AF773167

Gas Explosion Technology and Biomass Refinery

Hongzhang Chen

Gas Explosion Technology and Biomass Refinery

Chemical Industry Press

Springer

Hongzhang Chen
State Key Laboratory of Biochemical Engineering
Institute of Process Engineering, Chinese Academy of Sciences
Beijing
China

ISBN 978-94-017-7412-3 ISBN 978-94-017-7414-7 (eBook)
DOI 10.1007/978-94-017-7414-7

Jointly published with Chemical Industry Press, Beijing
ISBN: 978-7-122-18388-0 Chemical Industry Press, Beijing

Library of Congress Control Number: 2015950863

Springer Dordrecht Heidelberg New York London

Translation from the Chinese language edition: 气相爆破技术与生物质炼制 by Hongzhang Chen,

Printed on acid-free paper

Springer Science+Business Media B.V. Dordrecht is part of Springer Science+Business Media (www.springer.com)

Preface

Steam explosion technology is considered as one of the most cost-effective pretreatments of biomass. Steam explosion is the process in which the solid material especially lignocellulosic feedstock is pretreated with saturated steam or high-pressure gas for a certain time, and the solid material is then instantaneously exploded. In 1928, W.H. Mason from USA invented firstly the steam explosion technology, which only used 7–8 MPa saturated steam as a medium steam. This steam explosion technology was used only for the research of fiberboard preparation. Due to high pressure, this steam explosion technology is difficult to be applied. However, from the beginning of the 1980s, the steam explosion technology has attracted more attention again.

After decades of development, the steam explosion technology has made great progress. Most research still uses chemicals to pretreat biomass feedstocks at home and abroad. Based on the differences in the chemical composition and structure of straw and wood, author proposed the low pressure and unpolluted steam explosion technology of straw without any chemicals addition. And then the new low pressure and unpolluted steam explosion technology is extended to tobacco processing, herbal extracts, cleaning degumming of hemp fiber, etc.

On the basis of steam explosion, author extended the explosion media from the traditional steam to mix media, and developed inert medium steam explosion technology and mixed media steam explosion technology. Steam explosion technology has been used to the gradient temperature steam explosion process and other low-temperature steam explosion process of herbal treatment. A series of clean, efficient, and economical combinatorial pretreatment technologies taking steam explosion as the core have been invented, by which a clean and efficient separation of biomass components is achieved. Explosion technology is no longer limited to a single steam explosion. The media of explosion technology have been upgraded to multi-gas medium based on the requirements of process. Because the steam explosion media have been developed to a variety of gaseous medium, the steam explosion is named gas phase explosion in order to enrich and enhance the connotation of traditional steam explosion technology. Currently, gas explosion technology is mainly applied for lignocellulosic feedstock, whose common aim was to achieve a multi-component separation and utilization, namely biomass refining.

In 2006, we published the first monograph about the introduction of steam explosion technology. Based on our research of gas explosion technology and academic exchange with domestic and foreign peer in recent decades, authors write this book—Gas Explosion Technology and Biomass Refining. Authors hope to throw out a minnow to catch a whale and promote the better development of gas explosion technology.

This book analyzes the principle of gas explosion technology and the separation mechanism of solid material multi-component, and introduces gas explosion equipment and process. Additionally, the application process of biomass refining is described systematically. This work was financially supported by the National Basic Research Program of China (973 Project), the National High Technology Research and Development Program of China (863 Program), and the Knowledge Innovation Program of the Chinese Academy of Sciences. In addition, the works of my doctors and masters were essential preconditions for publishing this book. In particular, Dr. Zhihua Liu, Master Lanzhi Qin, Master Yang Liu, Dr. Wenjie Sui, Dr. Guanhua Wang, Dr. Yuzhen Zhang, Master Meixue Shao, Dr. Guanhua Li, Dr. Litong Ma, Dr. Junying Zhao, and Dr. Ning Wang participated in writing this book. Many references of our predecessors and colleagues are cited. I wish to express my sincere thanks to all of them.

Some errors may exist in this book. I sincerely hope to receive criticism and guidance from readers in this regard.

Beijing
July 2015

Hongzhang Chen

Contents

Chapter 1
Gas Explosion Technique Principles and Biomass Refining Pandect

1.1 Gas Explosion Technical Overview

1.1.1 History of Gas Explosion Technique

Biomass refining uses lignocellulose biorenewable resources as the main raw materials. To achieve high efficiency and value of biomass conversion, pretreatments are needed to destruct compact complex structures for structural separation. Among them, gas explosion technique has been developing a biomass feedstock pretreatment method in recent years. The main components of lignocellulosic materials are cellulose, hemicellulose, and lignin. The gas explosion is to deal with fiber raw materials by the use of high-temperature and pressure steam or other vapor media. In the physical and chemical effects, hemicellulose is hydrolyzed partially and the softening lignin becomes readily biodegradable, so that the timber lateral coupling strength decreases. The pores of cells are filled with high-pressure gas becoming soft and plastic. During sudden decompression, the rapid expansion of gas in the cavity produces an explosion, bursting into fine wood fiber bundles, in order to achieve separation of components and structural changes in the feedstock.

Steam explosion pretreatment technology was first started in 1928, when it was intermittent production, mainly used in the production of man-made fiber board. From the beginning of the 1970s, this technology was also widely used in animal feed production and extraction of ethanol from wood fiber and specialty chemicals. After the 1980s, the technology has a great development and has gradually expanded field of use, and there has been a continuous blast of steam production technology and equipment; for example, Canada Stake Technology has developed a continuous steam explosion technique and equipment. In the late 1980s, Stake Technology Corporation, the technology will be applied to the field of pulp and paper, through cooperation with the University of Quebec, Canada, on poplar and

H. Chen, *Gas Explosion Technology and Biomass Refinery*,
DOI 10.1007/978-94-017-7414-7_1

many non-wood fiber raw materials for a large number of steam burst test. On this basis, they developed a steam explosion pulping technology and related equipments, as well as the pulping waste reuse technology for the production of animal feed [1].

Steam explosion technique after decades of research has been developed to be used in different countries on different pretreatment of raw materials and is used in many fields, such as food industry, pharmaceutical industry, bioenergy, materials, chemicals, and environment protection. The prospects and advantages are increasingly highlighted [2]. But there is a certain limit to any technology. For example, the fibrous tissue and parenchyma, which are of different compositions, are bursting under the same conditions in steam explosion process. Because of both composition differences, blasting conditions are inconsistent. It is difficult at the same time to achieve the purpose of increasing the hydrolysis rate and avoiding the generation of fermentation inhibitors [3]. For example in herbal steam explosion process, high-temperature steam would destroy some of the effective herbal ingredients, and reduce the efficacy or cause changes in efficacy [4, 5]. Similarly for food processing, a higher temperature will cause gelatinization and coking deterioration phenomenon. Depending on the purpose of pretreatment, low temperature and appropriate pressure can damage the oil fruit (peanut, rapeseed), so that extraction of oil is difficult [4]. While for hemp fiber degumming process, the high temperature would result in excessive degumming, causing darkening of hemp fiber and strength reduction.

In response to these deficiencies existing in steam explosion technique, researcher Chen Hongzhang, Institute of Process Engineering, Chinese Academy of Sciences, developed a series of gas explosion techniques based on the principle of blasting. Inert medium steam explosion and mixed media gas explosion were developed by broadening the blasting medium from the traditional steam to the hybridvapor media. And the gas explosion technique was broadened to the perfect temperature gradient gas explosion and low gas explosion technology such as herbal treatment process. Meanwhile, with respect to the movement of raw materials in steam explosion reactor, in situ gas explosion process was developed based on the current non-in situ process to meet the pretreatment of food and hemp. What is more, a two-stage gas explosion technology was developed based on the different choice of gas explosion process of fibrous tissue and parenchyma, simultaneously achieving better hydrolysis result and less use of fermentation inhibitors. Gas explosion technology is no longer limited to only steam explosion, while the medium has been upgraded to a variety of permutations and combinations of vapor medium based on process requirements. Steam explosion has not completely covered its meaning, so Prof. Hongzhang Chen first proposed the concept of gas explosion, which is designed to enrich and enhance traditional steam explosion technology. And the applications of gas explosion have been greatly widened.

1.1.2 *Technical Classification of Gas Explosion*

1.1.2.1 Steam, Inert Medium, and Mixed Media Gas Explosion

Gas explosion technique is divided into steam gas explosion, inert medium explosion, and mixed media explosion according to the gas medium. The medium of steam gas explosion is water vapor, including saturated steam and superheated steam. The steam, the medium of gas explosion, plays the three roles of rehydration, catalysts of the autocatalytic process of materials and the power source of physical tearing. Steam explosion omits the presoaking process such as rehydration operations and simplifies gas explosion process.

The inert media of gas explosion contain air, N_2, CO_2, carbon dioxide ice, and liquid nitrogen. These serve only as a power source of the instantaneous pressure relief process, does not function as a catalytic chemical reaction, and change the moisture content of the material. For inert medium gas explosion, the temperature is room temperature or below room temperature, and the process only has physical tearing function, which leads to the increased specific surface area. Without the risk of chemical reactions, the chemical composition does not change. Therefore, the inert medium gas explosion can be widely used in the field of food and herb processing.

The media of mixed media gas explosion contain the combination of steam, air, N_2, CO_2, liquid nitrogen, and other media, depending on the purpose of gas explosion to select different combinations of gas as gas explosion media. For example, a mixed medium of water vapor with an inert gas can adjust the temperature and humidity by changing the ratio of steam vapor and inert gas, in order to selectively control chemical reactions and physical tearing effect and to achieve different pretreatment purposes.

1.1.2.2 Batch and Continuous Gas Explosion

Gas explosion technology is divided into batch and continuous gas explosion according to the mode of operation. The batch processing refers to the raw material fed in a closed reactor followed by high temperature and pressure, and then a sudden explosion. During this process, no second feeding is conducted. The batch processing of fractionation process for lignocellulose was first found in DeLong patent [6]. Masonite process reactor was used for separating hemicelluloses from wood and then continuously to remove lignin by water and ethanol extraction to yield pure cellulose. Batch processing equipment was originally developed by Marchessault et al. [7] and was applied in a patent. He also made a technical line about extraction and separation of the components in the patent. Then DeLong and Foody, respectively in 1983 [8] and 1984 [9, 10] applied for patents on the detailed operation and application Fields of batch processing to separate lignocellulosic materials. Soon, the technology was gradually applied to non-wood pulp fiber materials.

Continuous processing refers to the feeding at a constant speed into gas explosion reactor. After treatment, the material is discharged at a constant speed, so that the entire reactor material loading remains constant. Continuous gas explosion process began in 1973, which was originally used for animal feed processing. Then, this process is applied to the separation of components of lignocellulose. Currently, continuous gas explosion equipments contain Stake gas explosion systems developed by Stake Technology. The system consists of a horizontal high-pressure digester (reactor) and a discharge valve system structure. The digester can realize continuous feeding through a coaxial feeder. Material residence time in the digester can be controlled by the feeder and the discharge valve system. The feeder of Stake system is 25.4 cm and can handle 100,000 tons of biomass every year [1].

Batch processing with simple equipment and low cost is suitable for laboratory and material handling small factories, but its efficiency is relatively lower than continuous treatment process. The advantages of continuous processing are the large processing capacity, high efficiency and suitable for large-scale industrial applications. But the continuous processing equipment is little. Currently, only Canadian company Stake Technology owns this product and the equipment is expensive. Chinese researchers also develop continuous processing equipments and have made a great progress. Continuous gas explosion equipment developed in Institute of Process Engineering, Chinese Academy of Sciences, which is currently in process.

1.1.2.3 Non-In situ and In situ Gas Explosion

Gas explosion technique is divided into non-in situ and in situ gas explosion by the movement of solid materials. During traditional gas explosion operations, the material is always delivered to the intended receivers in the relief process due to the media pressure, which is called non-in situ gas explosion. In situ gas explosion technique developed by Prof. Chen Hongzhang refers to steam and other gas explosion media is separated in the relief process, and the material stays in its original position inside the reactor. The advantage of this process is that: ① When applied to the vapor explosion pretreatment hemp fibers, the damage to the fiber structure of the raw material is reduced, and the problem of winding and knotting of raw material was solved to facilitate the subsequent separation and carding process; ② the recovery is simple and the recovery rate of material is up to 100 %; ③ it broadens the application area of raw materials which can be used in food or medicine and other raw material with high health and safety factor; and ④ gas is recovered which not only reduces pollution of the environment, but also makes full recovery and utilization of resources. It facilitates mass balance calculation and quantitative and qualitative analysis of the explosion process [11].

In addition, in situ gas explosion technology could be improved continually. When the gas media are mixed media with high-temperature air and superheated steam or vapor, the in situ gas explosion and drying of raw material could be realized by multiple flash operations and gas explosion. On the one hand, raw material could be crushed during this process, and on the other hand, the moisture content could be reduced effectively. Besides, for some material, in situ gas explosion treatment could be the role of digestion and sterilization. Thus, its application range is wide and it is suitable for the processing of a variety of materials, such as poultry and animal feces, and activated sludge. And through multiple flash, the purpose of drying for multiple times could be achieved; thus, the process has advantages of high drying efficiency, and low energy consumed and costs.

1.1.3 Latest Developments of Gas Explosion Technique

After decades of development, gas explosion technology has made great strides. Because of the heterogeneity of biomass and the limitation of a single gas explosion pretreatment technique, it is still difficult to achieve the efficient separation of three major components of biomasss. Chen Hongzhang developed a series of clean, efficient, and economical combined pretreatment system based on the clean low-pressure gas explosion pretreatment technology.

1.1.3.1 Establishment of Low-Pressure Gas Explosion Clean Technology

According to the structural and chemical differences between straw and wood, Prof. Chen Hongzhang improved the previous gas explosion process. He proposed low-pressure gas explosion technique without addition of chemicals and developed 3 M^3 and 5 M^3 fast open-door gas explosion reactors with a number of national patents. Non-polluted gas explosion technology solved the problem of pollution by gas explosion fundamentally and resulted in a significant reduction of production costs.

The production processes for the batch explosion mainly contain high-pressure steam generator, the gas explosion cylinder, the acceptor, etc. Raw materials before adding into the gas explosion workshop should be presoaked firstly after removal of dust. The difference of the initial moisture content of the material impacts the rate to reach the highest temperature, thus affecting gas explosion effect. Experiments confirmed that the material with 34 % moisture content resulted in the best result of gas explosion, the highest recovery of hemicellulose, and the best properties of cellulose and pulp. After presoaking, raw material is fed to the gas explosion tank with aeration of high-pressure steam to the desired pressure and temperature to maintain a certain time, and then, the pressure is released quickly. Gas explosion process temperature (pressure), pressure time, and initial moisture content of materials are the main technological factors affecting gas explosion, which are adjusted to meet the required specifications based on the nature of the raw material, and the applications of exploded materials and the explosive devices.

The process is not only used to achieve the clean comprehensive utilization of straw, but also has been used in tobacco processing, paper industry, herbal extracts and hemp fiber cleaning unglued, and other industries. It has important economic and practical significance [1].

Figure 1.1 shows the latest gas explosive device developed by our laboratory [12]: on the basis of high-pressure steam generator 1, gas explosion reactor 2 and the receiver 3, also equipped with a temperature sensors (4, 5, 6), high-frequency pressure sensors (7, 8, 9), solids flowmeter (10), dynamic data acquisition and analysis system (11), a gas and condensate recovery system (12), a portable image acquisition device (13), and the sight glass window (14). The device has some new features: ① dynamic data acquisition system to collect instantaneous discharge pressure and temperature changes, thus conducting the energy, mass, and momentum accounting of gas explosion process; ② endoscopy through the window and image capture equipment, the continuous monitoring of the discharge pressure, and instant-dimensional morphology of materials and moisture vaporization, to intuitively understand gas explosion effect; and ③ through the discharge port of the solid flowmeter, multi-phase materials can be dynamically monitored by the instantaneous mass flow discharge, instantaneous density, and total mass flow

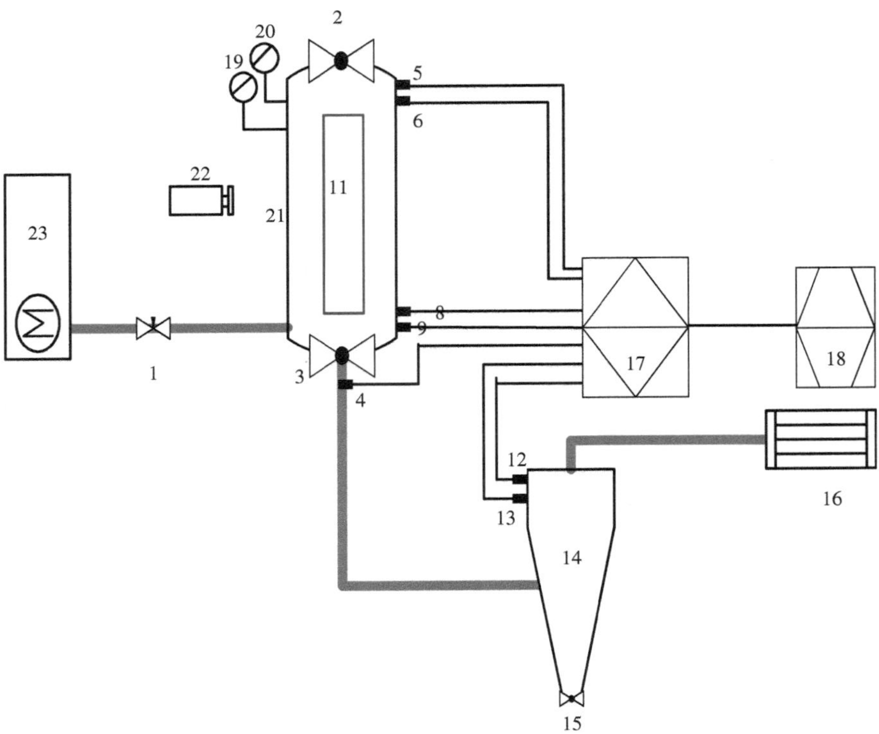

Fig. 1.1 Laboratory gas explosion apparatus

rate parameters, to facilitate the calculation of energy, mass, and momentum transfer during the process. And energy, mass, momentum transfer, and reaction engineering show the main parameters affecting the gas phase and gas explosion process dynamic model of blast effects and parameters to facilitate engineering scale-up design of devices and the development of application fields.

1.1.3.2 Gas Explosion—Solvent Extraction Combined Pretreatment Technology

(1) Gas explosion—ethanol extraction combined pretreatment

In an organosolv pulping, a mixed solution of organic solvents and water is usually as the stewing liquor, such as aqueous ethanol, aqueous acetone, and aqueous methanol [13]. Xu et al. [14] used 0.1 % HCl as a catalyst in aqueous acetic acid, formic acid–acetic acid–water, methanol–water, and ethanol–water solutions for pretreating dewaxed wheat straw. The lignin removal rate by methanol–water (60/40, v/v) and formic acid–acetic acid–water (30/60/10, v/v/v) was 37.4 and 94.1 %, respectively. The preprocess of Loblolly pine, with 65 % aqueous ethanol for 1 h at 170 °C and the addition of 1.1 % sulfuric acid as a catalyst, decreased the fiber crystallinity of loblolly pine and improved the availability of cellulose [15]. Chen and Liu [16] combined ethanol gas explosion pretreatment extraction. The lignin removal rate reached 82.33 %, which is significantly higher than that by direct extraction. Hemicellulose can be effectively recovered in gas explosion process. In the same processing conditions, gas explosion–ethanol extraction can effectively separate the wheat straw lignin and sugar recovery rate is 2.5 times higher than direct straw ethanol extraction [17]. Exploded straw after ethanol extraction in the electron microscopy showed that fiber cells were dispersed and the accessibility of cellulose can be increased so that raw enzymolysis and fermentation performance were improved.

(2) Gas explosion and high boiling organic solvent combined pretreatment

With respect to the low boiling organic solvents such as ethanol, a high boiling organic solvent has a higher safety degree. Rodríguez et al. [18, 19] reported that the pulping performances of high boiling organic solvent were significantly higher than those of ethylene glycol, such as the use of vinyl-ethyleneglycol, diethyleneglycol, ethanolamine and diethanolamine. Glycerol as a new pretreatment solvent with high boiling point (290 °C) can achieve low-voltage high-temperature pretreatment. Glycerol is strong heat-sensitive property and can achieve rapid heating and cooling treatment. In addition, it is a triol and can alter the chemical structure of lignin by the reaction of oxidation and alcoholysis to remove lignin from cellulose and hemicellulose to achieve the separation of the three chemical components. Sun and Chen [20] used gas explosion pretreatment coupling glycerol microwave to achieve component separation of lignocellulosic feedstock. First, conduct the material by gas explosion and water-washing, then mixing with glycerol for intermittent microwave treatment. Keep stirring to dissolve after adding hot water treatment, washing and filtering. The filter residue is the crude fiber. Finally, the filtrate was precipitated to obtain lignin. Gas explosion pretreatment and glycerol microwave coupling process can be separated from the lignocellulosic feedstock to about 70 % by weight of dry raw crude fiber, and isolated hemicellulose and lignin content accounted for 80 % of the raw material of the Central Plains and 85 % around [21–23].

(3) Gas explosion—ionic liquid dissolution combined pretreatment

Compared with conventional organic solvents and electrolytes, ionic liquids are colorless, odorless, less pollutant, and chemically stable. Ions are designed to adjust its solubility inorganic, water, organic matter and a polymer, and its acidity reach to super acid [24]. Swatloski et al. [25] found that the ionic liquid 1-butyl-3-methy-limidazolium chloride can dissolve cellulose, to open new doors for the ionic liquid applications of biomass research. Liu and Chen [26] studied the dissolution properties of straw and found [BMIM] Cl destroy the molecular chain of hydrogen bonds by Cl^-, thereby dissolving cellulose and hemicelluloses. [BMIM] Cl can dissolve a low-molecular lignin, lignin macromolecules but not dissolved. So combine gas explosion pretreatment with ionic liquid solubility to achieve an effective separation of hemicellulose, lignin and cellulose. After the treatment of ionic liquid [BMIM] Cl, wheat straw and wheat straw pretreated with gas explosion was conducted hydrolysis and fermentation and had significantly higher hydrolysis rates. What was more, the cellulose activity of the latter (118.64 FPU/g dry matter) was higher than those of the former (99.20 FPU/g) [26].

(4) Gas explosion—alkaline peroxide combined pretreatment

Alkaline hydrogen peroxide can effectively remove lignin and swelling cellulose, which mainly uses H_2O_2 to remove lignin in an alkaline medium and has a mild solubilizing function of macromolecular hemicellulose [27, 28]. Chen et al. [29] combined that the gas explosion pretreatment with alkaline hydrogen peroxide treatment led to the results that the cellulose content of gas exploded straw increased to 67.2 % and the sugar concentration increased to 110.9 g/L. Yamashita et al. [30] used 1 % (v/v) hydrogen peroxide and 1 wt% sodium hydroxide solution for pretreatment of bamboo, and bamboo hydrolysis rate was reached 568 mg/g dry matter. Yao et al. [31] demonstrated that the significance of impact factors of alkaline hydrogen peroxide treatment was NaOH concentration > H_2O_2 dosage > liquid to solid ratio > reaction temperature > reaction time, and they determined the optimal reaction conditions of 1 % hydrogen peroxide, 10 g/L sodium hydroxide, and 18 h at 70 °C.

1.1.3.3 Gas Explosion—Wet Superfine Combined Pretreatment

Superfine particles can be crushed to micron level, which greatly increases the surface area of particles. From the perspective of a measure to increase the reaction surface areas, the energy of superfine is not higher than traditional mechanical grinding [32]. Jin and Chen [32] combined gas explosion with wet ultrafine grinding technology, for the study of low-intensity coupling gas explosion technique of straw for ultrafine material effect fractionation effects. The results showed that the process made straw separated into easily digested powder and partially digested residue efficiently without damaging straw main chemical components and producing inhibitory substances. But the process had crushing and damaging the fiber. Therefore, the high moisture content material was separated high fiber content and high cellulose fibrous tissue sections in wet grinding technology using FJM-200 fluidized bed. In the optimization of process parameters, gas explosion-wet superfine separated technology, will initially separate straw into two parts: the fibrous tissue section and the non-fibrous tissue. Fibrous tissue separation reaches 2.04 (fibrous tissue separation original straw 1.00), and fibrous tissue partial gas exploding straw isolated yield of 70.4 % dry weight.

1.1.3.4 Gas Explosion—Mechanical Carding Grading Combined Pretreatment

Gas explosion pretreatment makes corn stalk fiber fully exposing, which makes hybrid cell broken or deformed, and hemicellulose partially degraded. Chen et al. [33] combined gas explosion pretreatment technology with the mechanical carding to realize the separation of tissues of miscellaneous cells and fibers cells at the level of organization. Mechanical carding can remove hybrid cells and small fibers adhered in the surface of fiber bundles. Hybrid cell tissue has a good fermenting property, and the highest cellulase production reached to 194.18 FPU/g dry matter. And fibrous tissue has an excellent performance in pulp. With 180 °C and 50 % ethanol concentration for 2 h, pulp yield is up to 45 %, and lignin content is less than 3.5 %.

1.1.3.5 Gas Explosion and Carding Two-Stage Technology

Some scholars studied inhibitor properties produced by biomass after dilute acid hydrolysis or gas explosion pretreatment. There are big differences of inhibitor properties, composition and the final concentration with different intensity (temperature and time), the nature of the raw material (hardwood, cork, and herbs), the presence of an acid catalyst, etc. [34–36]. These inhibitors were divided into three categories based on their chemical structures [37]: (1) Weak acid such as acetic acid, formic acid, and levulinic acid. Acetate is generated by deacetylation of hemicellulose, and formic acid and levulinic acid are degradation products of 5-hydroxymethylfurfural, while formic acid may also be produced by degradation of furfural in the acidic environment. (2) Furan aldehydes mainly furfural (Furfural) and HMF are, respectively, from pentoses and hexoses by dehydration under acidic conditions. (3) Phenolic compounds are mainly formed by lignin degradation. Klinke et al. [38] detailed the phenolic compounds formed during the pretreatment. In addition, there are still presumed trace and unclear microbial growth inhibitors in lignocellulose pretreatment solution. These inhibitors have become one of the major bottlenecks of lignocellulosic biorefinery processes. We need to take the necessary measures to deal with inhibitors to reduce or eliminate their inhibitory effect.

Various methods have been tried to detoxify lignocellulosic hydrolyzate before fermentation, including biological, physical, and chemical methods [39] and the combination of different measures. However, detoxification increases the cost of fermentation of cellulose products, makes the process more complicated, and leads to some loss of fermentable sugars [40–42] and so minimize the detoxification process in the fermentation process. Breeding highly resistant strains is considered as a feasible method [43], but the most fundamental way is to optimize the hydrolysis process to reduce the inhibitor, controlling the generation of inhibitors [37].

Lignocellulosic feedstock has complex, non-uniform, multi-level structures, which include fibrous cells and parenchyma cells (including vascular cells, parenchyma cells, and epidermis cells). Fiber cells are the most important and basic cells of plant fiber and support organization. The fibers typically have well-developed secondary cell walls. Parenchyma cells play the role of nutrition stored in plant growth, which have features of cavity large, thin wall, short length [44]. Different pretreatment conditions are required due to the differences in structure and in morphology between the two cell types. Fibrous cells, with high degree of lignification and compact tructure, have high heat and mass transfer resistance and are hard to break. On the other hand, thin-walled cells are sensitive to heat and mass transfer and are easily torn physically. Pretreatment conditions for the different tissues and cells should be optimized according to achieve the best hydrolysis effect and to minimize simultaneously side reactions.

Chen Hongzhang developed a new two-stage gas explosion carding pretreatment based on gas explosion inhibitor and structural properties of materials. Two-step steam explosion pretreatment, with the first step performed under mild conditions to hydrolyse parenchyma cells and fibrous cells. And the second step is steam explosion under normal conditions. Two-stage gas explosion is a way where materials were pretreated selectively according to characteristics of its organization's requirements. This process is beneficial not only in achieving a moderate degradation of fibrous tissue but also in avoiding excessive degradation of parenchyma cells. The methods increase the rate of hydrolysis of fiber raw materials, but also effectively reduce the inhibitor content, eliminating the detoxification unit operations. In addition, the methods for separation and selective pretreatment of fibrous tissue and parenchyma provide a new way for stratified multistage conversion of lignocellulosic feedstock.

1.1.3.6 Low-Temperature Gas Explosion Technique

Efficient preprocessing is to achieve the dual purposes: to improve the rate of hydrolysis of lignocellulosic feedstock and to reduce fermentation inhibitors. Currently, pretreatments of lignocellulosic feedstock are multitudinous. The current chemical pretreatment (dilute acid pretreatment, etc.) and some new pretreatment technology (gas explosion technique and hydrothermal pretreatment, etc.) are all involved in chemical reactions which degrade hemicellulose, making fiber exposure, thereby increasing the rate of cellulose hydrolysis. The physical pretreatment generally processes before chemical pretreatment, which is criticized due to the limitation of hydrolysis rate and high energy consumption. So now trends of the pretreatment of biomass refining are chemical pretreatments and some physicochemical pretreatment.

The advantage of chemical pretreatment which is to improve the degree of fiber explosion cannot be questioned, but the biggest disadvantage is the inhibitors of fermentation, which has become one of the largest bottlenecks on lignocellulosic biomass refinery industry. Faced with this phenomenon, we should refocus on the advantages of physical pretreatment.

In physical pretreatment, it will also increase the specific surface area of the material without causing inhibitor production. The traditional view is that the problem of high energy consumption is mainly for milling and crushing technology. However, gas explosion can still achieve the purpose of physical pretreatment.

Therefore, gas explosion technique which is out of the shackles of traditional chemical action, if necessary, can be developed either toward the direction of chemical pretreatment or toward the direction of physical pretreatment.

Chen and Li [45] had proposed a "low-pressure gas explosion" technology. The root of inhibitor problems is that the high temperature and pressure in the process of gas explosion prompt further degrade sugars and lignin, forming so-called fermentation inhibitors. Thus, in this basis, Chen Hongzhang put forward a novel gas explosion process by increasing the pressure and reducing the temperature to fully play the tearing role of gas explosion technology and appropriately inhibit chemical reactions. It can achieve the dual purpose of the fiber exposure and decreasing inhibitors.

"The low-temperature gas explosion" is no longer the operation about adjusting the moisture content, the time, and the pressure in the traditional sense, but a new mode of operation. The media may be dry air, N_2, or mixing media with CO_2 and water vapor and may be liquid nitrogen, dry ice, ozone, or a combination of each object which can not only realize the fiber exposure, but also solve the problem of fermentation inhibitors. In addition, the low-temperature gas explosion also plays a greater advantage in herbal medicine and food processing.

1.2 Biomass Refinery and Gas Explosion Technology

1.2.1 Biomass Concept and Biomass Refining

Biomass refers to all organic matter formed through photosynthesis, including agricultural and crop stalks, wood and wood waste, energy plants, medicinal plants, and aquatic plants. Plants in the growth process stored the solar energy in the form of carbohydrates by photosynthesis. Stored solar energy can be directly utilized as fuel energy by a suitable method. And the largest yield is biomass resources such as straw [46].

China is one of the countries with the most abundant plant resources in the world and has a variety of plant resources from the tropical, subtropical, and temperate to frigid zones. There are more than 30,000 kinds of higher plants, and more than 50 % higher plants are endemic species in China. China is also the world's most rich country for the resources of medicinal plant. According to a recent survey, a total of 12,807 kinds of Chinese herbal medicine resources are found in China, including plant medicine in which there are 21,146 species (distributed in 383 families, 2309 genera). At present, the annual trade amount of natural drugs in the world has reached $15 billion. The trade of medicinal plants and their products, health products, natural cosmetics, and natural spices can reach more than $30 billion [47].

Crop straw is the most abundant renewable resource on earth. According to statistics, the annual straw produced in China is more than 700 million tons, which is the top of the world. Crop straw accounts for 90.5 % of the total straw, mainly cornstalks (36.7 %), rice straw (27.5 %), and wheat straw (15.2 %) [48].

However, since the main ingredients of biomass are difficult to degrade, the development and utilization of straw are very limited. For the straw harvested in one year, about 28 million tons are used in papermaking, 213 million tons are used as feed or feed raw material, 108.9 million tons are lost in the process of returning and collecting, and the remaining 376.1 million tons have been burned or discarded directly. With the development of industrial modernization, these data will also increase year by year, causing serious waste of resources and environmental pollution.

The utilization development of straw biomass resources by biomass refinery has important significance to alleviate the energy crisis and protect the environment. Although the economy is highly developed in today's world, the resources, energy shortage, and environmental pollution are the difficulties faced by countries at the same time. Existing energy and chemical industry rely too much on fossil fuels which are mainly composed of oil, coal, and natural gas. However, due to the environmental pollutions caused by fossil fuel combustion and the gradual reduction of fossil fuel reserves, mankind is faced with more and more serious crisis of energy and resources. The unique chemical compositions and renewability of plant biomass provide a possibility for human to solve the energy crisis and food crisis [49].

Biorefinery technology is to use biomass (starch, lignocellulose etc.) as raw materials to produce various kinds of bioenergy and bio-based chemicals such as ethanol and furfural. The USA, Brazil, Japan, Canada, and other countries are vigorously developing biorefinery industry using agricultural and forestry wastes and switchgrass energy crops as raw materials. Implement of converting biomass efficiently, however, is still a worldwide problem, and the high value utilization and commercialization are still unable to achieve. Chen and his coworkers comprehensively analyzed the years' work results and demonstrated that relying on a single technology or using a single component to implement the conversion of biomass preparation to bio-based products is difficult to succeed. And the breakthrough could only be achieved by the fully aware of physical, chemical, and biological properties of straw biomass raw material in view of the key problems of the existing technology and major improvements in research methods and ideas [50].

1.2.2 Lignocellulosic Biomass Recalcitrance to Degradation

Lignocellulose is the structure of the plant and support organism. In the long-term evolutionary process, plants have evolved complex structure and chemical mechanism to deal with microbial and animal's attack, which results in the complex composition and structure of lignocellulose resources and the formation of natural barrier to biological and enzymatic attack. Currently, key technologies of low-cost biomass bioconversion are still lacking and the efficiency of biological conversion cannot adapt to the requirement of large-scale industrialization. To strengthen the basis of related research and develop the new generation of biomass refining technologies which convert lignocellulose feedstock to liquid fuels and chemicals is necessary to solve the urgent task to realize sustainable development.

Lignocellulose feedstock mainly contains three kinds of chemical components: cellulose (35–35 %), hemicellulose (20–40 %), and lignin (15–25 %). At the molecular level, glucose in the cellulose chain presents a chair conformation. The hydroxyl group is linearly arranged and forms strong hydrogen bond interaction between two adjacent chains. Hydrogen bonds result in the close combination between sugar chains which make the cell walls of microfibril crystalline cellulose arranged very closely. It is hard for enzyme molecules to enter into the cellulose crystalline region. And between the cellulose microfibrils, hemicellulose and lignin are also filled by covalent bonds to reinforce the cell wall structure and make the structure difficult to be degraded by chemical and biological methods.

Therefore, the current lignocellulose bioconversion process is still not cost-effective. Only, technological progress can realize sustainable supply of biofuels and chemicals and form the advantage on price. There are some important ways to improve the economy of lignocellulose bioconversion: increasing the sugar producing rate by cellulose enzymatic hydrolysis and improving the fermentation yield, lignin removal, and utilization [51].

1.2.3 Effective Methods to Expose Cellulose in Cell Wall by Physicochemical Pretreatments

There are not microbes which could directly and effectively attack the natural plant. Physicochemical pretreatments are still necessary to remove hemicellulose and lignin and expose cellulose for the effective enzymatic hydrolysis. These pretreatment should be able to destroy the contact structure of lignocellulose for the enzymatic hydrolysis but not severe enough to produce toxic substances for the microbial fermentation [52, 53].

In recent years, a lot of pretreatment methods have been developed, including acid pretreatment, alkali pretreatment, steam explosion pretreatment, and hydrothermal pretreatment. Various pretreatment methods can obtain high sugar rate. For agricultural waste, especially the corn straw, the hydrolysis yield is more than 90 % of the theoretical value.

How to chose and evaluate the pretreatment technologies? First, the treatment efficiency of pretreatments is different for different lignocellulose feedstock; for example, the alkali pretreatment could effectively decrease the lignin content in the agricultural residues, but its delignification is limited for softwood [54]. Secondly, the pretreatment is closely related to the subsequent conversion. A pretreatment should be chosen according to the degradability of cellulose, the formation of harmful substances, and the energy consumption during conversion process [55]. Chen and Li [56] suggested that the development of pretreatment technologies should not overemphasize the conversion of single cellulose component but to obtain the maximum utilization of the three components. Thus, the pretreatment technologies should have the three characteristics: technically feasible; energy saving and pollution free, and economically feasible. After summary about the choice of pretreatment technology at home and abroad [56–59], main bases include the followings:

(1) Economic effective separation of the various components of the substrate to make it convenient for production use. Pretreatment is not for the purpose of a particular component and cannot blindly stress on the complete separation of components. In order to achieve this goal, the combination of a variety of pretreatment techniques can be used. Although organic solvent treatment could obtain lignin and hemicellulose with certain purity, the loss rate of hemicellulose is as high as 50 %. If the most hemicellulose is firstly separated by steam explosion and the lignin is then isolated by organic solvent extraction, the recovery yield of both hemicellulose and lignin could be increased.
(2) To implement effective separation of each component in the raw materials, reduce the mutual inhibitions among each component in the subsequent transformation process. For example, the invalid adsorption of cellulase by lignin decreases the efficiency of cellulase and the removal of 20–65 % lignin in the substrate will significantly improve the efficiency of cellulose enzyme. Thus, it is not necessary to remove all lignin, which essentially reduces the cost of processing.

(3) To control the generation of harmful substances. The optimized pretreatment conditions should reduce the fermentation inhibitors for the subsequent pretreatment process. The inhibitors produced in the pretreatment process include acids (acetic acid, oxalic acid, and levulinic acid), furan derivatives (furfural and 5-HMF), and phenolic compounds (lignin degradation substances).
(4) To reduce the addition of chemicals and decrease the cost of subsequent treatment.
(5) To reduce the processing units for raw material crushing or grinding and decrease the energy consumption and cost.

1.2.4 Advantages of Steam Explosion-Derived Biomass Refining

Through more than ten-year study, Chen Hongzhang from Institute of Process Engineering, Chinese Academy of Science established a steam explosion-derived biomass refining platform. Based on this platform, a series of biorefinery processes are developed, and in these processes, numerous products such as bio-based energy, bio-based chemicals, and bio-based materials are obtained.

The advantages of steam explosion-derived biorefinery are as follows [1, 60]:

(1) Steam explosion is suitable for different kinds of plant biomass, and the conditions of pretreatment are adjustable.
(2) Hemicellulose, lignin, and cellulose could be fractionated in three different processes, which are water-soluble fraction, alkaline-soluble fraction, and alkaline-insoluble fraction.
(3) The enzymatic conversion of cellulose could reach the theoretical maximum.
(4) Lignin after steam explosion could also be converted to other chemicals.
(5) The sugars produced by the hemicellulose could be utilized completely and converted into liquid fuels.
(6) The fermentation inhibitors produced in the steam explosion process could be decreased by the control of steam explosion conditions.
(7) The pressure and temperature of steam explosion could be controlled individually to realize explosion effect under lower temperature, which is suitable for the specific process requirement of food and Chinese traditional medicines.
(8) The in situ steam explosion of hemp materials could avoid the twining of hemp fiber.
(9) The cost for steam explosion process is relatively low compared with other pretreatment processes.

Taking unpolluted steam explosion as an example, 0.2–0.5 ton steam is consumed for per ton raw material, which means the energy consumption for steam explosion is low. The costs for reagent consumption and labor are also lower

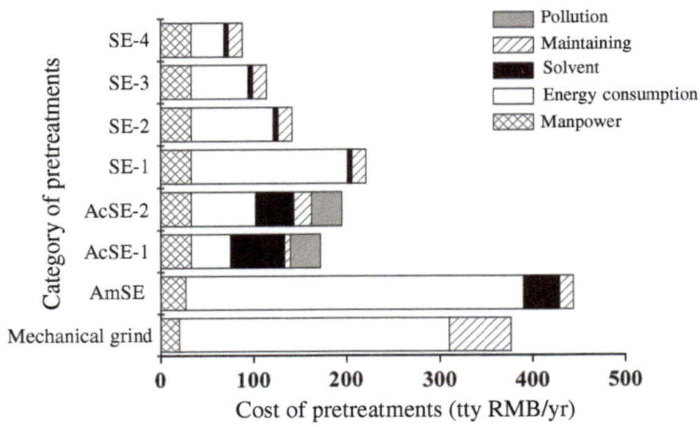

Fig. 1.2 Economic cost of pretreatments under different conditions

compared with other pretreatment technologies. The detailed costs of steam explosion process are shown in Fig. 1.2.

The conditions of steam explosion-1/2/3: 167 °C, charge coefficient 80 kg/m^3, pressure maintaining 5 min. The moisture content 0.7, 0.5 and 0.3, respectively. The conditions of steam explosion-4: 167 °C, charge coefficient 87.6 kg/m^3, pressure maintaining 5 min, moisture content 0.3. The conditions of acid-addition steam explosion-1/2: 164 °C, 1.6 % SO_2 (dry straw), charge coefficient 80 kg/m^3, pressure maintaining 5 min, moisture content 0.5 and 0.3 respectively; The conditions of ammonia-addition steam explosion: 0.1 % ammonia (dry straw), charge coefficient 80 kg/m^3, temperature 164 °C, pressure maintaining time 5 min, moisture content 0.3 tty RMB/year: 10,000 CNY per year.

Based on the structural characteristics and the requirements of target products, selective structural deconstruction according to the functional requirements of products aims to obtain the optimized efficiency and maximum value by least energy consumption and realize the usage of lignocellulose as the new main feedstock for

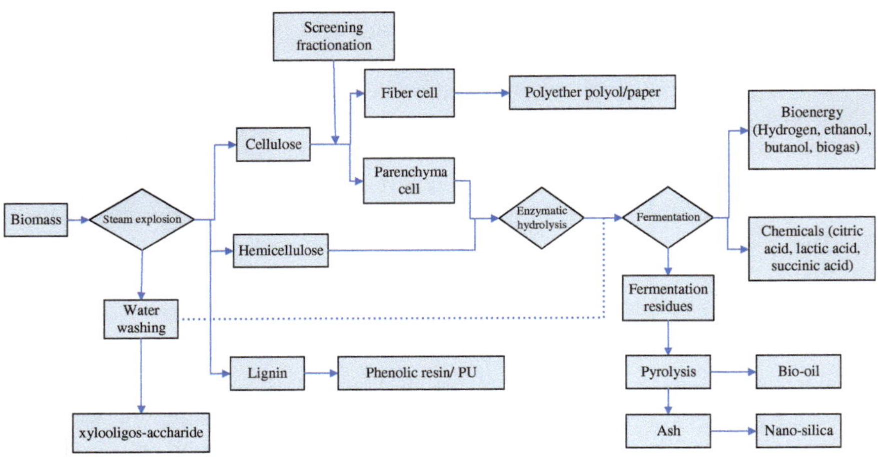

Fig. 1.3 Schematic diagram of steam explosion-derived biomass refining process

the biological and chemical industries. The biomass refining process using steam explosion as the core is exactly based on this idea and objectives, which aims to realize the maximum of economic efficiency of biomass resource. Figure 1.3 is the schematic diagram of steam explosion-derived biomass refining processes.

1.3 Foreground and Prospect

1.3.1 Preface

The high cost of the biomass pretreatment is mainly due to the high strength condition to destroy the structure. The choice of strength mainly depends on the pretreatment of acidity, temperature, and time under a certain temperature. Chemical composition of plant cell walls and the ultrastructural changes in the pretreatment process need more in-depth and detailed study, such as the study of the relationship between the structure and composition of plant material. Thus, it is advantageous to the development of better methods of chemistry and enzyme treatment. To solve the problem of yield and to design the pretreatment with the integration of high efficiency, low cost, and no pollution require a comprehensive analysis of complex plant tissue structure, chemical pretreatment, and enzyme hydrolysis process [51].

1.3.2 Cognition of Biomass Supermolecule Structure and Necessity of Selective Structural Deconstruction

The current biomass conversion technology is achieved by the use of chemical or physicochemical pretreatments to remove hemicellulose and lignin on the surface of the microfibril. The removal of hemicellulose and lignin makes crystalline cellulose more suitable for the reaction of cellulose enzyme. In addition, the pretreatment can reduce macroscopic stiffness and the physical barrier of mass transfer process. Cellulose degradation (saccharification process) is a combined action of multiple enzymes, including cellulase, hemicellulose, and other enzymes. In this process, the cell wall is destroyed at the molecular level, resulting in the in situ hydrolysis of hemicellulose and lignin and the exposure of crystalline cellulose. In the end, the polysaccharide is depolymerized to simple sugars for microbial fermentation. Now, the technical bottleneck is the high cost of cellulose conversion process, low sugar yield, and the low efficiency of enzyme molecules. In order to overcome these problems and to improve the efficiency of the process, the super molecular structure of the substrate structure and enzymatic hydrolysis mechanism are needed for further study [61].

For straw biomass, it is mainly composed of cellulose, hemicellulose, and lignin. The cellulose is formed by the crystallization and amorphous phase. Most hydroxyl groups of glucose in the amorphous phase are in the free state; a lot of hydroxyl groups in cellulose crystal phase form a large number of hydrogen bonds, which constitute enormous hydrogen bonding grid and directly led to the formation of the compact crystalline structure of aggregation state. The compact crystalline structure seriously impedes the effective contact and function of chemical reagents or cellulase on the surface of cellulose, which is also the important reason for the difficulty to hydrolyze natural cellulose [2].

On the other hand, the distribution, content, and physicochemical properties of the main components vary significantly with sources and kinds of straw. From the point of chemical composition, the content differences of main components in the each part of the straw are obvious. The straw skin has the highest content (36.66 %) of cellulose. The leaf has the highest content (33.86 %) of hemicellulose. And lignin is mainly concentrated in skin and knot, whose contents are 14.23 and 12.52 %, respectively. Ash is mainly concentrated in the leaf (11.63 %). From the perspective of the fiber morphological characteristics, straw has high content of tiny fiber cells and parenchyma cells (up to 40–50 %) and low content of fiber cells (40–70 %), while wood has low content of parenchyma cells and high content of fiber cells. The fiber cells content of broad-leaved timber is 60–80 %, and the value is 90–95 % for softwood [62, 63]. From different parts, the chemical composition and fiber morphology from stem, leaf, spike, and sheath of straw are also different. The fiber from some parts of straw is even better than the fiber from some broad-leaved woods, such as the fiber from internode and leaf sheath of wheat straw. The length of fiber from these parts is similar to that of poplar fiber, which has very high aspect ratio. This indicates that these parts of the straw have the value utilization potential.

Pretreatment technologies directly influence the properties and operational performance of cellulose products and cellulose functional materials. Pretreatment can change or remove hinders from the physical structure and chemical composition, realizing the directional separation and conversion of raw materials and the adequate degradation of cellulose and hemicellulose by microorganisms or enzymes. For the actual straw resources, due to the complexity of its structure, using a single pretreatment technology is often difficult to achieve the ideal goal. Component separation proposed by Chen [2] in the early stage of the China 973 project is the upgrade on the basis of pretreatment process, which is not only a kind of pretreatment method, but also an allocation process of macromolecular component resource in the straw. After cognition of the non-uniformity of straw components, the unpolluted steam explosion of straw is established, the autohydrolysis mechanism during the steam explosion is revealed, and the component fractionation and oriented conversion routes of straw using steam explosion as the core technology are proposed. The combination of steam explosion with solvent extraction (ethanol, ionic liquid, and glycerol) realizes the component separation of lignocellulosic feedstock in the chemical level, which includes the conversion of hemicellulose into xylooligosaccharide, directional enzymolysis and fermentation of cellulose and lignin isolation, and value-added utilization routes. The combination of steam explosion with wet ultrafine grinding realizes the separation of fiber tissues and non-fiber tissues in the raw materials and forms the directional enzymolysis and fermentation of cellulose tissues and the thermochemical conversion of non-fiber tissue into levulinic acid. The combination of steam explosion with mechanical fractionation realizes the separation of long fiber, show fiber, and parenchyma cells [2]. Component fractionation technology which is suitable for the straw refining is based on the structural characteristics of raw materials and the requirements of target products to realize the functional deconstruction process. The aim of this process is not only to produce a few products but also to realize the universality of straw as main raw material for biological and chemical industries.

1.3.3 Analysis of Biomass Recalcitrance and Breaking Pathways

In the evolutionary progress from aquatic environment to terrestrial environment, excellent protection mechanisms of plant are evolved to protect its own structure and macromolecules from microbial and animal attack. The protection mechanisms are thought to be the natural barriers for the chemical and enzymatic degradation of biomass. These protection mechanisms include the following: (1) the skin tissue of plant body especially skin and cuticular wax; (2) the distribution and density of vascular bundles; (3) the heterogeneity of the structure and the complexity of cell wall components; (4) the microfibril structures of cell wall; (5) the intertwining of hemicellulose and lignin; (6) the crystallinity of cellulose; (7) enzymatic process on the insoluble substrate; (8) natural inhibition factors in the cell wall; and (9) inhibition facts from the pretreatment and the subsequent fermentation process. The chemical and structural characteristics affect solution infiltration, and the adsorption and hydrolysis of enzyme molecules ultimately affect the total cost of the whole process of bioconversion.

To date, the biomass recalcitrance is still not systematically studied. The function mechanism of biomass recalcitrance to the enzymatic hydrolysis is still unclear. Therefore, from the view of biomass recalcitrance to study the biomass supramolecular structures, the effects of pretreatments on the lignocellulosic feedstock and the structure–function relationship of lignocellulosic feedstock with enzyme molecule are necessary to finally provide the effective, economic, and practical pretreatment technology to break the barriers from biomass recalcitrance.

1.3.4 Changes of Biomass Mechanical Properties During Refining Process

During the pretreatment and the conversion process of biomass, the deformation of biomass skeleton is significant. Skeleton deformation is mainly influenced by its own degradation. With the destruction of structure and chemical composition, the macromolecule cracks into small molecules and the porosity and mechanical properties of biomass are also affected.

During the chemical pretreatment of biomass, the hemicellulose is degraded and lignin is softened, resulting in the decrease of mechanical properties of cell wall. In the steam explosion process, biomass is also torn by instantaneous pressure release, in which the brittle fracture of cell occurs and the macrostructure of material is changed. During the enzymatic hydrolysis of biomass, the cellulose skeleton is gradually degraded and the strength and porosity of materials are also decreased. The changes of material properties induce the growing of flow resistance during the enzymatic process. And the degradation of solid skeleton is influenced by the seepage field and diffusion field. Thus, the interactions of solid skeleton deformation and seepage/diffusion field are particularly obvious in transfer phenomenon of biorefinery. In the biomass refining, besides the coupling among different scales, the dynamic coupling effects of the stress field, strain field, diffusion field, and seepage field should also be considered.

1.3.5 Thermodynamics and Dynamics During Biomass Refining Processes

Thermodynamics is to study the conversion and trend of material system energy. There are hydrogen bond, van der Waals force, and hydrophobic interaction force in the straw supermolecule. The intermolecular interaction force under certain conditions could form strong interaction force with certain directivity and selectivity and provide the main force for supramolecular formation and molecular recognition, which has important influence on the physical and chemical characteristics of straw supramolecule. Through the energy calculation and thermodynamics analysis, exploring molecular interactions of the three main components of straw can provide theoretical basis for choosing appropriate pretreatment intensity.

He [64] found that the intermolecular interaction energy is much smaller than the covalent bond in the straw supramolecular system by molecular modeling and Gaussian software calculation. The total hydrogen bond energy on the cellulose crystal is −79.743 kJ/mol, and the average hydrogen bond energy is about −40 kJ/mol. The total hydrogen bond energy between cellulose and hemicellulose is 59.747 kJ/mol, and the average hydrogen bond energy is about 30 kJ/mol. The van der Waals force between two cellulose chains on the diagonal of cellulose crystal is 51.632 kJ/mol. Although the interaction energy between the molecules is very small, it has an important influence on the stability and properties characteristics of the straw super molecular structure. At room temperature, the formation process of complex system is the decreasing process of Gibbs free energy, which indicates that the cellulose chains and cellulose and hemicellulose could spontaneously form complexes by the intermolecular interaction forces. The hydrogen bond forces between cellulose chains and the hydrogen bond forces between cellulose and hemicellulose are the forces for the self-assembly of straw supramolecule. In the formation process of the complex system, the changes of Gibbs free energy (ΔG) are approximately equal to 0 at 375 and 515 K, respectively, which indicate that the hydrogen bond fracture temperature of cellulose chain is about 375 K and the fracture temperature of hydrogen bonds between cellulose and hemicellulose is about 515 K.

In the biomass refining process, the efficiency of degraded small molecule is closely related to its content and the energy density. Particularly, the energy state of sugar molecule is the key factor to limit its utilization in the dissolution process of small molecules during the pretreatment process and sugar dissolution during the enzymatic hydrolysis process, as well as the utilization of fermentation substrates. Taking the dissolution of degraded products during the steam explosion process as an example, the degraded small molecules are firstly absorbed in the pore of lignocellulosic materials. Thus, the recovery of sugars and other soluble molecules should be performed under certain extraction conditions (pH value, temperature, and liquid–solid ratio).

Chemical thermodynamics is used to study the possibility of reactions, and the dynamics can indicate the practical significance of reactions, which is also the powerful evidence as the guidance of industrial scale-up. Thermodynamics theory could be used as guidance to choose the appropriate pretreatment conditions, but it provides only a range of conditions. The dynamics can provide information about the generation of products and the reaction mechanisms, which further makes the better manipulation of biorefinery conditions possible.

1.3.6 Basis of Biomass Engineering Science

The research object of biomass process engineering is the chemical, physical, and biological conversion process of biomass. The research content is the movement of biomass, the transfer, the feasibility, and limitation of chemical reaction and the reaction rate. The mission is to create clean and effective process and equipment to solve the key bottlenecks of industrialization [65]. Chen proposed three focuses for the process engineering development of bio-based products. The first is to realize the non-uniformity of biomass materials. The second is the technique barriers of pretreatment, enzymatic hydrolysis, and product separation during the biomass conversion process. The third is the integration of methods and technologies during the biomass conversion process and the understanding of biomass raw material properties, and process engineering principle of biomass conversion is the core scientific problem of biomass refining process.

It is known that both the operation strengthening and design optimization will involve the method and limitation issues of process. The in-depth exploration of process essence is necessary for the exact scalp-up of process especially for the high-rate scale-up. The scientific bases of biomass conversion process engineering are three transfers and three conversions (mass transfer and conversion, energy transfer and conversion, information transfer and conversion). Thermodynamics is used to study the conversion and trend of material system energy. The thermodynamics study of biomass energy state and change trend is the important pathway for the research of dissolution, absorption, and migration of material during the biomass degradation, extraction, and enzymatic hydrolysis process. Dynamics is used to study the rate of chemical reactions and the reaction mechanisms, and its research object is the unbalance dynamic system varied with time. Thermodynamics can predict the possibility of reactions, and dynamics can indicate the true engineering significance of reactions. Dynamics parameters are the effective data to explore the reaction mechanism and provide theoretical guidance for the engineering optimization and scale-up.

Therefore, the scientific bases of biomass process engineering are the cognition of complexity and non-uniformity of biomass, the transfer principles of conversion process, thermodynamics, dynamics, mechanical principles, and the economic analysis of biorefinery routes, which are shown in Fig. 1.4.

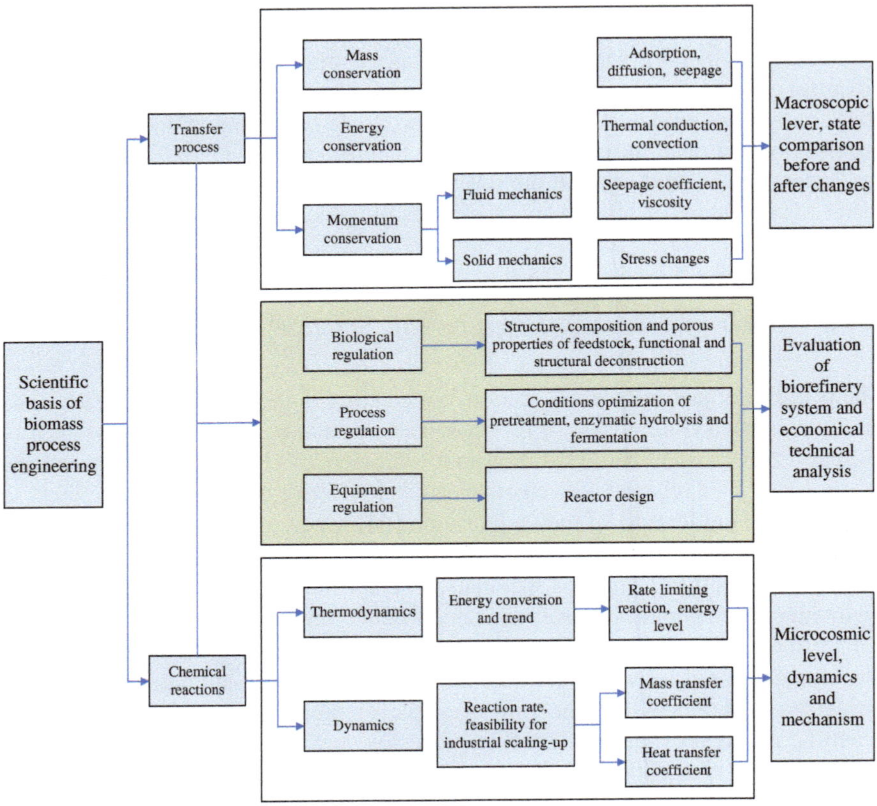

Fig. 1.4 Principle of biomass conversion engineering

References

1. Chen HZ, Liu LY. Principle and applications of steam explosion technology. Beijing: Chemical Industry Press; 2007.
2. Chen HZ. Process engineering in plant-based procucts. New York: Nova Science Publishers; 2009.
3. Zhang YZ, Fu XG, Chen HZ. Pretreatment based on two-step steam explosion combined with an intermediate separation of fiber cells-optimization of fermentation of corn straw hydrolysates. Bioresour Technol. 2012;121:100–4.
4. Chen GZ, Chen HZ. Extraction and deglycosylation of flavonoids from sumac fruits using steam explosion. Food Chem. 2011;126(4):1934–8.
5. Chen HZ, Peng XW. A steam explosion and biological coupling method to convert resveratrol glucoside into resveratrol; 2010. China patent, 201010128286.3.
6. DeLong E. Method of rendering lignin separable from cellulose and hemicellulose in lignocellulosic material and the product produced; 1981. Canadian patent, 1096374.
7. Marchessault R, Malhotra S, Jones A. The wood explosion process: characterization and uses of lignin/cellulose products. In: Wood and agricultural residues. New York: Academic Press; 1983.
8. DeLong EA. Method of rendering lignin separable from cellulose and hemicellulose in lignocellulosic material and the product produced; 1983. Canadian patent, 1141376.
9. Foody P. Method for increasing the accessibility of cellulose in lignocellulosic materials, particularly hardwoods agricultural residues and the like; 1984. US Patents, 4461648.
10. Foody P. Method for obtaining superior yields of accessible cellulose and hemicellulose from lignocellulosic materials; 1984. CA patent CA1,163,058.
11. Chen HZ, Zhang YZ. Insitu steam explosion and its equipments; 2011. China patent, 201110068899.7.
12. Chen HZ, Zhang YZ. Steam explosion equipments at laboratory scales; 2011. Chinese patent, 201110069290.1.
13. Araque E, Parra C, Freer J, Contreras D, Rodríguez J, Mendonça R, Baeza J. Evaluation of organosolv pretreatment for the conversion of *Pinus radiata* D. Don to ethanol. Enzyme Microb Technol. 2008;43(2):214–9.
14. Xu F, Sun JX, Sun RC, Fowler P. Comparative study of organosolv lignins from wheat straw. Ind Crops Prod. 2006;23(2):180–93.
15. Sannigrahi P, Miller SJ, Ragauskas AJ. Effects of organosolv pretreatment and enzymatic hydrolysis on cellulose structure and crystallinity in Loblolly pine. Carbohydr Res. 2010;345 (7):965–70.
16. Chen HZ, Liu LY. Unpolluted fractionation of wheat straw by steam explosion and ethanol extraction. Bioresour Technol. 2007;98(3):666–76.
17. Chen HZ, Li ZH. Studies on ethanol extraction of steam exploded wheat straw. Chem Ind For Prod. 2000;20(3):33–9.
18. Rodríguez A, Serrano L, Moral A. Pulping of rice straw with high-boiling point organosolv solvents. Biochem Eng J. 2008;42(3):243–7.
19. Rodríguez A, Serrano L, Moral A. Use of high-boiling point organic solvents for pulping oil palm empty fruit bunches. Bioresour Technol. 2008;99(6):1743–9.
20. Sun FB, Chen HZ. Evaluation of enzymatic hydrolysis of wheat straw pretreated by atmospheric glycerol autocatalysis. J Chem Technol Biotechnol. 2007;82(11):1039–44.
21. Sun FB, Chen HZ. Enhanced enzymatic hydrolysis of wheat straw by aqueous glycerol pretreatment. Bioresour Technol. 2008;99(14):6156–61.
22. Sun FB, Chen HZ. Organosolv pretreatment by crude glycerol from oleochemicals industry for enzymatic hydrolysis of wheat straw. Bioresour Technol. 2008;99(13):5474–9.
23. Sun FB, Chen HZ. Comparison of atmospheric aqueous glycerol and steam explosion pretreatments of wheat straw for enhanced enzymatic hydrolysis. J Chem Technol Biotechnol. 2008;83(5):707–14.

24. Hayes DJ. An examination of biorefining processes, catalysts and challenges. Catal Today. 2009;145(1):138–51.
25. Swatloski RP, Spear SK, Holbrey JD. Dissolution of cellose with ionic liquids. J Am Chem Soc. 2002;124(18):4974–5.
26. Liu LY, Chen HZ. Enzymatic hydrolysis of cellulose materials treated with ionic liquid [BMIM] Cl. Chin Sci Bull. 2006;51(20):2432–6.
27. Saha BC, Cotta MA. Ethanol production from alkaline peroxide pretreated enzymatically saccharified wheat straw. Biotechnol Prog. 2006;22(2):449–53.
28. Zhao X, Peng F, Cheng K. Enhancement of the enzymatic digestibility of sugarcane bagasse by alkali-peracetic acid pretreatment. Enzyme Microb Technol. 2009;44(1):17–23.
29. Chen HZ, Han YJ, Xu J. Simultaneous saccharification and fermentation of steam exploded wheat straw pretreated with alkaline peroxide. Process Biochem. 2008;43(12):1462–6.
30. Yamashita Y, Shono M, Sasaki C. Alkaline peroxide pretreatment for efficient enzymatic saccharification of bamboo. Carbohydr Polym. 2010;79(4):914–20.
31. Yao X, Zhang Q, Yang X. Pretreatment process for lignocellulose by alkaline H_2O_2. Chem Eng. 2009;26(003):34–7.
32. Jin SY, Chen HZ. Fractionation of fibrous fraction from steam-exploded rice straw. Process Biochem. 2007;42(2):188–92.
33. Chen HZ, Liu LY, Jin SY, Zhai W. Components fractionation of crop straw; 2006. China patent, 200610075690.2.
34. Oliva JM, Sáez F, Ballesteros I. Effect of lignocellulosic degradation compounds from steam explosion pretreatment on ethanol fermentation by thermotolerant yeast *Kluyveromyces marxianus*. Appl Biochem Biotechnol. 2003;105(1):141–53.
35. Luo C, Brink DL, Blanch HW. Identification of potential fermentation inhibitors in conversion of hybrid poplar hydrolyzate to ethanol. Biomass Bioenergy. 2002;22(2):125–38.
36. Martinez A, Rodriguez ME, Wells ML. Detoxification of dilute acid hydrolysates of lignocellulose with lime. Biotechnol Prog. 2001;17(2):287–93.
37. Palmqvist E, Hahn-Hägerdal B. Fermentation of lignocellulosic hydrolysates. II: inhibitors and mechanisms of inhibition. Bioresour Technol. 2000;74(1):25–33.
38. Klinke HB, Thomsen A, Ahring BK. Inhibition of ethanol-producing yeast and bacteria by degradation products produced during pre-treatment of biomass. Appl Microbiol Biotechnol. 2004;66(1):10–26.
39. Palmqvist E, Hahn-Hägerdal B. Fermentation of lignocellulosic hydrolysates. I: inhibition and detoxification. Bioresour Technol. 2000;74(1):17–24.
40. Mussatto SI, Roberto IC. Alternatives for detoxification of diluted-acid lignocellulosic hydrolyzates for use in fermentative processes: a review. Bioresour Technol. 2004;93(1):1–10.
41. Almeida JRM, Bertilsson M, Gorwa-Grauslund MF. Metabolic effects of furaldehydes and impacts on biotechnological processes. Appl Microbiol Biotechnol. 2009;82(4):625–38.
42. Liu ZL, Slininger PJ, Gorsich SW. Enhanced biotransformation of furfural and hydroxymethylfurfural by newly developed ethanologenic yeast strains. Appl Biochem Biotechnol. 2005;121:451–60.
43. Li H, Zhang X, Shen Y. Inhititors and their effects on *Saccharomyces cerevisiae* and relevant countermeasures in bioprocess of ethanol production from lignocellulsoe—a review. Chin J Biotech. 2009;25(9):1321–8.
44. Chen HZ. Cellulose biotechnology. Beijing: Chemical Industrial Press; 2005.
45. Chen HZ, Li ZH. No-contaminative steam explosion and its application. J Cellul Sci Technol. 2002;10(3):47–52.
46. Xu FJ, Chen HZ. New developments of solid state fermentation in the applied aspects of resource and environment. Chin Biotechnol Bull. 2002;3:27–30.
47. Yang S, Ding WY, Chen HZ. Enzymatic hydrolysis of steam explosion rice straw in membrane bioreactor. Environ Sci. 2005;26(5):161–3.
48. Zhai W, Chen HZ, Ma RY. Structure characteristics of cellulose after dissolution and regeneration from the ionic liquid [bmim] Cl. J Beijing Univ Chem Technol. 2007;34(2):138–41.
49. Chen HZ, Li ZH. Bioreactor engineering. Adv Bio-eng. 1998;18(4):46–9.

50. Chen HZ, Qiu WH. The crucial problems and recent advance on producing fuel alcohol by fermentation of straw. Prog Chem. 2007;19(7):1116–21.
51. Qu Y. Lignocellulose enzymatic hydrolysis and biorefinery. Beijing: Chemial Industry Press; 2011.
52. Ding SY, Himmel ME. The maize primary cell wall microfibril: a new model derived from direct visualization. J Agric Food Chem. 2006;54(3):597–606.
53. Wyman CE, Dale BE, Elander RT. Coordinated development of leading biomass pretreatment technologies. Bioresour Technol. 2005;96(18):1959–66.
54. Chandra R, Bura R, Mabee W. Substrate pretreatment: the key to effective enzymatic hydrolysis of lignocellulosics? Biofuels. 2007;108:67–93.
55. Galbe M, Zacchi G. Pretreatment of lignocellulosic materials for efficient bioethanol production. Biofuels. 2007;108:41–65.
56. Chen HZ, Li ZH. Lignocellulose fractionation. J Cellul Sci Technol. 2003;11(4):31–40.
57. Alvira P, Tomás-Pejó E, Ballesteros M. Pretreatment technologies for an efficient bioethanol production process based on enzymatic hydrolysis: a review. Bioresour Technol. 2010;101 (13):4851–61.
58. Mosier N, Wyman C, Dale B. Features of promising technologies for pretreatment of lignocellulosic biomass. Bioresour Technol. 2005;96(6):673–86.
59. Yang B, Wyman CE. Pretreatment: the key to unlocking low-cost cellulosic ethanol. Biofuels, Bioprod Biorefin. 2008;2(1):26–40.
60. Saddler J, Ramos L, Breuil C. Steam pretreatment of lignocellulosic residues. Oxford: Oxford University Press; 1993.
61. Wang L, Zhang Z, Qu Y. Biomass recalcitrance: deconstructing the plant cell wall for bioenergy. Beijing: Chemical Industrial Press; 2012.
62. Chen HZ, Wang L. Research progress on key process and integrated eco-industrial chains of biobased products-proposal of biobased product process engineeing. Chin J Process Eng. 2008;8(4):676–81.
63. Jin SY, Chen HZ. Structural properties and enzymatic hydrolysis of rice straw. Process Biochem. 2006;41(6):1261–4.
64. He L. Straw super molecular characterization. North China Electric Power University; 2009.
65. Song P, Hu M, Yao J. Process equipment and control engineering and process engineering. High Educ Chem Eng. 2004;2:79–82.

Chapter 2
Principle of Gas Explosion Technology

Based on non-pollution low-pressure gas explosion technology, the author has successfully established a series of new gas explosion technology such as clean pulping, hemp clean degumming, preparation of humic acid, and low-activity xylo-oligosaccharide from straw and industrialization demonstration. The author broaden gas explosion technology to processing field of food, fruits, vegetables, and other natural materials and to development area of biobased chemicals, material, and energy. Gas explosion technology has been exploited as a common platform technology for biomass refining, but there is no analysis of transfer laws and action mechanism in gas explosion process based on the perspective of biomass feedstock characteristics. This chapter systematically analyzed the influence of raw material parameters, operating parameters, equipment parameters, and product parameters on gas explosion performance. The relationship between the mechanical properties of cell wall and heat and mass transfer, and momentum transfer of gas explosion process in transfer perspective were also analyzed. The relationship between maximum energy dissipation on material of the instantaneous discharge pressure stage and temperature, and moisture content were explored. Additionally, the relationship between discharge port area and material particle size based on the maximum energy dissipation was optimized. Material moisture content, particle size, and discharge area were further taken into gas explosion intensity factor R, and the meaning of gas explosion intensity was enriched. In the view of heat transfer, the energy consumption of the gas explosion process and the relationships between them were analyzed; the effect of initial moisture content, height-to-diameter ratio of gas explosion tank, loading coefficient, and temperature factors on gas explosion energy consumption was systemically observed. Based on the purpose of removing the secondary barrier in cellulose enzymatic hydrolysis, which is brought by pretreatment process, this chapter studied the thermodynamics and kinetic rules of hemicellulose and lignin degradation, generation, and dissolution in gas explosion process.

H. Chen, *Gas Explosion Technology and Biomass Refinery*,
DOI 10.1007/978-94-017-7414-7_2

2.1 The Main Parameters Affecting the Gas Explosion Process

2.1.1 Overview

There are several factors affecting the gas explosion process [1].

① Acid hydrolysis and thermal degradation. In gas explosion process, the hot steam with high pressure penetrates into the cellulosic feedstock and then the internal void of fibers. The combined effects of water vapor and heat result in acidic degradation and thermal degradation of cellulosic feedstocks. The low molecular weight substances then dissolve out, and the polymerization degree of fiber drops down.

② Mechanical tearing. When high-pressure steam is released, the hot steam molecules penetrate into internal void of fiber in the form of airflow speed released from closed pores. The hot steam inside or around the fiber flows out at high speed, which makes the fiber mechanical breakage to a certain extent. The fault is not only manifested as the fracture of glycosidic bonds in cellulose macromolecules and breakage of cellulose internal hydrogen bonds, but also reflected in the destruction of amorphous region and partial destruction of the crystalline regions.

③ Destructive effects of hydrogen. In gas explosion process, water steam penetrates into pores of fibers, and hydrogen bonds with partial hydroxyl on cellulose molecule chain were formed. At the same time, the high-temperature and high-pressure water conditions will exacerbate the destruction of hydrogen bonds inside cellulose, free new hydroxyl, and increase the intramolecular hydrogen bonds of cellulose. When intramolecular hydrogen bonds were broken, cellulose was rapidly cooled to room temperature. The supramolecular structure of cellulose was then frozen, and only a small part of the hydrogen bond was recombined. This allows solvent molecules easy go into space between the sheets and further damages the residual intramolecular hydrogen bonds and accelerates completely broken of other grain zone.

④ Structural rearrangement. Under the high temperature and high pressure, hydrogen bonds within cellulose molecules are destroyed to a certain extent. The mobility of cellulose chain increases which is conducive to orderly structure of cellulose. At the same time, the cellulose molecular chain is broken, so that the cellulose chain is more easily rearranged.

It is generally believed that in the process of gas explosion, hemicellulose is partly hydrolyzed and converted into monosaccharides and oligomers, while the lignin is degraded into sugars and phenolic oligomer. The acetyl hydrolyzed from hemicellulose chain would generate acetate under the high temperature, which would intensify the hydrolysis of glucosidic bond in hemicellulose and β-ester bond in lignin. Therefore, the bigger the intensity of pretreatment in a certain range, the greater the degree of degradation of hemicellulose and lignin, and the fractionation effect is more obvious.

Operation conditions for gas explosion are related to raw material type, material use, and the performance of explosion tank. (1) There is a great difference of gas explosion conditions between straw and wood. (2) The requirements of plant raw material for pulping, chemical fiber, and biotransformation vary greatly. Therefore, different conditions of gas explosion can also be taken into account. For example, in order to get high yield pulp, appropriate measures are taken to prevent the cellulose degradation. From total utilization of biomass point of view, it should be at the lowest cost to obtain maximum yield of three components. (3) Considering gas explosion conditions from the engineering point of view, it is mainly the uniformity of gas cooking, namely the vapor transfer characteristics, which are highly correlated with the initial moisture content, particle size, material bulk density, and loading coefficient. (4) Performance of gas explosion tank also has influence on pretreatment effect, such as the ratio of discharge port diameter to the tank diameter, decompression velocity, shape of outlet pipe, and the volume of buffer tank. In addition, holding pressure and holding time are the main factors affecting gas explosion performance.

2.1.2 *Effect of Material Parameters on Gas Explosion*

2.1.2.1 The Structure and Composition of Raw Material

The influence of gas explosion on component separation and supramolecular structure is closely related to the types and sources of the lignocellulose materials. For different kinds of lignocellulose materials, the chemical compositions (cellulose, hemicellulose, and lignin) are not the same. For example, the herbaceous and woody material requires different intensities of gas explosion. Even for the same kind of material, morphology, structure, and content of the cell are also different, such as the fiber cells with wall thickness and small cavity and parenchyma cells within wall and big cavity. Thus, vapor permeation and physical resistance for tearing are different, which affect the gas explosion pretreatment efficiency.

Herbal lignocellulosic materials have the following characteristics [2].

1. Structure is loose with low lignin content and high hemicellulose content; therefore, acetyl groups in hemicellulose are hydrolyzed in gas explosion process. The content of acetic acid is high, which has catalytic effect on raw materials. Herbal lignocellulosic materials are easily degraded in gas explosion process.
2. Phenolic hydroxyl group content of lignin in herbal lignocellulose is higher than that in wood materials.

According to the characteristics and properties, the wood is divided into softwood and hardwood.

Needlebush was named by its conifer leaves. At the same time, because needlebush is relatively soft, it is also called the softwood. Softwood is commonly represented by red pine, white pine, pinus, picea, basswood, poplar, etc. The cavity of softwood includes resin and tannin compounds. So softwood is often colored, elastic, and waterproof and is not easily affected by chemical reagent. It is a poor conductor of electricity, heat, and sound. The diameter of atypical cell of softwood is 30 μm, and the thickness is 1–2 μm. There are catheters between cells. Softwood material contains tracheid, ray cells, and ray tracheid. Tracheid is accounted for more than 90 % of material volume, which length is about 1.5–5.6 mm and width about 30–75 μm.

Broadleaf wood is named by its broad leaves. Because broadleaf wood is hard, it is generally called the hardwood. Hardwood is commonly represented by walnut, yellow pineapple, camphor wood, catalpa wood, phoebe, willow, schimasuperba, locust, maple, teak, rosewood, red sandalwood, oak, aspen, west African rosewood, mahogany, cherry, beech, etc.

Hardwood contains libriform wood fiber, fiber tracheids and tracheid, which are both called wood fiber. Wood fiber with length of 0.7–1.7 mm, width of 20–40 m, accounts for 25–35 % of the wood volume, among which libriform wood fiber accounts for the most. Because of the tight structure, lignin content (20–24 %) is lower than softwood, and the pentosan content is high, which is generally between 21 and 24 %.

Comparison of structure and composition of hardwood, softwood, and herbage as well as their effects on gas explosion is shown in Table 2.1.

2.1.2.2 Particle Size and Pore Size Distribution

The best acting site for gas explosion is within cells. The cell size for different materials is not the same. So as to achieve the best effect of gas explosion, the particle size of the material should be at the cellular level. If particle size of the material is too large, it is not easy for steam permeation, the power of explosion is weakened, and tearing resistance is increased. If the particle size is too small, the steam cannot be maintained within cells, which lost the physical tearing effect and increases the energy consumption for precrushing material. It is also closely related to the gas explosion effect and the porosity of raw material. The morphology and structure of materials depend on the material porosity. High porosity is beneficial to steam or media to penetrate, which is conducive to the explosion pretreatment It is difficult to penetrate with small porosity and the tear resistance is high in these media. It then requires more severe gas explosion conditions.

The dead cells of plant are the cavity structure and assume each cell as a mini-tank of gas explosion. In the moment of instantaneous decompression, water intracellular vaporizes, further increasing the initial pressure inside the cell. A large different pressure forms inside and outside the cell. This state is not stable and will work on the cell wall, causing cell wall tore. Therefore, in order to achieve good tear effect, ideal explosion sites are in cavity, rather than in the boundary of cells.

Table 2.1 Structure and composition of hardwood, softwood, herbage, and their effects on gas explosion

	Hardwood	Softwood	Herbage	Gas explosion effect
Classification	Dicotyledon in angiosperm	Gymnosperm	Monocotyledon in angiosperm	
Secondary xylem	Catheter (0.2–1.3 mm), wood fiber (tracheid, fiber tracheids-bordered pit, libriform wood fiber-simple pit), wood parenchymatous cell, wood ray parenchyma cells	Tracheid (2–5 mm), no perforated wood ray cells and ray tracheid	Catheter and fiber cell	Tracheid arranged regular in softwood but scattered arranged in hardwood; thus, softwood is difficult pretreated for gas explosion. For herbage, secondary xylem is embedded in parenchymal cell, and it is easy for gas explosion
Cross-field	No	Ray cells crossed with fiber cells	No	Heat and mass transfer resistance of media is high in cross-field; thus, the pretreatment effect for softwood is bad under the same intensity as hardwood and herbage
Resin duct	No	Partly have	No	Resin duct will hinder heat and mass transfer, decreasing the gas explosion effect
Tracheal tissue	Have porous	No porous	Have	No porous imply the high penetration resistance
Fiber characteristics	Fiber length 0.7–1.7 mm, width 20–40 μm, accounted for 25–35 % of the total volume	Tracheid accounted for 90 % of the total volume, with length of 1.5–5.6 mm, width of 30–75 μm	Fiber cell with length of 1.0–2.0 mm, width of 10–20 μm	Softwood with larger length of fiber cell is hard for gas explosion (the larger the length fiber cell, the bigger the binding force with surrounding tissue)
Fiber arrangement regularity	Fiber arrangement is not regular and depends on the species	Fiber arrangement is regular, and structure is uniform	Fiber arrangement is regular, but the content of fiber cell is low	Fiber cell with highly lignification, fiber cell with high content and arranged regular is difficult for gas explosion

(continued)

Table 2.1 (continued)

	Hardwood	Softwood	Herbage	Gas explosion effect
Parenchymatous tissue	20–30 %, 2 times of softwood	7–8 %	The main structure	Softwood with low content of parenchyma cell is difficult for steam permeation and hard to break
Fiber cell wall	Partly have S3 layer	S3	S3	Possessing S3, it is hard for heat and mass transfer
Secondary wall of fiber cell	Thickness of S1 is larger than that of softwood	Degree of lignification is low, but crystalline degree is high in S1, vertical angle with fiber axis	/	/
	S2	3–10 μm, accounted for 70–80 % of total thickness of cell wall, the angle with fiber axis is 10–40°	/	Fibrillation in pulping is to loose the microfiber in S2, but S2 wrapped in S1 layer is hard for fibrillation
	S3	The angle with fiber axes 70–80°	/	/
Lignin	Low, 20–24 %	High	Low	Softwood with high content of lignin is hard for gas explosion
Pentosan	High, 21–24 %	Low	/	Softwood with low content of pentosan and acetyl groups is hard for gas explosion
Papermaking	Generally recognized that wood with uniform structure deep color is suitable for pulping	Density with too large or too small is both unsuited for pulping, and the appropriate density is 400–600 kg/m^3	/	/

(continued)

Table 2.1 (continued)

	Hardwood	Softwood	Herbage	Gas explosion effect
Air-dry density	/	0.32–0.70 g/m^3	/	0.240–1.130 g/m^3
Ratio of channel volume to the total volume	Moderation	Small	Large	The heat and mass transfer rate of herbal is much higher than that of wood
Lignin monomer	Syringyl, with ultraviolet absorption peak at 274–276 nm, is easily removed in alkali treatment	Guaiacyl, with ultraviolet absorption peak at 281–285 nm, is hard to remove by alkali treatment	Compared with wood, the content of phenolic hydroxyl group in herbal is the highest	In gas explosion, the chemical reaction is mainly the acid catalytic reaction. Guaiacyl, which is hard to remove by acid, would hinder the cell wall degradation
Molecular weight of lignin	High molecular weight, such as molecular weight of birch is 18,000		Low molecular weight, such as molecular weight of wheat straw is 8854	Lignin with low molecular weight is easy for dissolving out, so as to improve the accessibility of cellulose
Hemicellulose	Xylan	Glucan	Xylan with low molecular weight and low degree of polymerization	Under the acidic conditions of gas explosion, glucan in softwood is hardly degraded, and the herbal is easily degraded
Chemical bond	No ester bond	Few ester bond	A large number of ester bond	Ester bond is easily hydrolyzed and broken; thus, the herbal is easily degraded in gas explosion

Material used for gas explosion is best to reach the cell scale rather than the organization level. Because of the particle size with the organization scale, penetration resistance for steam and tear resistance are high. Once the work of steam on the material did not reach the modulus of rupture of cell wall, energy would convert into heat and sound, resulting in a waste of energy.

It can be seen in Table 2.2: (1) Thickness of fiber cell wall for *gramineae*, hardwood, and softwood progressively increases, while the cell wall thickness directly determines the resistance in gas explosion process; (2) The fiber length of *gramineae*, hardwood, and softwood is obvious, which determines the different particle size of materials before gas explosion. Taking corn straw as an example, the average fiber cell length of corn straw is 0.99 mm. If the particle size of material prepared for gas explosion is less than 0.99 mm, almost every cell is broken. There is no integrated cell wall structure to maintain the internal pressure of cell and to cause pressure rebound in the process of instantaneous decompression. In that case, steam is not likely to do volume work on the cell wall, losing the significance of physical tear. However, if the particle size of material is too large and composed of multi-cells, it would cause huge pressure rebound in instantaneous decompression, but tissue resistance and permeation resistance for steam are large, which would reduce the tearing effect. Therefore, the proper particle size directly determines the gas explosion pretreatment effect, which obeys the same law for softwood and hardwood.

Figure 2.1 shows the experimental results of gas explosion of corn straw. It can be seen that the best particle size of corn straw for gas explosion is 8 mm. At 8 mm, the degradation rate of hemicellulose and enzymatic hydrolysis rate reaches the maximum. When the particle size is less than 2 mm, the exposure rate of the carbohydrate and the specific surface area of material increases, respectively, with the particle size decreasing. The hemicellulose degradation rate and enzymatic hydrolysis yields increase with the increase of particle size, but they are still lower than that of with particle size at 8 mm. It is known that the average length of corn straw fiber cells is 1 mm [3], and the optimum size of 8 mm is larger than the single cell length. When the particle size is too large, which is beyond 15 mm, the enzymatic hydrolysis yields and hemicellulose degradation rate both decrease, indicating that the oversize of material increase the heat and mass transfer resistance and tear resistance and decrease gas explosion performance. The undersized material destructs its cell integrity, which is not conducive to holding pressure, thereby reducing the physical tear effect.

2.1.2.3 Initial Moisture Content and Rehydration Operation

Rehydration before gas explosion is also one of the most important factors affecting pretreatment efficiency. Rehydration operation is intended to regulate the initial moisture content and softens the fiber, which is conducive to fractionate the fiber without mechanical damage in gas explosion. At the same time, rehydration operation makes the fiber swelling to a certain extent and increase the degree of

Table 2.2 Comparison of fiber morphology of common plant materials [3]

	Materials	Average length/mm	Average width/μm	Ratio of length to width	Cell wall thickness/μm	Cavity diameter/μm	Ratio of cell wall to cavity	Non-fiber cell content/%
Gramineae	Rice straw	0.92	8.1	114	3.3	1.5	4.4	54.0
	Wheat straw	1.32	12.9	102	5.2	2.5	4.16	37.9
	Reed	1.12	9.7	115	3.0	3.4	1.77	35.5
	Silvergrass	1.36	17.1	80	6.17	3.7	3.6	34.5
	Miscan stem	1.64	16.4	100	–	–	–	53.1
	Bamboo reed	1.28	14.6	88	–	–	–	61.5
	Bagasse	1.73	22.5	77	3.28	17.9	0.36	35.7
	Chinese alpine rush	2.10	10.4	202	3.3	3.1	2.13	29.5
	Moso bamboo	2.00	16.2	123	6.6	2.90	4.55	31.2
	Sinocalamusaffinis	1.99	15.0	133	–	–	–	16.2
	Corn straw	0.99	13.2	75	–	–	–	69.2
	Sorghum stalk	1.18	12.1	109	–	–	–	51.3
	Cotton core	0.83	27.7	30	2.7	18.9	0.28	28.7
	Cotton bast	2.26	20.6	113	5.8	4.3	2.70	–

(continued)

Table 2.2 (continued)

	Materials	Average length/mm	Average width/μm	Ratio of length to width	Cell wall thickness/μm	Cavity diameter/μm	Ratio of cell wall to cavity	Non-fiber cell content/%
Softwood	Spruce	3.06	51.9	59	–	–	–	–
	Masson pine	3.61	50.0	72	Early wood 3.8	Early wood 33.1	Early wood 0.23	1.5
					Late wood 8.7	Late wood 16.6	Late wood 1.05	
	Pinuskoraiensis	3.62	54.3	67	Early wood 3.5	Early wood 27.7	Early wood 0.25	1.8
					Late wood 4.3	Late wood 14.0	Late wood 0.61	
	Larch	3.41	44.4	77	Early wood 3.5	Early wood 33.6	Early wood 0.21	1.5
					Late wood 9.3	Late wood 12.6	Late wood 1.48	
	Abiesnephrolepis	3.29	51.9	63	–	–	–	–
Hardwood	Poplar	0.86	17.4	50	–	–	–	23.3
	White birch	1.21	18.7	65	–	–	–	26.7
	Red birch	1.27	19.6	65	–	–	–	–
	Eucalyptus	0.68	16.8	43	–	–	–	17.6
	Batai	1.14	36.4	31	–	–	–	–

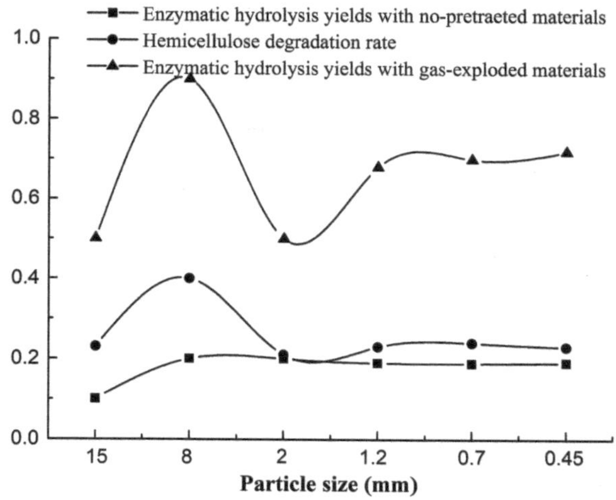

Fig. 2.1 Particle size and its effect on gas explosion

steam penetration, so as to improve the pretreatment efficiency. In addition, the water stored in the cell cavity will be flash evaporation and volume expansion in instantaneous decompression, doing volume work on the cell wall, which is equivalent to increase the power source for physical tear. However, the bigger initial moisture content is not the better. When moisture content increase, both the energy consumption and the steam condensation will be more, which will reduce the tearing effect. So the material before gas explosion needs to be adjusted to suitable moisture content, in order to promote high-temperature cooking and physical tear.

$$\text{Recovery rate of hemicellulose} = \frac{\text{sugar by water extract} - \text{sugar in control group}}{\text{raw material quantity} \times (1 - \text{miosture content}) \times \text{hemicellulose}} \times 100\,\%$$

$$\text{Loss of hemicellulose} = 1 - \frac{(\text{sugar by water extract} - \text{sugar in control group}) \times 0.9 + (1 - \text{water extraction rate}) \times \text{hemicellulose content in residue}}{\text{hemicellulose content in control group}} \times 100\,\%$$

Figures 2.2 and 2.3 show the properties change before and after gas explosion. It can be seen that the initial moisture content of materials with 30 % before gas explosion is beneficial to the recovery rate of hemicellulose and pulp properties improved. Therefore, the appropriate initial moisture content can promote gas explosion efficiency.

Considering gas explosion conditions from engineering aspect, it is mainly the uniformity of gas transmission, which is highly correlated with the initial moisture content. The above-mentioned study shows that when the moisture content is about 34 %, both the hemicellulose recovery and cellulose hydrolysis rate are high. The initial moisture content is highly correlated with heat transfer and also may relate with hemicellulose hydrolysis kinetics and lignin softening [1].

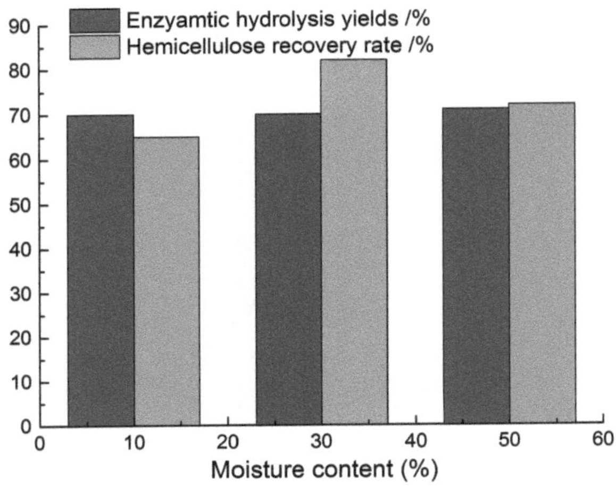

Fig. 2.2 Effect of the initial moisture content of materials on gas explosion effect (1.5 Mpa, 10 min) [1]

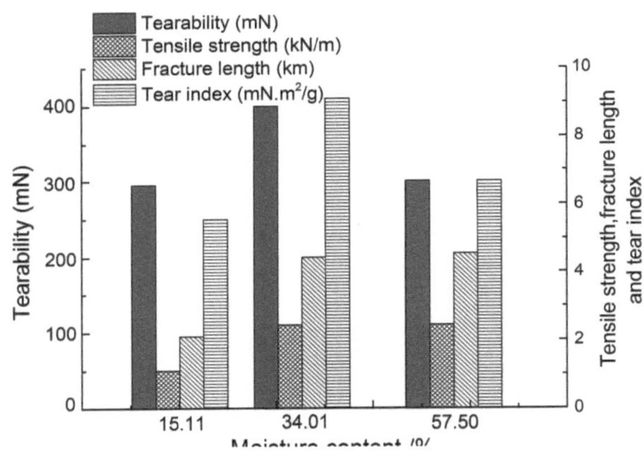

Fig. 2.3 Effect of the initial moisture content of materials on property of pulp (1.5 Mpa, 10 min) [1]

2.1.2.4 Loading Coefficient and Bulk Density

The loading coefficient and bulk density affect the heat and mass transfer rate and coefficient. When bulk density is too large, the heat and mass transfer resistance increases, causing the internal and external temperatures of the material are not uniform, resulting in inhomogeneous gas explosion efficiency.

2.1.3 Effect of Operating Parameters on Gas Explosion

2.1.3.1 Pre-impregnation

Pre-impregnation has a great influence on gas explosion effect. With or without the addition of chemical reagents, the amount of added chemical reagent, soaking time, temperature, and pressure will affect the rehydration. With or without the addition of chemical reagents, the dosage of chemical reagent, soaking time, temperature, and pressure will affect the rehydration, pH, density and hardness of materials, then has a significantly impact on steam penetration, reaction rate in high-temperature cooking, the physical tear resistance, and so on.

2.1.3.2 Holding Temperature

High-temperature cooking in gas explosion process is the premise of physical tear. Besides, auto-hydrolyze effect in high-temperature cooking process leads to hemicellulose degradation and lignin softening. According to the Arrhenius equation, the temperature is increased by 10 K and the degradation rate of raw materials is increased by 2–4 times. Therefore, the effect of temperature on gas explosion effect is significant.

2.1.3.3 Holding Pressure

Gas explosion process softens actually the fiber, hydrolyses the hemicellulose in high temperature, and weakens the bond between cellulose. Cellulose is torn in a sudden decompression. The pressure, namely temperature, affects the hemicellulose hydrolysis rate. At the same time, pressure is the only motivation power for physical tear. The time for holding pressure affects the degradation degree of hemicellulose and softening degree of lignin as well as the medium permeability.

2.1.3.4 Residence Time

Time aims at holding pressure process. As for chemical reaction, the temperature can increase the reaction rate, but formation rate of product is related to the reaction time. Thus, the time determines the product accumulation with a certain temperature. In the process of high-temperature cooking of gas explosion, hemicellulose would be degraded into pentose, and pentose would be further converted into furfural. Lignin would be degraded into small phenolic molecules. It has been known that furfural and phenolic compounds are potential inhibitors for fermentation, so the temperature of gas explosion could not be arbitrarily increased. To obtain a certain hemicellulose degradation rate and a smaller inhibitor formation rate, reducing the temperature and prolonging the time reasonably may be a good technical measure.

2.1.3.5 pH Value

The steam explosion process without the addition of acid and/or alkali is usually called autocatalytic process. Acetic acid is generated from acetyl in the cooking process, and it increases the acidity of the system. It also further promotes the degradation of hemicellulose, which also has a catalytic role in delignification. The acid–base gas explosion means to add acid and/or alkali as the catalyst in gas explosion process. Hydrochloric acid is beneficial to the degradation of hemicellulose and improves the cellulose hydrolysis rate, and ammonia or hydrogen peroxide is beneficial for degradation and dissolution of lignin.

2.1.4 Effect of Equipment Parameters on the Gas Explosion

2.1.4.1 Area of Discharge Port

The discharge port area influences the decompression velocity. It is generally acknowledged that the bigger discharge port area the better. First of all, there is no doubt that the bigger the discharge port area is, the greater the pressure drop (ΔP reaches the maximum and Δt reaches the minimum) and the bigger the superheat inside and outside cells. It illustrates that the greater the pressure rebound in material is, the larger the shock wave energy of steam acting on the cell wall, sharply tearing the cell.

2.1.4.2 Shape of Outlet Pipeline

In the process of instantaneous decompression of gas explosion, the material is transported at high speed through the pipeline to the receiver under the differential pressure of internal and external. Similar to the fluid flow in the pipeline, there is also the resistance of pipeline on transportation process of material, and the shape and structure of pipeline will cause inconsistent resistance. For example, straight pipe, bend pipe, or baffle and hammer in the inner wall of pipe all have the crushing effect on material to varying degrees. Therefore, according to the nature of material and product parameters, it should select the appropriate shape of outlet pipe.

2.1.4.3 Volume of Buffer Tank

In the first case, loading coefficient is small and the discharge port area is large enough; that is, the material can be discharged together in a very short period of time. In this case, the material does not represent a state of fluid being discharged successively, but discharged together as a group. So when the material enters into the pipeline, contacting with the barometric pressure, the pressure drop $\Delta P/\Delta t$ can reach the maximum. Because $\Delta P = P_1 - Pa$, $\Delta t = m/\rho A\ u$. In this case, the effect of buffer tank volume on gas explosion can be neglected.

In the second case, if loading coefficient is large, the discharge port area is relatively small, that is, the material is discharged in a period of time. So it can be imagined that the material discharged firstly would contact the atmospheric pressure, and the material would then contact the pressure, which is higher than atmospheric pressure caused by the flash of the preceding material. In this case, the pressure drop rate for the discharged material is not the same; that is, to say, the work for flash gas on material is not the same, causing a different physical tear effect. This is the fundamental reason for the inhomogeneity of gas explosion.

Therefore, based on the above analysis, the volume of buffer tank (or the outlet pressure) is an important factor influencing gas explosion effect, which has an effect on the uniformity of gas-exploded materials combined with the loading coefficient and discharge port area.

2.1.5 Relationship Between Product Parameters and Gas Explosion

2.1.5.1 Cell Inclusion

Generally speaking, vegetable oils and herbal medicine components both are in the cells, and gas explosion can destroy the cell wall to increase the extraction rate of these components. For cell inclusion extraction, gas explosion is aimed at to destroy the cell wall, not need to degrade hemicellulose. Moreover, high temperature may cause decomposition of drugs and oils to reduce the content or generate the toxic substances. Therefore, in this case, low-temperature gas explosion with the media of dry air or gas–steam mixture can play the role of physical tear, reducing the damaging effects of temperature on the chemical structure.

2.1.5.2 Degradation Products of Hemicellulose

Hemicellulose accounts for about 30 % of the dry matter in lignocellulose, and the recovery rate of hemicellulose sugar in the water washing solution of gas-exploded materials can reach about 80 %. This huge resource has aroused people's concern as a platform for ethanol fermentation or acid fermentation. A lot of researches have been done on hemicellulose degradation in gas explosion process and concluded that moderately reducing the temperature and the extension time of gas explosion can increase the degradation rate and recovery rate of hemicellulose.

2.1.5.3 Enzymatic Hydrolysis and Fermentation

When lignocellulose material used as enzymatic hydrolysis and fermentation substrate, the aim of the pretreatment is to increase the exposure rate of cellulose, improve the accessibility of cellulose, and reduce the content of fermentation inhibitors.

2.1.5.4 Degumming

Similar to the hemicellulose degradation, the aim of the pretreatment in this case is to increase the degradation rate of hemicellulose but avoiding damage of the cellulose. So the pretreatment conditions could not be too intense, and moderately reducing the temperature and prolonging the time of gas explosion contribute to degumming.

2.1.5.5 Pulping

As for pulping, the aim of pretreatment of lignocellulose is mainly to remove lignin, avoiding the damage of cellulose. The lignin removal of gas explosion is limited, so alkali cooking process is generally added subsequently. Because of gas-exploded materials with hemicellulose partly removed, pores increased and material density decreased, and alkali cooking time and temperature can be reduced.

2.2 Multi-scale Modeling of Biomass Pretreatment for Steam Explosion Condition Optimization

2.2.1 Overview

As it is one of the most economical and efficient biomass pretreatment technologies [4, 5], steam explosion was initially mistaken as a purely chemical process. The severity factor or modified severity factor of hydrothermal pretreatment processes is often used to describe the severity of the steam explosion process, as shown in Eqs. 2.1–2.6 in Table 2.3.

Two conclusions emerge from the effects of steam explosion on straw structure: (1) At high-temperature cooking, hemicellulose is degraded, lignin is solubilized, and cellulose binding is reduced [12]. (2) Under instantaneous decompression, superheated water flashes into steam and steam volume abruptly expands. The impact force generated by flashing and volume expansion destroys cell structure. In this stage, materials are torn into small pieces; fiber bundles are separated from one another and their structures loosen, thereby redistributing lignin; and cellulose is fully exposed.

The severity factor that currently used represents the relationship among time, temperature, and acid concentration. Although it enables the easy comparison of experimental results to facilitate process design and operation, it does not represent all the factors that affect pretreatment efficiency [9]. Unlike other hydrothermal pretreatment technologies, steam explosion is an effective fractionation technology that is characterized by physical tearing effects, which enhance lignocellulose defibration and increase specific surface area. Because the severity factor originates

Table 2.3 Severity factor or modified severity factor in hydrothermal pretreatment processes

No.	Equations	Literature derivation
(2.1)	$R = t \cdot \exp[(T_r - T_b)/14.75]$	Overend and Chornet [6]
(2.2)	$\text{In}\{[Pol]/[Pol]_0\} \propto [H^+]\exp[(T_r - T_b)/14.75]\Delta t + \text{constant}$	Chum et al. [7]
(2.3)	$R_{Br}^{+} = \frac{T}{T_{\text{iso}_r}}\exp\left[\frac{E_r}{ET_{\text{iso}_r}}\frac{T - T_{\text{iso}_r}}{T}\right]C_{H^+}t$ $R_{Bs}^{+} = \frac{T}{T_{\text{iso}_s}}\exp\left[\frac{E_s}{ET_{\text{iso}_s}}\frac{T - T_{\text{iso}_s}}{T}\right]C_{H^+}t$	Belkacemi et al. [8]
(2.4)	$R_O = \exp\left(\frac{T - T_{\text{ref}}}{\omega}\right)\frac{t_R^{\gamma}}{\gamma}$ $R_{OH} = \exp\left(\frac{X - X_{\text{ref}}}{\lambda X_{\text{ref}}}\right)\exp\left(\frac{T - T_{\text{ref}}}{\omega}\right)\frac{t_R^{\gamma}}{\gamma}$	Abatzoglou et al. [9]
(2.5)	$R_0 = \exp\left[\frac{1}{\omega_0}\left(1 - \frac{T_{\text{ref}}}{T}\right)\right]\frac{t^{\gamma}}{\gamma}$	Montane et al. [10]
(2.6)	$R = \frac{\frac{t}{\rho d^{1.5}}}{M\left(\frac{\phi D}{1 - \frac{1}{2}Ln\phi}\right)^{0.67}\left(\left(0.48\frac{\rho u}{\mu(1-\varepsilon)}\right)^{0.5}\left(\frac{\mu}{\rho}\right)^{0.33}\right)\cdot\Delta C} \cdot e^{\frac{T-100}{14.75}} \cdot 10^{-\text{pH}}$	Hosseini and Shah [11]

from hydrothermal pretreatment processes, it cannot represent the effects in the instantaneous decompression stage, but depicts those in the high-temperature cooking stage.

Hosseini and Shah [11] developed a model based on the diffusion of steam into biomass, taking particle size and process time into account (see Eq. 2.6). Although the mass transfer perspective dictates that chip size is considered first, Eq. (2.6) still represents the effects of high-temperature cooking on steam explosion. However, the equation does not depict the physical tearing effects of instantaneous decompression.

Physical tearing is affected by numerous factors such as chip size, material bulk density, material loading coefficient, and moisture content [13, 14]. The performance determinants of a pressure tank also considerably influences steam explosion results; these determinants include the height-to-diameter ratio of the tank, discharge port area [13], and buffer tank volume. Holding pressure (temperature) is an another important factor.

We analyze physical tearing in instantaneous decompression on the basis of the theories of mass transfer, heat transfer, and momentum transfer as well as on brittle fracture mechanics. We consider particle size, moisture content, and discharge port area in the analysis. An enriched and comprehensive severity factor represents the effects of high-temperature cooking on steam explosion and the physical tearing effects of instantaneous decompression. Such representations enable the comprehensive interpretation of the mechanism of steam explosion technology and serve as engineering reference in designing the equipment and selecting the conditions for steam explosion technology.

2.2.2 Multi-scale Model Eduction in the Instantaneous Decompression Stage of Steam Explosion

2.2.2.1 Model Assumption

We assume that the height-to-diameter ratio of a tank is unchanged and that loading density does not affect steam transfer. The volume of a buffer tank (also called a receiver) is sufficiently large, suggesting that the environmental pressure of exported materials stabilizes at normal pressure. Hence, the variable factors are holding pressure, holding time, chip size, moisture content, and discharge port area.

Ensuring effective fractionation necessitates physical tearing at the cellular level, implying that each cell is regarded as a "micropressure tank." A simple model for steam explosion at the cellular level is shown in Fig. 2.4.

The cell of a material is assumed to be a sphere with radius d; m denotes the total mass of the material; w (that is, $m_w = m \times w$, $m_s = m \times (1-w)$) represents the moisture content; P_1, T_1, ρ_1, and m_0 are the initial state (state 1) parameters of steam in the pressure tank; P_a, T_2, ρ_2, and $\mathrm{m}_0 + m_w$ denote the instantaneous explosion state (state 2) parameters of steam; and v_1, v_2 are the speeds of steam and solid material, respectively. The hypothetical intermediate state is easy to interpret and calculate. P_3, T_2, ρ_3, and $m_0 + m_\mathrm{w} \cdot q$ represent the intermediate state parameters of steam, and q is the vaporization ratio of heated water.

2.2.2.2 Establishment of a Brittle Fracture Criterion for Materials

The superheated water in cell lumens instantly flashes into steam under decompression, indicating that $P_3 \gg P_1$. When the brittle fracture process of materials is considered a quasi-static process, brittle fracture depends on maximal internal pressure P_3.

The stress in closed elastomers without external loads is expressed as follows:

$$\sigma_{iK} = -P\delta_{iK} \tag{2.7}$$

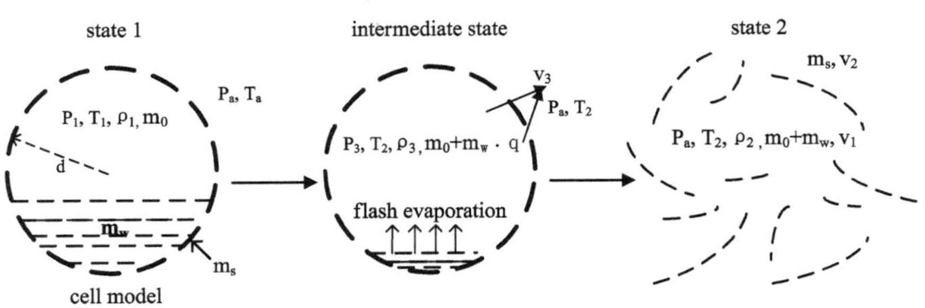

Fig. 2.4 Simple model for steam explosion at the cellular level

The elastic energy per unit mass of solid material before and after brittle fracture is written as follows [15]:

$$U_{s1} = \frac{P_3^2}{2K_s\rho_s} \tag{2.8}$$

$$U_{s2} = \frac{P_a^2}{2K_s\rho_s} \tag{2.9}$$

where K_s is the bulk modulus of solid material.

Therefore, dissipated energy E of solid material in the brittle fracture process is given as follows:

$$E = (U_{s1} - U_{s2}) \cdot m_s \tag{2.10}$$

Substituting U_{s1}, U_{s2} from Eqs. (2.8) and (2.9) into Eq. (2.10) yields the following:

$$E = \frac{P_3^2 - P_a^2}{2 \cdot K_s \cdot \rho_s} \cdot m_s \tag{2.11}$$

In instantaneous decompression, the superheated water releases a reasonable amount of heat, thereby inducing partial vaporization into steam:

$$m_w \cdot c_m \cdot (T_1 - T_2) = m_w \cdot q \cdot r \tag{2.12}$$

where c_m is the specific heat of water, kJ/kg; and r denotes the heat of water vaporization at T_a.

According to the state equation of ideal gas,

$$P_1V = n_1RT_1 \tag{2.13}$$

$$P_3V = n_2RT_2 \tag{2.14}$$

Thus,

$$\frac{P_3}{P_1} = \frac{n_2T_2}{n_1T_1} = \frac{m_0 + m_w \cdot q}{m_0} \times \frac{T_2}{T_1} \tag{2.15}$$

Because

$$m_0 = \frac{MP_1V}{RT_1} \tag{2.16}$$

Substituting Eqs. (2.12) and (2.16) into Eq. (2.15) yields the following:

$$P_3 = \left[\frac{rMP_1V + m_w \cdot c_m(T_1 - T_2) \cdot R \cdot T_1}{rMV}\right] \times \frac{T_2}{T_1} \tag{2.17}$$

Assume

$$\frac{T_2}{T_1} \approx 0.8, P_3 = P_1 + \frac{0.2 \times m_w c_m T_1^2}{rMV} \tag{2.18}$$

Substituting P_3 from Eq. (2.18) into Eq. (2.11) results in the following:

$$E = \frac{\left(P_1 + \frac{0.2 \times m_w c_m T_1^2}{rMV}\right)^2 - Pa^2}{2 \cdot K_s \cdot \rho_s} \cdot m_s \tag{2.19}$$

2.2.2.3 Establishment of Conservation Equations

1. Energy conservation equation

The energy in the intermediate state includes internal energy $e_1 \cdot (m_0 + m_w \cdot q)$ and potential energy $\frac{\kappa}{\kappa-1} \cdot \frac{(m_0+m_w) \cdot P_3}{\rho_3}$. The energy in state 2 includes internal energy $e_2 \cdot (m_0 + m_w \cdot q)$, kinetic energy $\frac{1}{2}(m_0 + m_w \cdot q)v_1^2 + \frac{1}{2}m_s v_2^2$, and potential energy $\frac{\kappa}{\kappa-1} \cdot \frac{(m_0+m_w \cdot q) \cdot P_a}{\rho_2}$.

According to the law of energy conservation,

$$\begin{aligned} e_1(m_0 + m_w \cdot q) &+ \frac{\kappa}{\kappa - 1} \cdot \frac{(m_0 + m_w \cdot q) \cdot P_3}{\rho_3} \\ &= e_2(m_0 + m_w) + \frac{1}{2}(m_0 + m_w \cdot q)v_1^2 + \frac{1}{2}m_s v_2^2 \\ &+ \frac{\kappa}{\kappa - 1} \cdot \frac{(m_0 + m_w \cdot q) \cdot P_a}{\rho_2} + E \end{aligned} \tag{2.20}$$

where e_1 and e_2 are the internal energy of the unit mass of steam in the intermediate states 1 and 2, respectively, and κ denotes the polytropic exponent of steam [16].

The condensate state equation indicates that

$$P = A \cdot \rho^{-\kappa} \tag{2.21}$$

$$e = \frac{A}{\kappa - 1} \cdot \rho^{\kappa-1} \tag{2.22}$$

where A is a constant that depends on steam.

We can determine the relationship among e, P, and ρ as follows:

$$e = \frac{P}{\rho(\kappa - 1)} \tag{2.23}$$

Thus,

$$e_1 = \frac{P_3}{\rho_3(\kappa - 1)} \tag{2.24}$$

$$e_2 = \frac{P_a}{\rho_2(\kappa - 1)} \tag{2.25}$$

Substituting e from Eqs. (2.24) and (2.25) into Eq. (2.20) yields the following:

$$\begin{aligned}
&\frac{P_3}{\rho_3(\kappa - 1)}(m_0 + m_w \cdot q) + \frac{\kappa}{\kappa - 1} \cdot \frac{(m_0 + m_w \cdot q) \cdot P_3}{\rho_3} \\
&= \frac{P_a}{\rho_2(\kappa - 1)}(m_0 + m_w \cdot q) + \frac{1}{2}(m_0 + m_w \cdot q)v_1^2 + \frac{1}{2}m_s v_2^2 \\
&+ \frac{\kappa}{\kappa - 1} \cdot \frac{(m_0 + m_w \cdot q) \cdot P_a}{\rho_2} + E
\end{aligned} \tag{2.26}$$

Substituting E from Eq. (2.19) into Eq. (2.26) results in the following:

$$\begin{aligned}
&\frac{P_3}{\rho_3(\kappa - 1)}(m_0 + m_w \cdot q) + \frac{\kappa}{\kappa - 1} \cdot \frac{(m_0 + m_w \cdot q) \cdot P_3}{\rho_3} \\
&= \frac{P_a}{\rho_2(\kappa - 1)}(m_0 + m_w \cdot q) + \frac{1}{2}m_s v_2^2 + \frac{1}{2}(m_0 + m_w \cdot q)v_1^2 \\
&+ \frac{\kappa}{\kappa - 1} \cdot \frac{(m_0 + m_w \cdot q) \cdot P_a}{\rho_2} + \frac{\left(P_1 + \frac{0.2 \times m_w c_m T_1^2}{rMV}\right)^2 - P_a^2}{2 \cdot K_s \cdot \rho_s} \cdot m_s
\end{aligned} \tag{2.27}$$

2. Momentum conservation equation

The impulse that acts on solid material is equal to the increased momentum of materials in instantaneous decompression.

Because the cell of a material is assumed to be a sphere, its total stress is given as follows[17]:

$$\sigma = (P_3 - P_a)\pi d^2 \tag{2.28}$$

$$(P_3 - P_a)\pi d^2 \times t = m_s \cdot v_2 \tag{2.29}$$

where t is assumed as the decompression times, which is inversely proportional to discharge port area A.

We assume that the speed of escaping steam is constant as sound velocity [18]. Hence, the time at which steam escapes depends on the discharge port area, and $t = \frac{\eta}{A}$, where η is a coefficient that depends on the design of the discharge port. Therefore,

$$\frac{(P_3 - P_a)\pi d^2 \times \eta}{A} = m_s \cdot v_2 \tag{2.30}$$

Substituting Eq. (2.30) into Eq. (2.27) results in the following:

$$\begin{aligned}
&\frac{P_3}{\rho_3(\kappa - 1)}(m_0 + m_w \cdot q) + \frac{\kappa}{\kappa - 1} \cdot \frac{(m_0 + m_w \cdot q) \cdot P_3}{\rho_3} \\
&= \frac{P_a}{\rho_2(\kappa - 1)}(m_0 + m_w \cdot q) + \frac{\left(P_1 + \frac{0.2 \times m_w c_m T_1^2}{rMV} - P_a\right)^2 \cdot \pi^2 \cdot d^4 \cdot \eta^2}{2 \cdot A^2 \cdot m_s} \\
&\quad + \frac{1}{2}(m_0 + m_w \cdot q)v_1^2 + \frac{\kappa}{\kappa - 1} \cdot \frac{(m_0 + m_w \cdot q) \cdot P_a}{\rho_2} \\
&\quad + \frac{\left(P_1 + \frac{0.2 \times m_w c_m T_1^2}{rMV}\right)^2 - P_a^2}{2 \cdot K_s \cdot \rho_s} \cdot m_s
\end{aligned} \tag{2.31}$$

Substituting Eqs. (2.12), (2.16), and (2.18) into Eq. (2.31) yields the following:

$$\begin{aligned}
&\frac{\left(P_1 + \frac{0.2 \times m_w c_m T_1^2}{rMV}\right)(MP_1 Vr + 0.2 \times m_w c_m R T_1^2)(\kappa + 1)}{\rho_3 R T_1 r(\kappa - 1)} \\
&= \frac{P_a \cdot (MP_1 Vr + 0.2 \times m_w \cdot c_m \cdot RT_1^2) \cdot (\kappa + 1)}{RT_1 r \rho_2(\kappa - 1)} + \frac{\left(P_1 + \frac{0.2 \times m_w c_m T_1^2}{rMV} - P_a\right)^2 \cdot \pi^2 \cdot d^4 \cdot \eta^2}{2 \cdot A^2 \cdot m_s} \\
&\quad + \frac{1}{2}\left[\frac{MP_1 Vr + 0.2 \times m_w \cdot c_m \cdot RT_1^2}{RT_1 r}\right] v_1^2 + \frac{\left(P_1 + \frac{0.2 \times m_w c_m T_1^2}{rMV}\right)^2 - P_a^2}{2 \cdot K_s \cdot \rho_s} \cdot m_s
\end{aligned} \tag{2.32}$$

In instantaneous decompression, speed of steam v_1 is equal to sound velocity. The sound velocity is expressed as follows [18]:

$$c = \sqrt{\left(\frac{\partial P_1}{\partial \rho_1}\right)_s} = \sqrt{\kappa \frac{P_3}{\rho_3}} \tag{2.33}$$

Substituting v_1 from Eq. (2.33) into Eq. (2.32) results in the following:

$$\frac{\left(P_1+\frac{0.2\times m_w c_m T_1^2}{rMV}\right)(MP_1Vr+0.2\times m_w c_m RT_1^2)(\kappa+1)}{\rho_3 RT_1 r(\kappa-1)}$$
$$=\frac{P_a\cdot(MP_1Vr+0.2\times m_w\cdot c_m\cdot RT_1^2)\cdot(\kappa+1)}{RT_1 r\rho_2(\kappa-1)}+\frac{\left(P_1+\frac{0.2\times m_w c_m T_1^2}{rMV}-P_a\right)^2\cdot\pi^2\cdot d^4\cdot\eta^2}{2\cdot A^2\cdot m_s}$$
$$+\frac{1}{2}\frac{(MP_1Vr+0.2\times m_w\cdot c_m\cdot RT_1^2)\left(P_1+\frac{0.2\times m_w c_m T_1^2}{rMV}\right)}{RT_1 r\rho_3}+\frac{\left(P_1+\frac{0.2\times m_w c_m T_1^2}{rMV}\right)^2-P_a^2}{2\cdot K_s\cdot\rho_s}\cdot m_s \tag{2.34}$$

2.2.3 *Multi-scale Model Connotation*

2.2.3.1 Condition Optimization for Steam Explosion Pretreatment on the Basis of Maximum Dissipated Energy E of Materials

Equation (2.19) shows that moisture content and holding pressure (or temperature) are the key factors that affect physical tearing.

The Antoine equation is widely used in calculating the saturated vapor pressure of water, but it is difficult to use in converting pressure to temperature. Thus, we fit a simple unary quadratic equation to represent the relationship between pressure and temperature:

$$P=3.6\times10^7-179876T+224.9T^2(\mathrm{R}=0.999) \tag{2.35}$$

Therefore, Eq. (2.19) can be converted into

$$E\approx\frac{\left(P_1+\frac{0.2\times m_w c_m T_1^2}{rMV}\right)^2}{2\cdot K_s\cdot\rho_s}\cdot m_s$$
$$=\frac{\left(3.6\times10^7-179876T_1+224.9T_1^2+\frac{0.2\times m\cdot w\cdot c_m T_1^2}{rMV}\right)^2\cdot m(1-w)}{2\cdot K_s\cdot\rho_s} \tag{2.36}$$

Equation (2.36) shows that

$$E=\frac{\left(3.6\times10^7-179876T_1+224.9T_1^2+\frac{0.2\times m\cdot w\cdot c_m T_1^2}{rMV}\right)^2\cdot m(1-w)}{2\cdot K_s\cdot\rho_s} \tag{2.37}$$

$$E=(A+Bw)^2(1-w)(0<\mathrm{w}<1) \tag{2.38}$$

$$A = \frac{\left(3.6 \times 10^7 - 179876T_1 + 224.9\,T_1^2\right)\sqrt{m}}{\sqrt{2 \cdot K_s \cdot \rho_s}} \tag{2.39}$$

$$B = \frac{0.2 \times m \cdot c_m T_1^2 \sqrt{m}}{rMV\sqrt{2 \cdot K_s \cdot \rho_s}} \tag{2.40}$$

When first derivative

$$E' = -(A + Bw)^2 + 2B(1 - w)(A + Bw) = 0 \tag{2.41}$$

$$w_{\text{opt}} = \frac{2B - A}{3B} \tag{2.42}$$

$$E_{\max} = \frac{4(A + B)^3}{27B} \tag{2.43}$$

Figure 2.5 illustrates that every temperature T (range, 160–235 °C) corresponds to an optimal value for moisture content w_{opt}. In this case, dissipated energy E of solid material in the brittle fracture process reaches its maximum value. The relationship between T and w_{opt} is expressed as $w_{\text{opt}} = \frac{2B-A}{3B}$ [A and B are shown in Eqs. (2.39) and (2.40)]. The tearing effect of solid material reaches the highest under T and w_{opt}. Hence, the effects of increased component fractionation and specific surface area also reach their best level.

As shown in Eq. (2.36),

$$E \propto T_1^4 \tag{2.44}$$

Equation (2.44) demonstrates that as temperature T increases, dissipated energy E of solid material in the brittle fracture process rises, indicating that high

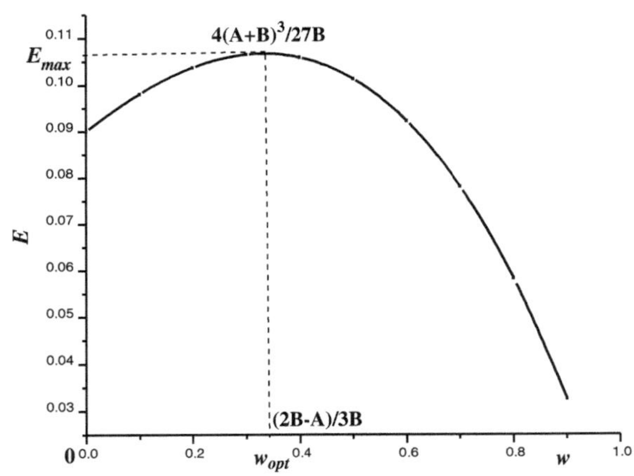

Fig. 2.5 Effect of moisture content w on dissipated energy E of materials in instantaneous decompression stage of steam explosion

temperature facilitates the tearing of solid material and the increase in specific surface area.

2.2.3.2 Optimizing Chip Size of Biomass and Discharge Port Area of the Steam Explosion Tank

Using the above-mentioned equations as bases, we consider holding pressure, holding time, chip size, moisture content, and discharge port area as follows:

$$\begin{aligned}&\frac{2\left(P_1+\frac{0.2\times m_w c_m T_1^2}{rMV}-P_a\right)(MP_1Vr+0.2\times m_w c_m RT_1^2)(\kappa+1)-(MP_1Vr+0.2\times m_w\cdot c_m\cdot RT_1^2)\left(P_1+\frac{0.2\times m_w c_m T_1^2}{rMV}\right)(\kappa-1)}{2\rho_3RT_1r(\kappa-1)}\\&=\frac{\left(P_1+\frac{0.2\times m_w c_m T_1^2}{rMV}-P_a\right)^2\cdot\pi^2\cdot d^4\cdot\eta^2}{2\cdot A^2\cdot m_s}+\frac{\left(P_1+\frac{0.2\times m_w c_m T_1^2}{rMV}\right)^2-P_a^2}{2\cdot K_s\cdot\rho_s}\cdot m_s\end{aligned}\tag{2.45}$$

Because $P_a \ll P_1$, we disregard P_a. Thus,

$$\begin{aligned}&\frac{(MP_1Vr+0.2\times m\cdot w\cdot c_m RT_1^2)(\kappa+3)}{2\rho_3RT_1r(\kappa-1)}\\&=\frac{\left(P_1+\frac{0.2\times m\cdot w\cdot c_m T_1^2}{rMV}\right)\cdot\pi^2\cdot d^4\cdot\eta^2}{2\cdot A^2\cdot m(1-w)}+\frac{\left(P_1+\frac{0.2\times m\cdot w\cdot c_m T_1^2}{rMV}\right)}{2\cdot K_s\cdot\rho_s}\cdot m(1-w)\end{aligned}\tag{2.46}$$

Substituting P_1 from Eq. (2.35) into Eq. (2.46) results in the following:

$$\begin{aligned}&\frac{[M(3.6\times10^7-179876T_1+224.9\,T_1^2)Vr+0.2\times m\cdot w\cdot c_m RT_1^2](\kappa+3)}{2\rho_3RT_1r(\kappa-1)}\\&=\frac{\left(3.6\times10^7-179876T_1+224.9\,T_1^2+\frac{0.2\times m\cdot w\cdot c_m T_1^2}{rMV}\right)\cdot\pi^2\cdot d^4\cdot\eta^2}{2\cdot A^2\cdot m(1-w)}\\&\quad+\frac{\left(3.6\times10^7-179876T_1+224.9\,T_1^2+\frac{0.2\times m\cdot w\cdot c_m T_1^2}{rMV}\right)}{2\cdot K_s\cdot\rho_s}\cdot m(1-w)\end{aligned}\tag{2.47}$$

Equation (2.47) can be rewritten as follows:

$$K_1T_1+K_2wT_1=\left[K_3T_1^2+K_4wT_1^2\right]\cdot\frac{d^4}{A^2\cdot(1-w)}+\left(K_5T_1^2+wK_6T_I^2\right)(1-w)\tag{2.48}$$

where

$$K_1 \approx \frac{MVr \times 224.9}{2\rho_3 Rr(\kappa - 1)} \quad (2.49)$$

$$K_2 = \frac{0.2 \times m \cdot w \cdot c_m(\kappa + 3)}{2\rho_3 r(\kappa - 1)} \quad (2.50)$$

$$K_3 \approx \frac{224.9\pi^2\eta^2}{2m} \quad (2.51)$$

$$K_4 = \frac{0.2 \times w \cdot c_m \cdot \pi^2 \cdot \eta^2}{2rMV} \quad (2.52)$$

$$K_5 \approx \frac{224.9m}{2 \cdot K_s \cdot \rho_s} \quad (2.53)$$

$$K_6 = \frac{0.2 \times m^2 \cdot w \cdot c_m}{2 \cdot K_s \cdot \rho_s \cdot rMV} \quad (2.54)$$

Using Eq. (2.48), we derive the following:

$$T_1 = \frac{(K_1 + K_2 w)A^2 \cdot (1 - w)}{(K_3 + K_4 w) \cdot d^4 + (K_5 + wK_6)(1 - w)^2 A^2} \quad (2.55)$$

As shown in Fig. 2.2, every T corresponds to an optimal w_{opt}. Hence, T and w_{opt} can be assumed constant.

$$T = \frac{\alpha A_1^2}{\beta d_1^4 + \chi A_1^2} = \frac{\alpha A_2^2}{\beta d_2^4 + \chi A_2^2} \quad (2.56)$$

$$\alpha = (K_1 + K_2 w_{\text{opt}})(1 - w_{\text{opt}}) \quad (2.57)$$

$$\beta = K_3 + K_4 w_{\text{opt}} \quad (2.58)$$

$$\chi = (K_5 + w_{\text{opt}} K_6)(1 - w_{\text{opt}})^2 \quad (2.59)$$

Using Eq. (2.56), we derive the following:

$$\frac{A_1}{A_2} = \left(\frac{d_1}{d_2}\right)^2 \quad (2.60)$$

i.e.,

$$A \propto d^2 \tag{2.61}$$

As depicted in Eqs. (2.60) and (2.61), discharge port area A and radius d are relevant under T and w_{opt}, and the relationship between these variables is expressed as $A \propto d^2$. This relationship indicates that materials with different chip sizes demand different discharge port areas or that equipment with fixed discharge port areas requires corresponding chip sizes to reach the best physical tearing effect. Hence, the chip size of materials that are pretreated by steam explosion is not randomly chosen but restricted by specific equipment requirements.

2.2.4 Establishing a Novel Severity Factor on the Basis of Chip Size, Discharge Port Area, and Moisture Content

If severity factor R is used to describe the severity of the steam explosion process, then chemical and physical effects are incorporated into the process.

Substituting T_1 from Eq. (2.55) into Eq. (2.6) yields the following:

$$R = \frac{t \cdot d^{-1.5}}{K_7} \cdot \mathrm{e}^{\frac{\frac{(K_1 + K_2 w)A^2 \cdot (1-w)}{(K_3 + K_4 w) \cdot d^4 + (K_5 + wK_6)(1-w)^2 A^2} - 373}{14.75}} \cdot 10^{-\mathrm{pH}} \tag{2.62}$$

where

$$K_7 = \frac{\rho}{M\left(\frac{\phi D}{1 - \frac{1}{2} Ln\phi}\right)^{0.67} \left(\left(0.48 \frac{\rho u}{\mu(1-\varepsilon)}\right)^{0.5} \left(\frac{\mu}{\rho}\right)^{0.33}\right) \cdot \Delta C} \tag{2.63}$$

In Eq. (2.63), ρ is the density of the fluid; μ denotes the dynamic viscosity of the fluid; u represents the velocity; ε is the dimensionless void fraction, which defined as the volume of void space over the total volume of packing; φ is the void fraction; D denotes the actual diffusion coefficient; t is the pretreatment time spent in steam explosion; d represents the equivalent spherical radius of the particle; A is the discharge port area; and w is the moisture content of materials.

Equation (2.62) shows that chip size d, discharge port area A, and moisture content significantly affect severity factor R.

As illustrated in Eqs. (2.61) and (2.62), $A \propto d^2$. Let us assume that $A = k'd^2$. If $A \neq k'd^2$, the R value would be lower than that if $A = k'd^2$. If $A = k'd^2$, then $R \propto d^{-1.5} \cdot \mathrm{e}^{w^{-1}}$. Both R values would decrease with increasing w and d. When we control the condition in $A \propto d^2$, a relatively small size d and a relatively low moisture content w result in a maximum R. Under these conditions, the effects of steam explosion reach their best level.

Except for traditional chemical factors, such as pretreatment time t and holding temperature T, enriched R causes physical effects. Enriched R improves the significances of the severity factor, enables the interpretation of the mechanism of steam explosion technology, and serves as theoretical guidance for further research. The enriched R serves as an engineering reference in designing the equipment and selecting the conditions for steam explosion under given treatment targets. However, this R should be further simplified and clarified. Issues such as the optimum ranges of chip size d and moisture content w for different materials, as well as the explicit relationship between A and d, necessitate additional research.

On the basis of maximum dissipated energy E of materials in the instantaneous decompression stage of steam explosion, we optimize moisture content w_{opt} with corresponding holding temperature T ($T \leftrightarrow w_{opt}$) and material chip size d by discharge port area A ($A \propto d^2$), which guides the selection of suitable operating temperatures and the matching of chip sizes and discharge port areas for materials with a certain moisture content. Efficient selection and matching generate the best physical tearing effects. The severity factor enriched with chip size, moisture content, and discharge port area represents the effects of high-temperature cooking on steam explosion and the physical tearing effects of instantaneous decompression. Such representations enable the comprehensive interpretation of the mechanism of steam explosion technology and guide equipment design and process parameter selection for steam explosion under a given set of materials, products, and treatment targets.

2.3 Mechanisms of the Physical and Chemical Coupling Effects of Gas Explosion

2.3.1 Overview

An effective pretreatment is required to achieve the dual purpose of enhancing the material enzymatic hydrolysis (EHY) and reducing the fermentation inhibitors at the same time. Currently, the growth of several pretreatment technologies makes it difficult to compare their advantages and disadvantages accurately. However, studies mostly focus on chemical pretreatment (e.g., dilute acid pretreatment) and several new pretreatment technologies (steam explosion (SE) and hot water pretreatment), which commonly involve the chemical reactions such as hemicellulose degradation and cellulose exposure, in order to enhance the EHY. Physical pretreatment, which is generally performed prior to chemical pretreatment, causes limited EHY improvement and high energy consumption. Thus, physical pretreatment is less likely to be used alone. Therefore, the general form of pretreatment is chemical and coupled physical–chemical.

Chemical pretreatment undeniably improves fiber exposure. However, its accompanying disadvantage of producing fermentation inhibitors of lignocellulosic materials is one of the bottlenecks in the fermentation industry. On the other hand, physical pretreatment increases the specific surface area of the materials and prevents the generation of fermentation inhibitors, and the idea of its high energy consumption only focuses on technologies such as milling and crushing. SE is a cost-effective and a widely used method for pretreating lignocellulosic materials [4, 5]. A previous study defines SE not as a purely chemical process but a combined physical and chemical process [19]. This process couples the hydrothermal effects of chemical pretreatment with the comminution and tearing effects of physical pretreatment. At high-temperature cooking, hemicellulose is degraded, lignin is solubilized, and cellulose binding is reduced. The reduced cell wall strength of the materials resulting from these chemical reactions gave way to the idea of physical tearing at instantaneous decompression process. The physical tearing effect following the chemical action further breaks the tissues and cells to increase the surface area and porosity of the materials. These phenomena lead to the adsorption and mass transfer of materials in the EHY process. Therefore, the coupling effect of SE is greater than exclusive physical or exclusive chemical pretreatment, making SE the most economical, efficient, and widely used pretreatment technology.

The sole effects of physical pretreatment and chemical pretreatment as well as their combined effect of SE are explored and compared by analyzing the hemicellulose degradation yields, lignin degradation yields, the conversation of inhibitors, EHY, and pore size distribution of materials. This reveals the mechanisms of the effects of the main physical and chemical factors on pore size distribution and EHY of the materials as well as their respective weighting coefficient affecting the EHY of the materials. It will provide theoretical guidelines for comprehensive evaluation of the pretreatment technologies and strengthening of the EHY of the materials.

2.3.2 *Effects of SE on Degradation of Hemicellulose and Lignin*

Table 2.4 shows that all groups under the pressure 1.5 MPa increased along with increased SE temperature such as the reducing sugars, furfural derivatives, weak acids, and phenolic compounds found in the steam-exploded straw hydrolysates [5]. The reducing sugars, weak acids, and furfural derivatives are the degradation products of hemicellulose; thus, the degradation rate of hemicellulose increases with the increased SE temperature. The phenolic compounds are the degradation products of lignin; thus, the degradation rate of lignin increases with increased SE temperature. Weak acids, furfural derivatives, and phenolic compounds are considered as potential fermentation inhibitors. Hence, the formation rate of inhibitors also increases with increased SE temperature. At 294 K, the operating conditions are regarded as feeding 1.5 MPa pure N_2 at room temperature. Hence, this group is considered as the purely physical pretreatment group. At 328–471 K, the medium

Table 2.4 Degradation of hemicellulose and lignin at the same pressure but different SE temperatures

Temperature (K; 1.5 MPa constant pressure)	Concentration (g/l; ratio of liquid to solid = 20)										
	Sugars	HMF	F	Acetic acid	Formic acid	Phenolic compounds	Degradation yield of hemicellulose (%)	Degradation yield of lignin (%)	Total inhibitors	Total degradation products	Enzymatic hydrolysis (EHY) (%)
No pretreatment	2.268	0.000	0.000	0.047	0.094	0.585	16.06	3.90	0.726	2.994	8.510
294	2.300	0.003	0.000	0.139	0.114	1.135	17.04	7.57	1.391	3.691	30.38
328	2.302	0.019	0.001	0.290	0.152	1.981	18.43	13.21	2.443	4.745	35.88
378	2.360	0.051	0.004	0.475	0.240	2.843	20.87	18.95	3.613	5.973	44.02
410	2.375	0.058	0.014	0.531	0.308	3.377	21.91	22.51	4.288	6.663	47.73
471	3.894	0.059	0.019	0.559	0.327	3.773	32.39	25.15	4.737	8.631	80.77

of SE is the gas mixture of saturated vapor and N_2; thus, these groups are considered as physical and chemical coupling pretreatment groups under gradient temperature. Table 2.2 shows the comparison of each product formation under gradient temperature in SE pretreatment, the chemical action significantly contributed to the hemicellulose degradation yields, lignin degradation yields, the conversation of inhibitors, and EHY, whereas the physical action showed no obvious effects on the degradation products generation.

2.3.3 *Effects of SE on Pore Distribution of Straw*

Figure 2.6 shows that as the SE temperature increases, the pore volume of the straw increases, and the pore volume of the steam-exploded straw are greater than the unprocessed straw. With increased SE temperature, the volume of the cracks (400,000–100,000 nm) and macropores (100,000–10,000 nm) is gradually increased. The volume of the mesopores (10,000–100 nm) and micropores (100–5 nm) increases at 294–328 K with the increase of SE temperature, whereas at 328–471 K, their volume decreased. Figure 2.7 shows that the area of the cracks and macropores is very small and almost negligible. The total pore area, the crack area, and the micropore area are larger than the unhandled straw at 294–328 K and increases with increased SE temperature, whereas at 328–471 K, they are lesser than the unhandled straw and decreased with increased SE temperature.

At low temperatures (294–328 K), the high-temperature-cooking function of SE was unnoticeable and its physical tearing effect predominates. On this event, the high-pressure gas within the pores of each straw tore all of its pores result in increased pore volume and pore area. At high temperatures (328–471 K), the

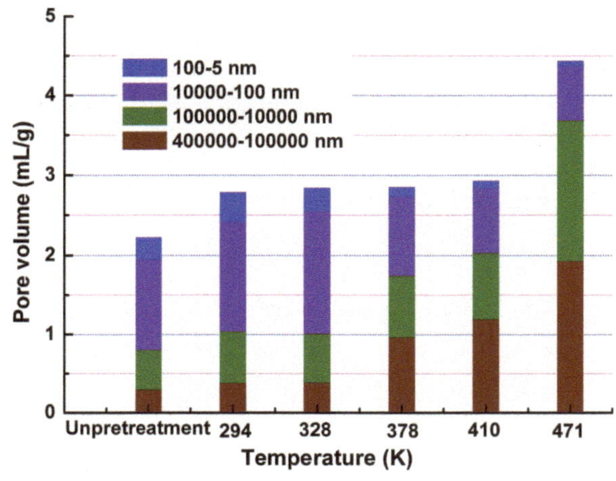

Fig. 2.6 Pore volume of straw at different steam explosion temperatures

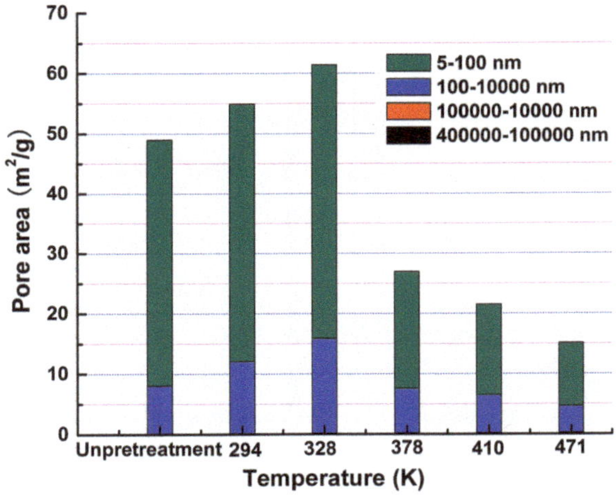

Fig. 2.7 Pore area of straw at different steam explosion temperatures

combined chemical high-temperature cooking and physical tearing occurs. Figures 2.1 and 2.2 show that the pore volume and pore area of the mesopores and micropores sharply decreased, but the crack volume and micropores dramatically increased. Table 2.1 shows the combination of the generation of the degradation products in the steam-exploded straw wherein high-temperature cooking plays a significant role in hemicellulose and lignin degradation as well as softening and exposure of the cellulose. The cell wall consists of cellulose which acts as its skeleton, and hemicellulose and lignin as the fillers. Thus, the filler degradation caused the increase of cracks and micropores and the decrease of mesopores and micropores, then cell wall porosity was increased. The proportion of cracks and macropores in the total pore areas is less than 10 %, and that of the mesopores and micropores is more than 90 %. Thus, the strengthening role of high-temperature cooking decreases the total pore areas of the steam-exploded straw.

Table 2.5 shows the influences of physical and chemical pretreatment in the pore size distribution of the steam-exploded straw. In the physical tearing process, the quantity of cracks and macropores slightly increases, whereas the mesopores and micropores noticeably increase. At low-temperature SE, the cracks and macropores account for 70 % in the total pore volumes and 10 % in the total pore areas, whereas mesopores and micropores account for 30 and 90 %, respectively, which indicated

Table 2.5 Physical and chemical effects of SE on the pore size distribution

Content	Physical tearing effects	Chemical cooking effects	Contribution to the pore volume (%)	Contribution to the pore area (%)
Crack/macropores	Slightly increased	Increased	70	10
Macropores/micropores	Increased	Decreased	30	90

that the pore volumes and pore areas both increased based on the physical effects. In the high-temperature-cooking process, because of the increase of cracks and micropores and the decrease of mesopores and micropores, resulted in increased total pore volumes and decreased total pore areas. Therefore, the combined effects of physical tearing and chemical high-temperature cooking in SE resulted in increased pore volumes and decreased pore areas.

2.3.4 *Effects of SE on Permeability of Straw*

Figure 2.8 shows that compared with the un-pretreated straw, the porosity (20 %) and permeability (400 %) of the steam-exploded straw are both increased. The porosity and permeability slowly increased at low temperature (294–328 K) but significantly increased at high temperature (328–471 K), indicating that the role of high-temperature cooking in improving the porosity and permeability of materials is greater than the physical tearing. Therefore, it shows that the effects of high-temperature cooking on filler degradation within the cell wall are beneficial in opening the mesopores and micropores to improve the porosity and permeability of the materials.

2.3.5 *Effects of SE on EHY of Straw*

Table 2.6 shows that with the increase of SE pretreatment temperature, the mass fraction of the carbohydrates in the materials increases resulting from the partial degradation of lignin and hemicellulose with almost no cellulose degradation. Consequently, the relative percentage of carbohydrates including cellulose and

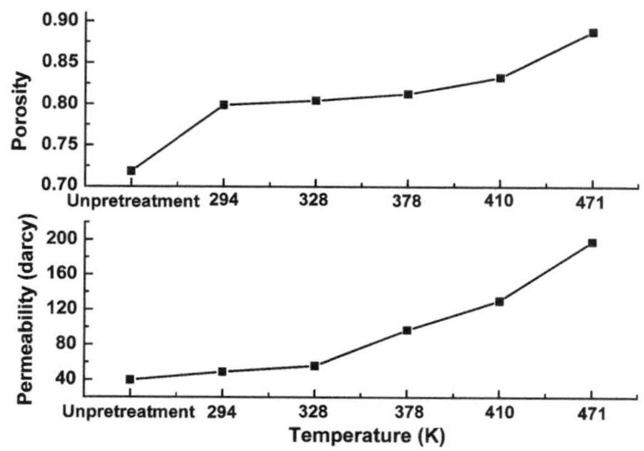

Fig. 2.8 Porosity and permeability of straw at different steam explosion temperatures

Table 2.6 Enzymatic hydrolysis of straw at different steam explosion temperature

Temperature (K; 1.5 MPa constant pressure)	Percentage of cellulose exposure (w)	EHY (%)
No pretreatment	0.70829	8.510
294	0.71627	30.38
328	0.72889	35.88
378	0.74219	44.02
410	0.75069	47.73
471	0.75713	80.77

hemicellulose increases. The increased mass fraction of carbohydrates and increased EHY in the materials are due to the exposure of a larger proportion of carbohydrates because of the degradation of lignin and hemicellulose. The content percentage of the carbohydrates is considered as the exposure proportion of carbohydrates (EPC) w, and is consistent with EHY, obtained as follows: $\text{EHY} = 2218.8 \times \omega^{21.224}$.

In a previous study, the effect of the pore areas (A) on EHY is calculated as follows: $\text{EHY} = 7.40635 \times 10^{-4} \cdot A^{1.707}$.

By comparing the two power exponents in Eqs. 2.1 and 2.2, the effects of EPC are found to be approximately 11.5 times larger than those of the pore area on the EHY of the materials, which cause the decreased material pore area and increases EHY with the increase of SE temperature. The significant increase of EPC to counter balance the negative impact of the decreased pore area on the EHY resulted in increased EHY with the increase of SE temperature.

In Table 2.3, the impact of temperature on EHY can also be measured as follows:

$$\text{EHY} = 2.15827 \cdot T^{2.2792}.$$

The impact of temperature on EHY is 1.707 compared with the lesser impact of pressure. This shows an inconsistent contribution of temperature and pressure to EHY with greater temperature effects than pressure effects. In general, for saturated steam SE, the pressure corresponds to the temperature. Hence, the strength formula of SE is $R_0 = t \cdot \exp^{T-100/14.75}$, where T and P refer to one parameter. However, in the present study, T and P cannot be mixed because of their different contributions to EHY. SE is a process of combined physical and chemical action that includes not only high-temperature cooking but also physical tearing, and the strength formula for SE should simultaneously contain T and P.

In SE pretreatment, chemical action significantly contributed to hemicellulose degradation yields, lignin degradation yields, the conversion of the inhibitors, and EHY, whereas physical action showed no obvious effects on the degradation products generation.

The cracks and macropores account for 70 % of the total pore volumes and 10 % of the total pore areas, whereas mesopores and micropores account for 30 and 90 %, respectively. The quantity of all pores increases in the physical tearing process, whereas the mesopores and microporesare decreased and cracks and micropores are increased in the high-temperature-cooking process. Hence, both the pore volumes and the areas increase in low-temperature SE based on the physical effects, whereas the total pore volumes increase and the total pore areas decrease in high-temperature-cooking process. Therefore, in the process of SE, the combined effects of physical tearing and chemical high-temperature cooking along with the increase of SE temperature resulted in increased pore volume and decreased pore area. With the increase of SE temperature, the pore area of the materials decreases. However, the EHY increased due to the increased EPC that is approximately 11.5 times larger than that of the pore area on EHY of materials.

2.4 Dissolution Thermodynamics of the Degradation Products of Steam-Exploded Straw

2.4.1 Overview

By pretreatment, lignocellulosic materials can destroy cell wall structures and increase the surface area of microfibrils [20]. However, a certain amount of xylan remains in the raw materials. Xylan covers the surface of a microfibril and forms hydrogen bonds, thus reducing the accessibility of cellulose to enzymes [21]. The US National Renewable Energy Laboratory (NREL, USA) analyzed the chemical composition of corn stover after different pretreatments. The results showed that 3.0–28.5 % of xylan remains in the substrates [22]. The affinity between xylan and cellulose resulted in the irreversible adsorption of xylan on the cellulose surface. The adsorption and dissolution of xylan are affected by environmental conditions such as temperature, substrate concentration, pH value, and ionic strength [23]. In addition, xylan accounts for about 20–30 % of the raw materials and 30 % of hydrolysates, and pentose fermentation is the key factor in determining the economical and efficient biotransformation of biomass resources [24, 25]. Thus, desorption and dissolution of xylose affect cellulose hydrolysis as well as its own conversion and utilization.

Steam explosion is used to enhance the enzymatic hydrolysis of lignocellulosic substrates into glucose and to produce hemicellulose hydrolysates with the highest yields of pentosan, which is a substrate for industrial fermentation. However, weak acids, furfural derivatives, and phenolic compounds in steam explosion hydrolysates are regarded as potential fermentation inhibitors [1] that should be removed to reduce inhibition to strains before fermentation. Therefore, the separation of oligosaccharides and potential fermentation inhibitors through dissolution eliminates the detoxification process for the fermentation industry and provides a reference for the recovery of oligosaccharides, which is beneficial to their subsequent self-conversion and utilization.

The effectiveness of oligosaccharides and fermentation inhibitors is related to their contents and energy levels. In particular, the energy state of oligosaccharides is a limiting factor to its utilization in the dissolution of degradation products during pretreatment and enzymatic hydrolysis. The energy states and the dissolution law of degradation products originating from steam-exploded straw (SES) are explored. By controlling the extraction conditions such as temperature, ionic strength, liquid-to-solid ratio (LSR) and pH, the energy states of the degradation products can be adjusted, in an attempt to realize the maximum dissolution of oligosaccharides and the minimum dissolution of potential fermentation inhibitors or hinder the dissolution of fermentation inhibitors to some extent. We aim to separate oligosaccharides and inhibitors by the dissolution process, eliminating the need for subsequent detoxification in the fermentation industry and simultaneously provide theoretical reference for the efficient dissolution and recovery of oligosaccharides.

2.4.2 *Effects of Temperature on the Dissolution Rate of Degradation Products*

As shown in Fig. 2.9, the effects of temperature on the dissolution of phenolic compounds are significant. However, temperature has little effect on the dissolution of sugars, weak acids, and furfural derivatives. With the increase of temperature, the dissolved amount of phenolic compounds also increases, whereas the dissolved amount of sugars slightly decreases. This result shows that increased temperature favors the dissolution of phenolic substances but not the dissolution of sugars.

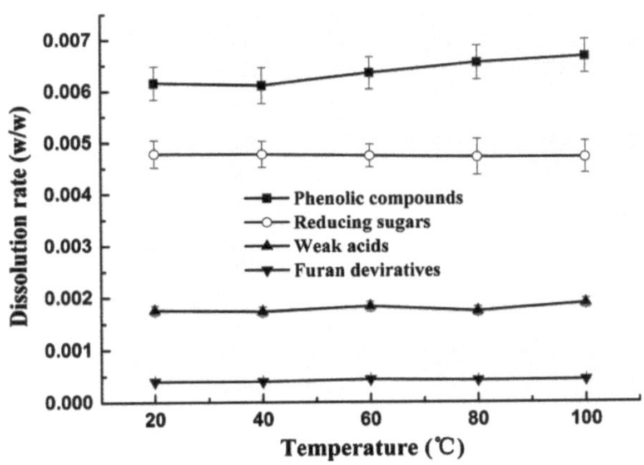

Fig. 2.9 Dissolution rate of degradation products of steam-exploded straw at different temperatures

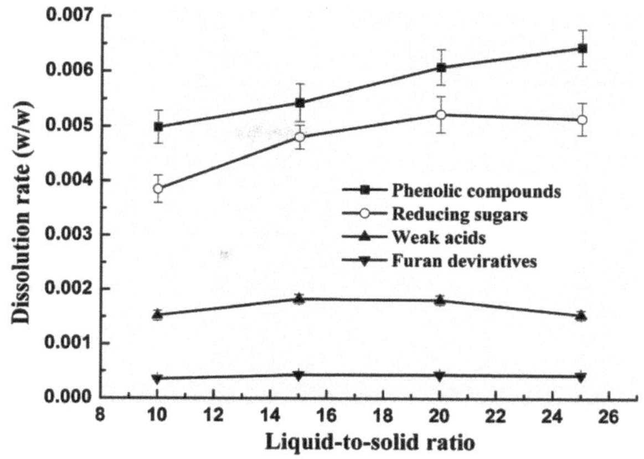

Fig. 2.10 Dissolution rate of degradation products of steam-exploded straw at different liquid-to-solid ratios

2.4.3 Effects of LSR on the Dissolution Rate of Degradation Products

Figure 2.10 shows that the dissolved amount of phenolic compounds and sugars increases with increased LSR. The dissolution amount of sugars can reach its maximum at LSR = 20. The dissolution of weak acids also reaches its maximum at LSR = 20. LSR almost has no effect on the dissolution of furfural derivatives.

2.4.4 Effects of Ionic Strength on the Dissolution Rate of Degradation Products

As shown in Fig. 2.11, the effects of ionic strength on the dissolution of sugars, phenolic compounds, weak acids, and furfural derivatives are uniform; that is, the dissolution decreases with increased ionic strength.

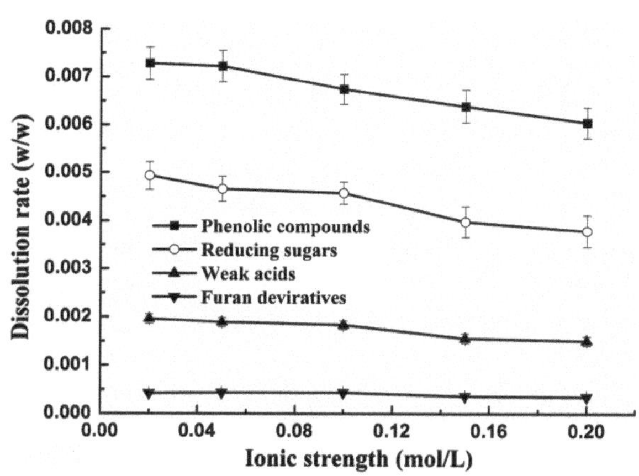

Fig. 2.11 Dissolution rate of degradation products of steam-exploded straw at different ionic strengths

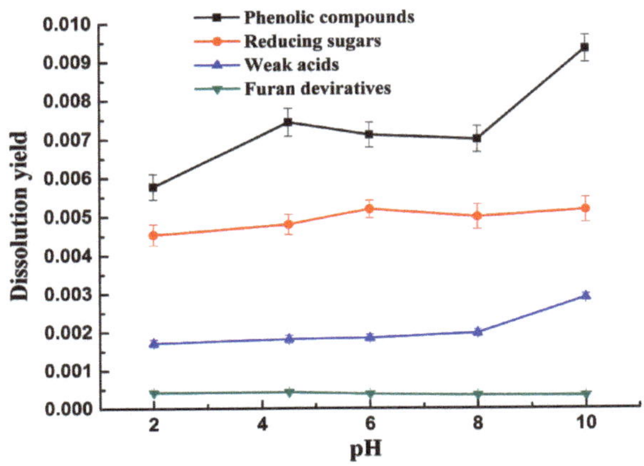

Fig. 2.12 Dissolution rate of degradation products of steam-exploded straw at different pH

2.4.5 Effects of pH on the Dissolution Rate of Degradation Products

It can be seen from Fig. 2.12 that the dissolution yields of carbohydrate and weak acids increase with the increase of pH. Dissolution yields of carbohydrate reached the maximum at pH 6. For dissolution of weak acids, the larger the pH, the better the dissolution efficiency. Dissolution yields of furan derivatives are decreased with the increase of pH, which illustrates that the acidic condition is beneficial for dissolution yields of furan derivatives. From Fig. 2.12, dissolution yields of phenolic compounds are increased with the increase of pH at pH 2.0–4.5, but decreased with the increase of pH at pH 4.5–8.0. The dissolution rate in pH 10 is increased sharply. The reason maybe that lignin is degraded again in the dissolution process under alkaline conditions, which increases the content of phenolic compounds. Thus, from the point of dissolution and no damage of the original structure of the material, it should not be selected alkaline conditions to dissolve the degradation products, and dissolution rate of phenolic compounds reached the maximum at pH 4.5.

2.4.6 Optimal Dissolution Conditions for Sugars and Phenolic Compounds

Steam explosion is used to enhance the enzymatic hydrolysis of lignocellulosic substrates into glucose and to produce hemicellulose hydrolysates with the highest yields of pentosan, which is a substrate for industrial fermentation. However, weak acids, furfural derivatives, and phenolic compounds in steam explosion hydrolysates are regarded as potential fermentation inhibitors that should be removed to reduce inhibition to strains before fermentation. Therefore, the separation of sugars and potential fermentation inhibitors through dissolution eliminates the detoxification process for the fermentation industry and provides a reference for the recovery of sugars, which is beneficial to their subsequent self-conversion and utilization.

The tolerances of different strains to different types of inhibitors are inconsistent. Phenolic compounds and furfural derivatives are the most toxic to common microorganisms. The effects of dissolution conditions on furfural derivatives are not obvious. Thus, the dissolution of phenolic substances is used as the basic reference for dissolution inhibition. Results indicates that the optimal dissolution conditions for phenolic compounds are 100 °C (the higher, the better), LSR of 25, and ionic strength of 0.020 mol/L (the smaller, the better). The most unfavorable dissolution conditions are 20 °C (the lower, the better), LSR of 10, and ionic strength of 0.20 mol/L (the higher, the better). The optimal dissolution conditions for sugars are 20 °C, LSR of 20, and ionic strength of 0.02 mol/L (the smaller, the better). Thus, dissolution conditions can be controlled at 20 °C (or room temperature), LSR of 20, and ionic strength of 0.02 mol/L (the ionic strength is not deliberately adjusted because its value in natural waters is lower than 0.02 mol/L) to maximize the dissolution of sugars and minimize dissolution of phenolic substances.

2.4.7 *Dissolution Thermodynamic Principles for Degradation Products in SE*

Chemical potential and activity are associated with the diffusion and desorption of products in the dissolution process for SES degradation. These products can transfer from high-chemical potential and high-activity systems to ones.

Figure 2.13 shows that the dissolution process of SES degradation can be considered as a change of state from 1 to 2. The main parameters in the solution are μ, α, γ, and C. μ is the chemical potential, α is the activity, γ is the activity coefficient, and C is the theoretical concentration.

The dissolution process of SES degradation products include desorption and dissolution. Thus, the partial molar free energy change from state 1 to state 2 is $\Delta G = \Delta G_1 + \Delta G_2$ (1 refers to desorption; 2 refers to dissolution). The material has

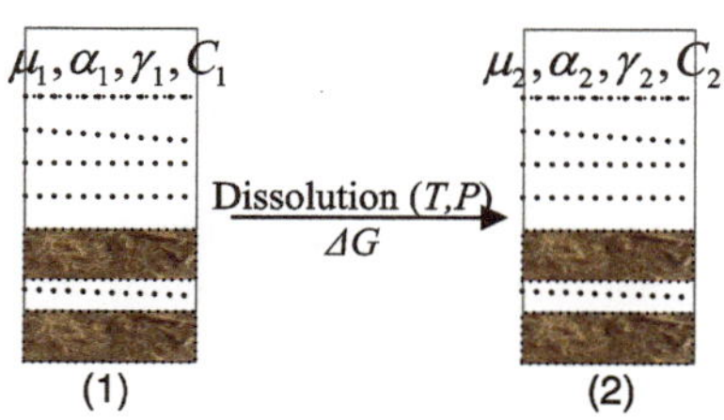

Fig. 2.13 Dissolution process of degradation products of steam-exploded straw

not yet begun to dissolve in state 1. Thus, the parameters considered are the intrinsic parameters of the steam-exploded materials (the sugar concentration depends on the steam explosion pretreatment): $C_1 = \Delta m/(m \times \chi_1)$ and $C_2 = \Delta m/(m \times \chi_2)$, where Δm is the reduction of hemicellulose or lignin in the materials, m is the mass of dry steam-exploded materials, χ_1 is the LSR for steam-exploded materials (in general, LSR is 0.5–0.7; in this equation, LSR = 0.6), and χ_2 is the LSR for the washing process.

In the desorption process,

$$\Delta G_1 = RT\text{In}\frac{C_2}{\alpha_2} = RT\text{In}\frac{1}{\gamma_2} \tag{2.64}$$

In the dissolution process,

$$\Delta G_2 = RT\text{In}\frac{C_2}{C_1} = RT\text{In}\frac{\chi_1}{\chi_2} = RT\text{In}\frac{0.6}{\chi_2} \tag{2.65}$$

Thus,

$$\Delta G = \Delta G_1 + \Delta G_2 = RT\text{In}\frac{0.6}{\gamma_2 \cdot \chi_2} \tag{2.66}$$

Therefore, the partial molar free energy change in the dissolution process of SES degradation products from state 1 to state 2 is given as follows:

$$\Delta G = RT\text{In}\frac{0.6}{\gamma_2 \cdot \chi_2} = -RT\text{In}K_a^{\Theta} + RT\text{In}Q_a = RT\text{In}\frac{K_a^{\Theta}}{Q_a} \tag{2.67}$$

where K_a^{Θ} is the dissolution equilibrium constant and Q_a is the activity provider. At dissolution time $t = 0$, the concentration of the soluble molecules in the solution is zero. Thus, $Q_a = 0$. When dissolution reaches equilibrium, $Q_a = K_a^{\Theta}$. Therefore, ΔG is a constant negative in the dissolution process, indicating that the dissolution of soluble molecules is spontaneous and accompanied by free steam explosion degradation.

According to Eq. (2.67), the factors affecting the dissolution process during water washing are the dissolution temperature T, activity coefficient γ_2, and LSR χ_2. The activity coefficient of the nonelectrolyte liquid mixtures is related with van der Waals forces, hydrogen bonding, complex forces in electronic transfer, and so on [26]. According to the literature [27], the activity coefficient γ of the nonelectrolyte solute is inversely proportional to the electrolyte concentration. The electrolyte concentration can be regarded as the ionic concentration. Therefore, a smaller ionic strength results in a higher activity coefficient of the nonelectrolyte solute. Equation (2.67) shows that higher activity coefficient γ_2 and LSR result in smaller free energy; a more negative ΔG value indicates easier dissolution of steam explosion degradation products.

According to the van't Hoff equation, $\frac{d\ln K^{\ominus}}{dT} = \frac{\Delta_r H^{\ominus}(T)}{RT^2}$. Thus, the dissolution of phenolic compounds is endothermic, whereas the dissolution of sugar molecules is exothermic. Therefore, steam-exploded materials can be washed at room temperature. This process benefits sugar molecules dissolution but not phenolic molecules dissolution.

Fractionation of sugars and phenolic compounds during the process of dissolution eliminates the need for subsequent detoxification in the fermentation industry. These results provide a theoretical reference for the efficient dissolution of sugars and for overcoming the barrier to cellulose hydrolysis.

2.5 Formation Kinetics of Potential Fermentation Inhibitors in a Steam Explosion Process of Corn Straw

2.5.1 Overview

Lignocellulose, which is a complex of cellulose, hemicelluloses, and lignin, only renders approximately 20 % of its theoretical glucose yield upon subjection to enzymatic hydrolysis due to its recalcitrance [28]. Therefore, lignocellulose needs to be pretreated to enable the cellulose to be more accessible to cellulolytic enzymes [29].

Various researchers have demonstrated the capability to identify and/or quantify sugars and lignin degradation products resulting from chemical pretreatment of biomass. Fenske et al. [30] compared aromatic monomers in lignocellulosic biomass dilute acid prehydrolysates. Luo et al. [31] identified potential fermentation inhibitors in the conversion of hybrid poplar hydrolyzate to ethanol. Palmqvist et al. [32] discussed the generation of inhibitors during degradation of lignocellulosic materials by dilute acid pretreatment and reviewed the inhibiting mechanisms of individual compounds on fermentation yield and productivity. Klinke et al. [29] systematically summarized the different inhibitors formed by pretreatment of lignocellulosic materials and their inhibition of ethanol production in yeast and bacteria. Du et al. [33] researched the effects of varying pretreatment chemistry–feedstock combinations on degradation product formation and accumulation of biomass hydrolysates is analyzed. But the formation rules of potential inhibitors in steam explosion process are not reported in one consolidated study.

2.5.2 Determination of Potential Fermentation Inhibitors in Steam Explosion Hydrolysates

Table 2.7 shows the quantitative determination of the identified degradation compounds in the hydrolysates from the steam-exploded corn straw. The acetic, formic

Table 2.7 Conversion of inhibitor at different temperature and time in steam explosion pretreatment

Time	T (K)	Conversions (MC × 100,000)									
		HMF	F	Syringic acid	4-hydroxybenzaldehyde	Vanillin	*p*-coumaric acid	Acetic acid	Formic acid	*p*-hydroxybenzoic acid	Ferulic acid
2 min	283	0.00	0.00	0.00	1.10	0.00	13.93	94.85	188.73	–	0
	294	1.97	0.00	0.00	4.91	4.80	40.73	249.58	171.85	–	0
	310	5.05	0.00	2.10	11.54	13.57	94.21	354.24	205.13	–	0
	328	16.99	0.00	2.14	12.30	18.23	96.28	579.97	239.14	–	0
	351	38.89	1.65	2.44	12.93	30.62	105.59	582.54	310.11	–	0
	378	44.80	3.15	2.67	14.77	30.36	68.71	635.40	341.47	–	0
	410	95.70	8.17	2.98	16.15	30.71	50.75	773.88	367.07	–	0
	471	96.96	17.74	4.32	20.07	36.93	37.77	1092.19	557.04	–	52.22
5 min	283	0.00	0.00	0.00	1.10	0.00	13.93	94.85	188.73	–	0
	294	6.67	0.00	0.00	6.94	5.19	43.16	278.70	227.93	–	0
	310	14.61	0.00	2.10	11.75	13.75	95.27	426.75	277.77	–	0
	328	35.84	1.41	2.24	16.02	26.46	99.36	585.55	304.87	–	0
	351	44.32	2.21	2.48	17.07	25.05	62.25	630.32	337.17	–	0
	378	102.04	7.75	2.83	17.46	32.12	39.66	750.89	479.27	–	0
	410	116.23	27.98	3.06	19.05	26.33	28.28	1062.70	616.28	–	0
	471	118.06	37.71	4.61	22.16	29.03	22.05	1118.04	654.03	–	58.13
8 min	283	0.00	0.00	0.00	1.10	0.00	13.93	94.85	188.73	–	0
	294	11.82	1.43	1.91	10.30	13.77	91.42	392.58	283.79	–	0
	310	19.23	1.98	2.14	12.33	20.41	96.34	517.91	335.71	–	0
	328	38.01	2.31	2.44	17.17	29.03	107.13	594.46	394.90	–	0
	351	47.98	2.57	2.54	17.07	26.42	76.60	670.26	419.30	–	0
	378	108.38	12.50	2.86	16.33	26.76	54.90	954.90	509.12	–	0
	410	119.58	56.75	4.32	16.31	27.23	38.30	1388.85	823.13	–	37.73
	471	138.39	73.52	5.04	16.13	27.06	35.04	1430.98	845.66	–	35.26

"–" mean trace

acids, HMF, and furfural acids from the hemicellulose degradation of corn straw are the main compounds present in the hydrolysate, which accounts for 82–96 % of the total inhibitors. *p*-coumaric acid, vanillin, 4-hydroxybenzaldehyde, and syringic acid constitute a large fraction of the lignin-derived compounds in the hydrolysate, which accounted for 3–14 % of the total inhibitors. Both *p*-hydroxybenzoic and ferulicacids are in small quantities in the hydrolysate, the sum of which accounts for less than 3 % of the total inhibitors. Vanillic and 4-hydroxybenzoic acids are not detected in the hydrolysate of steam explosion pretreatment.

In general, it is observed that the types and concentrations of degradation products produced during pretreatment are more dependent upon the feedstock utilized than on the type of pretreatment chemistry employed. However, formation and accumulation of select compounds are dependent upon both feedstock and pretreatment chemistry [33]. From Tables 2.7 and 2.8, the types of inhibitors observed in corn straw hydrolysates during different pretreatment technologies are almost the same. The yield of inhibitor is differed in various pretreatments. The yield of the weak acids is the highest in the $NH_3{\cdot}H_2O$ pretreatment, whereas the yield of furan derivatives is the highest in the dilute acid pretreatment. A few differences exist between the phenolic compound yields in different pretreatments. Vanillic and 4-hydroxybenzoic acids were not detected in the steam explosion pretreatment, whereas *p*-coumaric acid is detected only in the steam explosion pretreatment and not in other pretreatments.

Table 2.8 Inhibitor conversion observed in corn straw hydrolysates

	All pretreatments were carried out at 180 °C, for 8 min						
Weak acids	0.7 % H_2SO_4	0.07 % H_2SO_4	LHW	Wet oxidation	NH_3	Lime	Oxidative lime
Acetic acid	1700.0	830.0	340.0	580.0	1800.0	1200.0	1100.0
Formic acid	1200.0	760.0	550.0	790.0	2500.0	430.0	920.0
Furan derivatives							
5-Hydroxymethylfurfural (5-HMF)	440.0	110.0	23.0	28.0	8.9	23.0	38.0
Furfural	2200.0	260.0	80.0	65.0	4.0	15.0	32.0
Phenolic compounds							
Vanillic acid	33.0	15.0	26.0	43.0	32.0	33.0	51.0
4-hydroxybenzoic acid	0.3	0.3	0.6	0.7	0.7	0.5	0.9
Ferulic acid	66.0	26.0	22.0	10.0	42.0	66.0	7.6
4-hydroxybenzaldehyde	36.0	24.0	27.0	44.0	15.0	22.0	21.0
Vanillin	40.0	28.0	26.0	67.0	26.0	36.0	17.0
Syringic acid	20.0	15.0	18.0	21.7	15.4	17.0	14.0
p-coumaric acid	0.0	0.0	0.0	0.0	0.0	0.0	0.0

All dates were the yield of each compound multiplying by 100,000

2.5.3 *Yields of Inhibitors at Different Steam Explosion Conditions*

Figures 2.14, 2.15, and 2.16 show the yield of furan derivatives, weak acids, and phenolic compounds versus temperature and time during the steam explosion pretreatment.

Figures 2.14 and 2.15 show an increase in the yield of furan derivatives and weak acids with the increase of pretreatment temperature and time. The same trend is observed with syringic acid (Fig. 2.16). However, the 4-hydroxybenzaldehyde, vanillin, and *p*-coumaric acids show typical characteristics of continuous reaction ($A \xrightarrow[T]{k_1} B \xrightarrow[T]{k_2} C$, where A denotes original corn straw, B represents the objective inhibitor, C denotes secondary degradation products, and k indicates equilibrium constant). Their yield does not have a linear relationship with the pretreatment temperature T and time t. The yields of the objective inhibitors in these reactions are

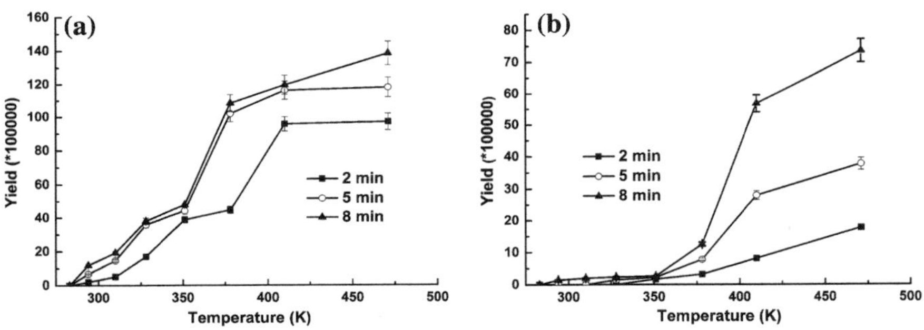

Fig. 2.14 Effects of temperature and time of steam explosion on the yield of furan derivatives. **a** HMF. **b** Furfural

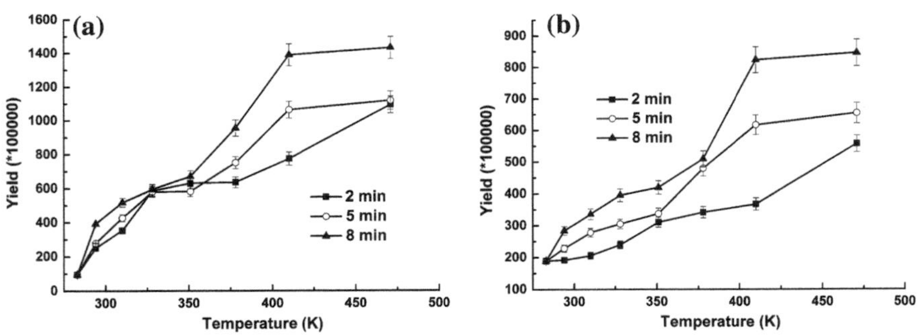

Fig. 2.15 Effects of temperature and time of steam explosion on the yield of weak acid. **a** Acetic acid. **b** Formic acid

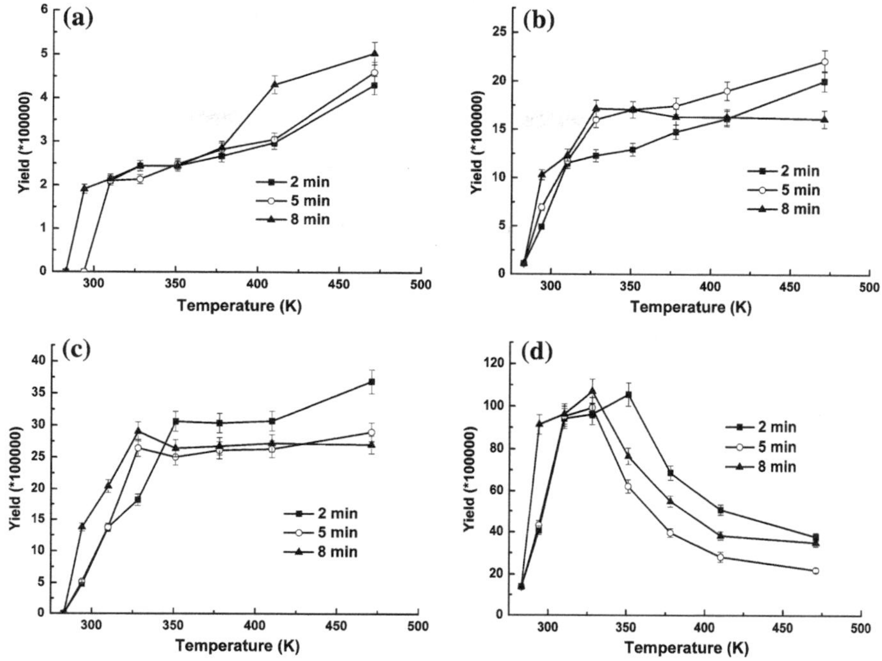

Fig. 2.16 Effects of temperature and time of steam explosion on the yield of phenolic compounds. **a** Syringic acid. **b** 4-hydroxybenzaldehyde. **c** Vanillin. **d** *p*-coumaric acid

affected by k_1/k_2 and time t. From the Arrhenius equation $k = A \times e^{\frac{-E_a}{RT}}$, k is affected by E_a and T. Thus, the yields of the objective inhibitors are $A_1 \times e^{\frac{-E_{a_1}}{RT}} / A_2 \times e^{\frac{E_{a_2}}{RT}} \cdot t$, in which the extremum exists at a given T or t.

Sun and Chen (27) found that some lignin and carbohydrates form the lignin recondensation and/or LCC during the drying process of fiber. Under severe enough pretreatment conditions, the cleaved linkages of hemicellulose and lignin form other linkages, i.e., lignin recondensation (28–29). Formed lignin recondensation or LCC may be the reasons for the yield of 4-hydroxybenzaldehyde, vanillin, and *p*-coumaric acids not having a linear relationship with the pretreatment temperature T and time t but first increasing then dropping.

As shown in Fig. 2.16, when the pretreatment time t is less than 5 min, the yield of 4-hydroxybenzaldehyde increased with temperature. However, when t is 8 min, the yield initially increases and then decreases. It finally reaches the maximum at 328 K. At the same pretreatment time t, the yield of vanillin increases with temperatures from 283 to 351 K but remains unchanged at temperatures higher than

351 K. Moreover, when pretreatment time t is longer than 2 min and temperature is higher than 351 K, the yield of vanillin shows a downward trend. When pretreatment time t increases, the yield of p-coumaric acid increases with temperature increasing from 283 to 328 K. However, the yield of p-coumaric acid decreases at temperature beyond 328 K. The yield of p-coumaric acid at 5 min is larger than that at 8 min. This difference may be due to the larger k_1/k_2 of p-coumaric acid at 8 min than that at 5 min.

2.5.4 Dynamic Parameters and Yield Equations of Inhibitors in Steam Explosion Process

Table 2.9 shows the equilibrium constants of the objective inhibitors at each temperature level. From Figs. 2.14, 2.15, and 2.16, the yield of HMF, furfural, syringic, acetic, and formic acids is positively correlated with pretreatment time and temperature. Thus, an equilibrium constant exists in each compound for each temperature level. The formations of 4-hydroxybenzaldehyde, vanillin, and p-coumaric acids are continuous reactions, and their yield is affected by several factors; thus, their equilibrium constants are difficult to express and not calculated here.

According to the equation In $\kappa = \text{In } A - \frac{E_a}{RT}$, the k versus $1/T$ plot would yield an activation energy E_a and pre-exponential factor A. Tables 2.10 and 2.11 show the dynamic parameters and Arrhenius equations of the five model inhibitors, respectively.

Table 2.12 shows the yield equations of HMF, furfural, syringic, acetic, and formic acids. The yields of the inhibitors could be associated directly with the time and temperature of the steam explosion pretreatment. Thus, the yields of inhibitors could be predicted and calculated before the actual determination, even before the steam explosion experiment.

The analysis of the formation kinetics of eight kinds of fermentation inhibitors in the steam-exploded material hydrolysates shows that formations of weak acids and furan derivatives are the first-order reactions, of which conversions increase with the pretreatment temperature and time. Formations of phenolic compounds show typical characteristics of continuous reaction, of which conversions are affected by both active energies in two stages, temperature and time, and existed extreme value. Inhibitor conversion equations and relationships of inhibitor conversion, temperature, and time in steam explosion process are further deduced. Such understanding may contribute to predict and calculate the inhibitors conversions and to provide theoretical references for limiting the production of certain inhibitors by artificially controlling the temperature and holding time in steam explosion process.

Table 2.9 Equilibrium constant of inhibitors in different temperatures

T(k)	Equilibrium constant $K \times$ quilib							
	$A \xrightarrow[T]{[}]kB$					$A \xrightarrow[T]{[}]k_1 B \xrightarrow[T]{[}]k_2 C$		
	HMF	Furfural	Syringic acid	Acetic acid	Formic acid	4-hydroxybenzaldehyde	Vanillin	*p*-coumaric acid
283	0	0	0	0	0	ND	ND	NE
294	1.4175	0.1282	0.1716	54.121	40.362	NE	NE	NE
310	2.5487	0.1782	0.3102	75.113	48.223	NE	NE	NE
328	5.5625	0.2747	0.3767	95.090	55.503	NE	NE	NE
351	7.3464	0.3756	0.4049	104.073	60.865	NE	NE	NE
378	15.7729	1.560	0.4558	136.177	76.905	NE	NE	NE
410	18.5933	6.5619	0.5995	193.248	111.833	NE	NE	NE
471	20.3367	8.7330	0.7743	206.693	119.887	NE	NE	NE

A original corn straw, *B* objective inhibitors, *C* secondary degradation products, *NE* not expressed

Table 2.10 Pre-exponential factor and activation energy of five model inhibitors

	HMF	Furfural	Syringic acid	Acetic acid	Formic acid
Pre-exponential factor A	0.03248	0.2847	0.000072	0.02237	0.008671
Activation energy E_a	18080.51	30907.05	8509.953	8835.853	7504.466

Table 2.11 Arrhenius equations of five model inhibitors

	Arrhenius equations
HMF	$K = 0.03248 \times e^{\frac{-2174.7}{T}}$
Furfural	$K = 0.2847 \times e^{\frac{-3717.47}{T}}$
Syringic acid	$K = 0.000072 \times e^{\frac{-1023.57}{T}}$
Acetic acid	$K = 0.02237 \times e^{\frac{-1062.8}{T}}$
Formic acid	$K = 0.008671 \times e^{\frac{-902.63}{T}}$

Table 2.12 Yield equations of five model inhibitors

	Yield (Y) (T temperature, K; t time, min)
HMF	$Y = 0.03248 \times e^{\frac{-2174.7}{T}} \times t$
Furfural	$Y = 0.2847 \times e^{\frac{-3717.47}{T}} \times t$
Syringic acid	$Y = 0.000072 \times e^{\frac{-1023.57}{T}} \times t$
Acetic acid	$Y = 0.02237 \times e^{\frac{-1062.8}{T}} \times t$
Formic acid	$Y = 0.008671 \times e^{\frac{-902.63}{T}} \times t$

2.6 Analysis of Energy Consumption on Steam Explosion Process

2.6.1 Overview

As an effective pretreatment method for biomass, although steam explosion technology is widely studied and applied [4, 5], most of existing research works only simply optimize the effect of holding pressure, holding time, and materials presoak treatment before steam explosion. Systematical research on heat transfer and energy consumption in steam explosion process is rare.

In view of this, the distribution of energy consumption in steam explosion process and their relationship are analyzed from heat transfer. Based on the actual steam explosion process, the effects of initial moisture content of materials, ratio of tank height to diameter, loading coefficient, and holding temperature on energy consumption are systematically investigated. The optimum condition where steam explosion energy consumption reaches the minimum value is obtained, and a retrieval table of steam explosion energy consumption at temperature of 143–212 °C (corresponding to the pressure of 0.4–2.0 MPa), holding time of 2–12 min, and the initial moisture content of 20–80 % is calculated, which provides valuable guides for further economic analysis and material balance calculation in steam explosion related process.

2.6.2 *The Composition of Steam Explosion Energy Consumption*

Take industrial 20-m^3 tank as an example. Corn straw in temperature 20 °C will be heated to preset temperature by 220 °C inlet steam. Holding time is 5 min. As shown in Fig. 2.17, energy consumption in steam explosion process includes five parts: heating materials energy Q_1, heating the liquid water in materials energy Q_2, holding pressure energy Q_3, heating tank energy Q_4, and tank radiation energy Q_5.

2.6.3 *Calculation Formulas for Each Part of Energy*

Heating materials energy

$$Q_1 = c_1 m_1 \Delta t = c_1 m_{\text{total}}(1-\omega)(T_1 - T_0) \tag{2.68}$$

Heating the liquid water in materials energy

$$Q_2 = c_2 m_2 \Delta t = c_2 m_{\text{total}} \omega (T_1 - T_0) \tag{2.69}$$

Holding pressure energy

$$Q_3 = c_2 m_3 (T - T_1) + m_3 r \tag{2.70}$$

$$m_3 = \frac{PVM_{\text{w}}}{RT_1 \cdot 1000} \tag{2.71}$$

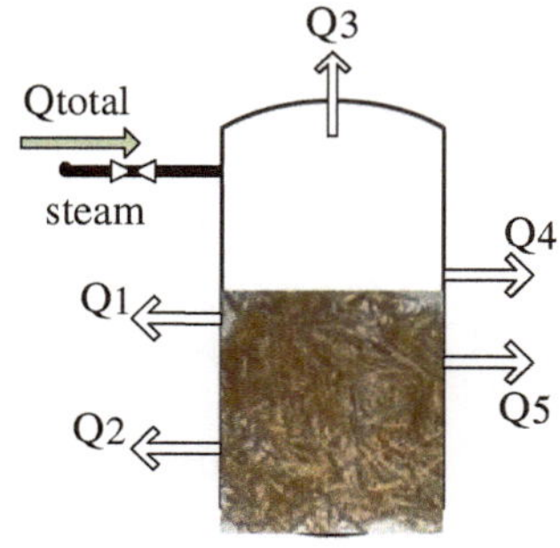

Fig. 2.17 The distribution of steam explosion energy consumption

Tank radiation energy

$$Q_4 = \varepsilon \cdot c_0 \cdot \left(\frac{T_1}{100}\right) \cdot A \cdot t \div 1000 \tag{2.72}$$

Heating tank energy

$$Q_5 = c_5 m_5 \Delta t = c_5 \cdot A \cdot \rho(T_1 - T_0) \tag{2.73}$$

Effective energy

$$Q_e = Q_1 + Q_2 + Q_3 \tag{2.74}$$

Ineffective energy

$$Q_{\text{ine}} = Q_4 + Q_5 \tag{2.75}$$

Total energy

$$Q_{\text{total}} = Q_1 + Q_2 + Q_3 + Q_4 + Q_5 \tag{2.76}$$

Steam consumption per unit mass dry basis

$$m' = \frac{Q_{\text{total}}}{m_{\text{total}}(1 - \omega)} \tag{2.77}$$

where c_1 is specific heat capacity of materials. Because the material is corn straw, then c_1 = 1.6 kJ/kg K^{-1} [34];

m_1 is the mass of dry material, kg;
m_{total} is the mass of wet material, kg;
m_2 is the mass of water in wet material, kg;
ω is moisture content of wet material;
T_1 is holding temperature of the material, K;
T_0 is initial temperature of the material, K;
c_2 is specific heat capacity of liquid water, taking c_2 = 4.2 kJ/kg K^{-1};
m_3 is steam consumption in holding pressure process, kg;
T is inlet saturated steam temperature, K;
r is condensing heat of saturated steam, kJ/kg;
P is holding pressure, Pa;
V is the volume of the tank, m^3;
M_w is molar mass of water;
ε is blackness of stainless steel, taking ε = 0.60 [35];
c_0 is blackbody radiation coefficient, taking c_0 = 5.67 W/(m^2 K^4);
A is the surface area of the tank, m^2;
t is holding time, s;

Table 2.13 Factor levels table on steam explosion energy consumption

Level of codes value	Ratio of height to diameter A	Charging coefficient B	Moisture of material C	Holding temperature D
2	5	100	0.9	212
1	4	80	0.7	197
0	3	60	0.5	182
−1	2	40	0.3	167
−2	1	20	0.1	152

c_5 is specific heat capacity of the tank material, and tank is made of stainless steel, then $c_5 = 0.46$ kJ/kg K^{-1};

m_5 is the mass of the tank, kg;

ρ is the density of stainless steel, $\rho = 7.8$ kg/m^3.

2.6.4 *Experiment Design and Data Processing*

Select the ratio of tank height to diameter, loading coefficient, initial moisture content of materials, and holding temperature as four factors. Design factor levels as Table 2.13 and adopt quaternary cubic regression analysis. The index is steam consumption per unit mass dry basis (kg steam/kg dry basis). Using design-expert 7.1.6 software to analyze the results.

2.6.5 *Relationship Between the Ratio of Tank Height to Diameter, Loading Coefficient, Initial Moisture Content of Materials, Holding Temperature, and Total Energy Consumption*

2.6.5.1 Regression Model Establishment and Significance Test

Using design-expert 7.1.6 software for multiple regression analysis based on calculation results, obtain regression model of steam consumption per unit mass of dry basis(kg steam/kg dry basis) *Y* on the ratio of tank height to diameter *A*, loading coefficient *B*, the initial moisture content of materials *C*, and holding temperature *D*.

$$y = 0.6596 - 0.1512B + 0.2203C + 0.1641D + 0.4883C^2 + 0.2656C^3 (R^2 = 0.961) \tag{2.78}$$

Table 2.14 Analysis of variance for response surface reduced cubic model

Source	Sum of squares	df	Mean square	*F* value	*p* value prob > *F*
Model	25.00	5	5.00	117.08	<0.0001
B–B	0.55	1	0.55	12.84	0.0015
C–C	0.39	1	0.39	9.09	0.0060
D–D	0.65	1	0.65	15.14	0.0007
C2	6.87	1	6.87	160.83	<0.0001
C3	3.39	1	3.39	79.28	<0.0001
Residual	1.02	24	0.043		
Lack of fit	1.02	19	0.054		
Pure error	0.000	5	0.000		
Corresponding total	26.02	29			

As shown in Table 2.14, the regression model p value is approximated to zero, significance level $\alpha = 0.05$, $P < \alpha$; then, it should reject the null hypothesis of regression equation significant test that the regression coefficient is not simultaneous as zero, and thus linear relationship between explanatory variables and independent variables is significant and linear model can be established. It also can be seen that the results of one degree term B, C, and D, quadratic term C2, and cubic term C3 all reach significant levels; then, using this model for analysis and forecasting steam consumption per unit mass of dry basis is reasonable. Coefficients of the standardization regression equation (2.78) reflect the effect of various factors on the index, and positive and negative coefficient reflects change direction of the index. It can be seen from one degree term of the four factors that the most influential factor on steam consumption per unit mass of dry basis is initial moisture content of materials, followed by holding temperature and loading coefficient, and the ratio of tank height to diameter has almost no effect on the index. Wherein the initial moisture content of materials and holding temperature both have positive impact on the index, loading coefficient has negative impact on it.

2.6.5.2 Single Factor Effect on Steam Consumption Per Unit Mass of Dry Basis (kg Steam/kg Dry Basis)

Other factors fixed at 0 level research the effect of one factor on steam consumption per unit mass of dry basis (kg steam/kg dry basis). Results are shown in Fig. 2.18.

As shown in Fig. 2.18, the change rate of initial moisture content of materials effect curve is maximum. When the code value of initial moisture content of materials is close to zero, the steam consumption per unit mass of dry basis is minimum (Theoretically, the code value of initial moisture content of material is the smaller the better, but it is difficult to achieve 10 % and below in actual situation, so the code value cannot be selected as −2). The larger loading coefficient lead to the

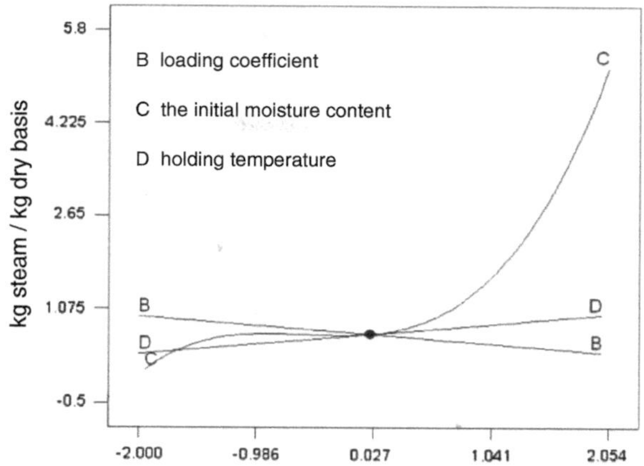

Fig. 2.18 Single factor response curve to steam consumption per unit mass of dry basis (kg steam/kg dry basis)

smaller steam consumption per unit mass of dry basis, but the actual loading coefficient should be selected according to particle size and density of materials. With holding temperature decreasing, steam consumption per unit mass of dry basis would reduce, and choosing actual temperature should consider the requirements of pretreatment. The ratio of tank height to diameter has almost no effect on the index.

2.6.5.3 Determination the Optimal Conditions and Validation Regression Model

According to analysis results by design-expert 7.1.6 software, the best operating conditions include that the ratio of tank height to diameter is 3, loading coefficient is 100 kg/m^3, initial moisture content of materials is 0.44, and holding temperature is 167 °C. Steam consumption per unit mass of dry basis is 0.1948 kg steam/kg dry basis under these conditions.

2.6.6 *Energy Analysis of Steam Explosion Process*

In steam explosion process, the energy consists of heating materials energy Q_1, heating the liquid water in materials energy Q_2, holding pressure energy Q_3, heating tank energy Q_4, and radiation energy of tank Q_5. Effective energy Q_e is defined as the sum of total heating energy of materials ($Q_1 + Q_2$) with holding pressure energy Q_3. Ineffective energy Q_{ine} is defined as the sum of heating tank energy Q_4 with radiation energy of tank Q_5. The ratio of each part of energy to total energy and the interrelation between each part of energy are seen as in the following analysis.

According to the formula,

$$\frac{Q_e}{Q_{\text{ine}}}=\frac{Q_1+Q_2+Q_3}{Q_4+Q_5}=\frac{(T_1-T_0)[c_1m_{\text{total}}(1-\omega)+c_2m_{\text{total}}\omega]+[c_2(T-T_1)+r]\cdot\frac{PVM_W}{RT_1\cdot 1000}}{\varepsilon c_0\cdot\left(\frac{T_1}{100}\right)^4\cdot A\cdot t+c_5A\rho(T_1-T_0)} \tag{2.79}$$

$$\frac{Q_e}{Q_{\text{total}}}=\frac{Q_1+Q_2+Q_3}{Q_1+Q_2+Q_3+Q_4+Q_5}=\frac{(T_1-T_0)[c_1m_{\text{total}}(1-\omega)+c_2m_{\text{total}}\omega]+[c_2(T-T_1)+r]\cdot\frac{PVM_W}{RT_1\cdot 1000}}{(T_1-T_0)[c_1m_{\text{total}}(1-\omega)+c_2m_{\text{total}}\omega]+[c_2(T-T_1)+r]\cdot\frac{PVM_W}{RT_1\cdot 1000}+\varepsilon c_0\cdot\left(\frac{T_1}{100}\right)^4\cdot A\cdot t+c_5A\rho(T_1-T_0)} \tag{2.80}$$

2.6.6.1 The Ratio of Each Part of Energy to Total Energy in Steam Explosion Process

Based on the above-optimized results, of which tank is 20 m^3, the ratio of tank height to diameter is 3, loading coefficient is 100 kg/m^3, initial moisture content of material is 0.44, and holding temperature is 167 °C. The results of ratios of each part of energy to total energy are shown in Fig. 2.19.

As shown in Fig. 2.19, the main energy are holding pressure energy (33.8 %), heating tank energy (27.3 %), and heating the liquid water in materials energy (23.9 %) in all compositions, and heating materials energy only accounts for 11.6 %. Tank radiation energy (3.3 %) can be negligible. Effective energy accounts for 70 % of the total energy, and ineffective energy is 30 %. According to the formulas (2.79) and (2.80), the ratio of effective energy to ineffective energy is mainly related to initial moisture content of materials and loading coefficient. It is inversely proportional to the ratio of tank height to diameter (mainly effect A) and has little relationship with holding temperature. On the optimized condition, of

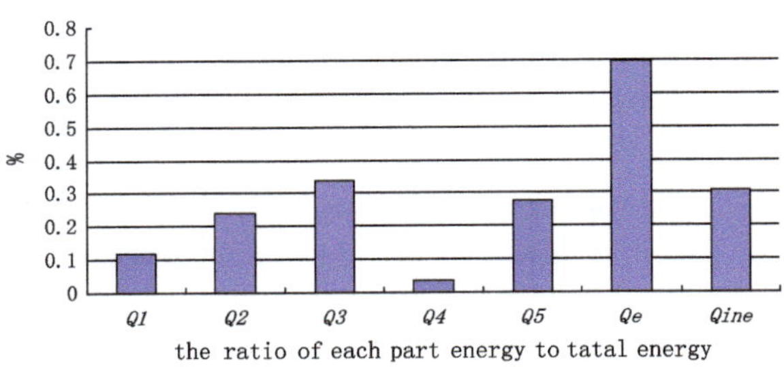

Fig. 2.19 The ratio of five parts energy, effective energy, and ineffective energy to total energy. (Q_1 heating materials energy, Q_2 heating the liquid water in materials energy, Q_3 holding pressure energy, Q_4 heating tank energy, Q_5 radiation energy of tank, effective energy $Q_e = Q_1 + Q_2$, and ineffective energy $Q_{\text{ine}} = Q_4 + Q_5$.)

which the ratio of tank height to diameter is 3, loading coefficient is 100 kg/m^3, initial moisture content of materials is 0.44, and holding temperature is 167 °C, and the ratio of effective energy to ineffective energy is 2.3 and the ratio of effective energy to total energy is 0.70. Thus, this result shows that the total energy mainly comes from the efficient energy, and effective energy mainly comes from the total heating materials energy. So the total energy can be optimized as long as we optimize the total heating materials energy. The total heating energy is only related to the initial moisture content of materials. That is, the initial moisture content of materials is the most important factor on total energy of steam explosion, which accords with the results of significant analysis and single factor analysis.

2.6.6.2 Relationship Between Each Part of Energy in Steam Explosion Process

According to the formula, the ratio of heating materials energy to heating the liquid water in materials energy is $(1-\omega)/\omega$, which is only related to the initial moisture content of materials. From Fig. 2.20, the ratio of heating materials energy to heating the liquid water in materials energy reduces with moisture content increasing. That is, the proportion of heating straw decreases with moisture content increasing. Furthermore, it is known that the initial moisture content of materials cannot be too high; otherwise, most of the energy is used to heat the liquid water in materials, and this part of energy does not contribute to heating straw.

According to the formula $\frac{Q_4}{Q_5}=\frac{\varepsilon \cdot c_0 \cdot \left(\frac{T_1}{100}\right)^4 \cdot t}{c_5 \cdot \rho \cdot (T_1-T_0)}$, the ratio of tank radiation energy to heating tank energy is related to the heating temperature based on the same holding time and the same volume of the tank. As shown in Fig. 2.21, the ratio of tank

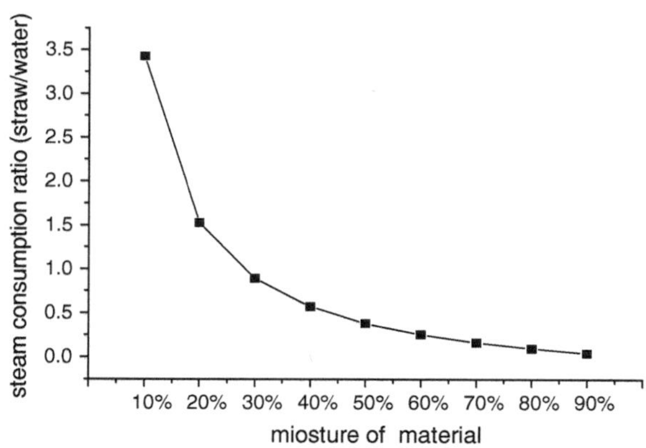

Fig. 2.20 Effect of material moisture content on the ratio of heating materials energy to heating the liquid water in materials energy. Prerequisite: 20-m^3 tank, inlet steam temperature 220 °C, heating the material from room temperature 20–182 °C, and holding time 5 min

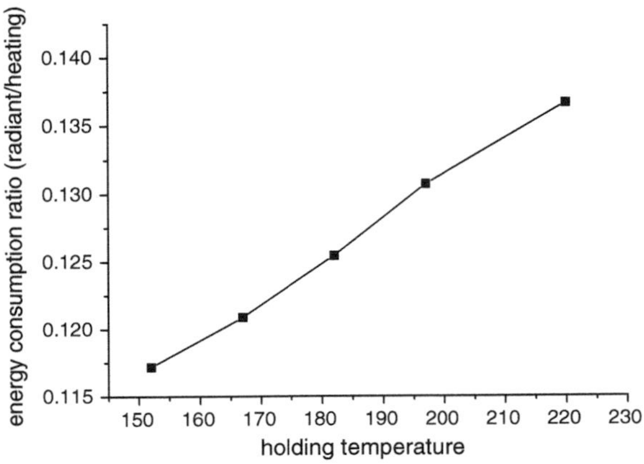

Fig. 2.21 The ratio of tank radiation energy to heating tank energy on different holding temperature

radiation energy to heating tank energy is very small, and the maximum does not exceed 0.15. This implies that the tank radiation energy has little effect on the total energy. In addition, the equipment for industrial production and laboratory research all have insulation outside the tank, so the actual energy consumption is far lower than calculated value of radiation. Thus, the radiation energy loss is negligible. Because holding time only affects the tank radiation energy in all parts of energy, the effect of holding time on the overall energy consumption can be ignored since the radiation energy can be ignored. Steam explosion severity parameter formula [6] $R_0 = t^{\exp(T-100)/14.75}$ (t is holding time, min; T is holding temperature, °C) shows that the strategy which holds low temperature and long time can be used to achieve the same steam explosion efficiency. Furthermore, based on the above analysis, holding low temperature is conducive to energy conservation. Thus, the strategy of holding low temperature and long time will not only ensure the same effect of steam explosion but also reduce energy consumption.

2.6.6.3 Building a Retrieval Table of Steam Explosion Energy Under Commonly Used Conditions

According to the formulas (2.68)–(2.77), calculate the steam consumption per unit mass of dry basis on the temperature conditions 143–212 °C (corresponding to the pressure 0.4–2.0 MPa), holding time 2–12 min, and the initial moisture content of materials 20–80 % .The results are shown in Table 2.15. Calculations are based on tank volume 20 m^3, the ratio of tank height to diameter 3, and loading coefficient 100 kg/m^3.

According to heat transfer, initial moisture content of materials is the most influential factor on total energy of steam explosion, and the best operating conditions are described as follows: the ratio of tank height to diameter is 3, loading coefficient is 100 kg/m^3, initial moisture content of materials is 0.44, and holding

Table 2.15 Steam consumption (kg steam/kg dry basis) under common conditions: temperature 143–212 °C (corresponding to the pressure 0.4–2.0 MPa), holding time 2–12 min, and the initial moisture content of materials 20–80 %

Y (kg steam/kg dry base)		*t* (min)						
T (°C)	*ω* (%)	2	4	5	6	8	10	12
143	20	0.207	0.208	0.209	0.209	0.211	0.212	0.213
	30	0.257	0.259	0.259	0.26	0.262	0.263	0.265
	40	0.324	0.326	0.327	0.328	0.33	0.332	0.333
	50	0.418	0.421	0.422	0.423	0.425	0.427	0.429
	60	0.56	0.562	0.564	0.565	0.568	0.571	0.573
	70	0.795	0.799	0.801	0.802	0.806	0.81	0.813
	80	1.266	1.271	1.274	1.277	1.282	1.288	1.293
152	20	0.234	0.235	0.227	0.237	0.239	0.241	0.243
	30	0.289	0.292	0.282	0.294	0.296	0.298	0.3
	40	0.364	0.366	0.355	0.369	0.371	0.374	0.376
	50	0.468	0.471	0.458	0.474	0.477	0.48	0.483
	60	0.624	0.628	0.612	0.632	0.636	0.639	0.643
	70	0.885	0.89	0.868	0.895	0.9	0.905	0.91
	80	1.406	1.414	1.381	1.421	1.429	1.436	1.444
164	20	0.253	0.255	0.255	0.256	0.258	0.26	0.261
	30	0.314	0.316	0.317	0.317	0.319	0.321	0.323
	40	0.395	0.397	0.398	0.399	0.401	0.403	0.406
	50	0.508	0.51	0.512	0.513	0.516	0.518	0.521
	60	0.678	0.681	0.683	0.684	0.688	0.691	0.694
	70	0.961	0.965	0.967	0.97	0.974	0.978	0.983
	80	1.527	1.533	1.537	1.54	1.547	1.553	1.56
175	20	0.279	0.28	0.281	0.282	0.284	0.286	0.288
	30	0.345	0.347	0.348	0.349	0.351	0.353	0.355
	40	0.433	0.435	0.437	0.438	0.44	0.443	0.445
	50	0.557	0.56	0.561	0.562	0.565	0.568	0.571
	60	0.742	0.746	0.748	0.749	0.753	0.757	0.76
	70	1.051	1.056	1.058	1.061	1.066	1.07	1.075
	80	1.668	1.676	1.68	1.683	1.691	1.698	1.705
180	20	0.296	0.298	0.299	0.3	0.302	0.304	0.306
	30	0.365	0.368	0.369	0.37	0.372	0.374	0.377
	40	0.458	0.461	0.462	0.463	0.466	0.468	0.471
	50	0.588	0.591	0.593	0.594	0.597	0.6	0.603
	60	0.783	0.786	0.788	0.79	0.794	0.798	0.802
	70	1.107	1.112	1.115	1.117	1.122	1.128	1.133
	80	1.756	1.764	1.767	1.771	1.779	1.787	1.795

(continued)

Table 2.15 (continued)

Y (kg steam/kg dry base)		t (min)						
T (°C)	ω (%)	2	4	5	6	8	10	12
192	20	0.321	0.323	0.324	0.325	0.328	0.33	0.332
	30	0.396	0.399	0.4	0.401	0.404	0.406	0.409
	40	0.497	0.499	0.501	0.502	0.505	0.508	0.511
	50	0.637	0.64	0.642	0.644	0.647	0.651	0.654
	60	0.847	0.852	0.854	0.856	0.86	0.864	0.869
	70	1.198	1.204	1.207	1.209	1.215	1.221	1.227
	80	1.9	1.908	1.912	1.917	1.925	1.934	1.942
198	20	0.339	0.341	0.342	0.343	0.345	0.348	0.35
	30	0.417	0.42	0.421	0.422	0.425	0.428	0.43
	40	0.522	0.525	0.527	0.528	0.531	0.534	0.537
	50	0.669	0.673	0.674	0.676	0.68	0.683	0.687
	60	0.889	0.894	0.896	0.898	0.903	0.907	0.912
	70	1.256	1.262	1.265	1.268	1.274	1.28	1.286
	80	1.991	2	2.004	2.009	2.018	2.027	2.036
204	20	0.355	0.358	0.359	0.36	0.363	0.365	0.367
	30	0.438	0.44	0.442	0.443	0.446	0.448	0.451
	40	0.547	0.55	0.552	0.553	0.557	0.56	0.563
	50	0.7	0.704	0.706	0.708	0.712	0.715	0.719
	60	0.93	0.935	0.937	0.94	0.944	0.949	0.954
	70	1.313	1.32	1.323	1.326	1.332	1.339	1.345
	80	2.08	2.089	2.094	2.099	2.108	2.118	2.127
210	20	0.372	0.374	0.376	0.377	0.379	0.382	0.384
	30	0.457	0.46	0.462	0.463	0.466	0.469	0.472
	40	0.571	0.575	0.576	0.578	0.581	0.585	0.588
	50	0.731	0.735	0.737	0.739	0.743	0.747	0.751
	60	0.97	0.975	0.978	0.98	0.985	0.99	0.995
	70	1.369	1.376	1.379	1.382	1.389	1.396	1.402
	80	2.167	2.177	2.182	2.187	2.197	2.207	2.217
212	20	0.379	0.381	0.383	0.384	0.387	0.389	0.392
	30	0.466	0.469	0.47	0.472	0.474	0.477	0.48
	40	0.582	0.585	0.587	0.588	0.592	0.595	0.598
	50	0.744	0.748	0.75	0.752	0.756	0.76	0.764
	60	0.987	0.992	0.994	0.997	1.002	1.007	1.012
	70	1.392	1.399	1.402	1.405	1.412	1.419	1.426
	80	2.202	2.212	2.217	2.222	2.233	2.243	2.253

temperature is 167 °C. Steam consumption per unit mass of dry basis is 0.1948 kg steam/kg dry basis under these conditions. The proportion of the energy for heating straw is decreased with the increasing of moisture content. Thus, the initial moisture content of materials cannot be too high; otherwise, most of the energy is used to heat the liquid water in materials, and this part of energy does not contribute to heating straw. The effect of holding time on the overall energy consumption is negligible since the radiation energy can be ignored. Thus, the conditions of low holding temperature and long holding time will not only ensure the same efficiency of steam explosion but also reduce energy consumption. A retrieval table of steam explosion energy consumption under common conditions is established to provide a foundation for further economic analysis and material balance calculation.

References

1. Chen HZ, Liu LY. Technology of steam explosion principles and application. Beijing: Chemical Industry Press; 2007.
2. Xie LS, Zhan HY. Pulping principle and engineering. Beijing: China Light Industry Press; 2001.
3. Yang SH. Plant fiber chemistry. Beijing: China Light Industry Press; 2001.
4. Alfani F, Gallifuoco A, Saporosi A. Comparison of SHF and SSF processes for the bioconversion of steam-exploded wheat straw. J Ind Microbiol Biotechnol. 2000;25(4): 184–92.
5. Datar R, Huang J, Maness PC. Hydrogen production from the fermentation of corn stover biomass pretreated with a steam-explosion process. Int J Hydrogen Energy. 2007;32(8):932–9.
6. Overend RP, Chornet E, Gascoigne JA. Fractionation of lignocellulosics by steam-aqueous pretreatments [and discussion]. Phil Trans R Soc Lond A. 1987;321(1561):523–36.
7. Helena L, Chum D, Stuart K. Organosolv pretreatment for enzymatic hydrolysis of poplars. 2. Catalyst effects and the combined severity parameter. Ind Eng Chem Res. 1990;29(2):156–62.
8. Belkacemi K, Abatzoglou N, Overend RP, Chornet E. Phenomenological kinetics of complex systems: mechanistic considerations in the solubilization of hemicelluloses following aqueous/steam treatments. Ind Eng Chem Res. 1991;30(11):2416–25.
9. Abatzoglou N, Chornet E, Belkacem K. Phennomenological kinetics complex systems: the development of a generalized severity parameter and its application to lignocellulosics fractionation. Chem Eng Sci. 1992;47(5):1109–22.
10. Montane D, Overend RP, Chornet E. Kinetic models for non-homogeneous complex systems with a time-dependent rate constant. Can J Chem Eng. 1998;76:58–68.
11. Hosseini SA, Shah N. Multiscale modelling of hydrothermal biomass pretreatment for chip size optimization. Bioresour Technol. 2009;100(9):2621–8.
12. Cantarella M, Cantarella L, Gallifuoco A. Comparison of different detoxification methods for steam-exploded poplar wood as a substrate for the bioproduction of ethanol in SHF and SSF. Process Biochem. 2004;39(11):1533–42.
13. Chen HZ, Chen JZ, Liu J, Li ZH. Stidies on steam explosion of wheat straw I. Effects of the operating conditions for steam explosion of wheat straw and analysis of the process. J Cellul Sci Technol. 1999;7(2):60–7.
14. Chen HZ, Liu LY. Unpolluted fractionation of wheat straw by steam explosion and ethanol extraction. Bioresour Technol. 2007;98(3):666–76.
15. Cherepanov GP. Mechanics of brittle fracture. New York: Mcgraw-Hill; 1979.

16. Ning J, Wang C, Ma T. Explosion and shock dynamics. Beijing: National Defence Industry Press; 2010.
17. BenhamPP Warnock FV. Mechanics of solids and structures. Sweden: Pitman Publishing; 1973.
18. Wang X. Gas dynamics. Xi'an: Northwestern Polytechnical University Press; 2006.
19. Zhang YZ, Chen HZ. Multiscale modeling of biomass pretreatment for optimization of steam explosion conditions. Chem Eng Sci. 2012;75:177–82.
20. MosierN Wyman C, Dale B. Features of promising technologies for pretreatment of lignocellulosic biomass. Bioresour Technol. 2005;96(6):673–86.
21. Himmel ME, Ding SY, Johnson DK. Biomass recalcitrance: engineering plants and enzymes for biofuels production. Science. 2007;315(5813):804–7.
22. Selig MJ, Adney WS, Himmel ME. The impact of cell wall acetylation on corn stover hydrolysis by cellulolytic and xylanolytic enzymes. Cellulose. 2009;16(4):711–22.
23. Köhnke T. Adsorption of xylans on cellulosic fibres-Influence of xylan composition on adsorption characteristics and kraft pulp properties. Gothenburg: Chalmers University of Technology; 2010.
24. Ji XJ, Huang H, Nie ZK. Fuels and chemicals from hemicellulose sugars. Adv Biochem Eng Biotechnol. 2012;128:199–224.
25. Chen YP, Yong Q, Liu CG, Xu Y, Yu SY. The microbes and selection of pentose fermentation. J Cellul Sci Technol. 2001;9(3):57–61.
26. Deng W, Shen B, Tang Y. The infinite dilition activity coefficient and selective molecules gravity. J Hangzhou Normal University 1991;(3): 55–59.
27. Bai T, Lu Y, Li Q. The infinite dilition activity coefficient of organic solutes in the mixture of formamide + salt. J Henan Normal University. 1996;24:48–51.
28. Chen HZ. Process engineering in plant-based products. Beijing: Chemical Industry Press; 2010.
29. Klinke HB, Thomsen A, Ahring BK. Inhibition of ethanol-producing yeast and bacteria by degradation products produced during pre-treatment of biomass. Appl Microbiol Biotechnol. 2004;66(1):10–26.
30. Fenske J, Griffin D, Penner M. Comparison of aromatic monomers in lignocellulosic biomass prehydrolysates. J Ind Microbiol Biotechnol. 1998;20(6):364–8.
31. Luo C, Brink DL, Blanch HW. Identification of potential fermentation inhibitors in conversion of hybrid poplar hydrolyzate to ethanol. Biomass Bioenerg. 2002;22(2):125–38.
32. Palmqvist E, Hahn-Hägerdal B. Fermentation of lignocellulosic hydrolysates. II: inhibitors and mechanisms of inhibition. Bioresour Technol. 2000;74(1):25–33.
33. Du B, Sharma LN, Becker C. Effect of varying feedstock–pretreatment chemistry combinations on the formation and accumulation of potentially inhibitory degradation products in biomass hydrolysates. Biotechnol Bioeng. 2010;107(3):430–40.
34. He F, Du SS, Li YJ. Heat emission qualification of agro-stalks dring smoldering. Biomass Chem Eng. 2007;41(1):5–8.
35. TanT Dou M, Zhou M. Principles of chemical engineering. Beijing: Chemical Industry Press; 1984.

Chapter 3
Gas Explosion Equipments

3.1 Cutter Bar and Dedusting Equipments

Before gas phase explosion, straw and other non-wood cellulose materials should be pretreated, and the required pretreatment equipments are given as follows:

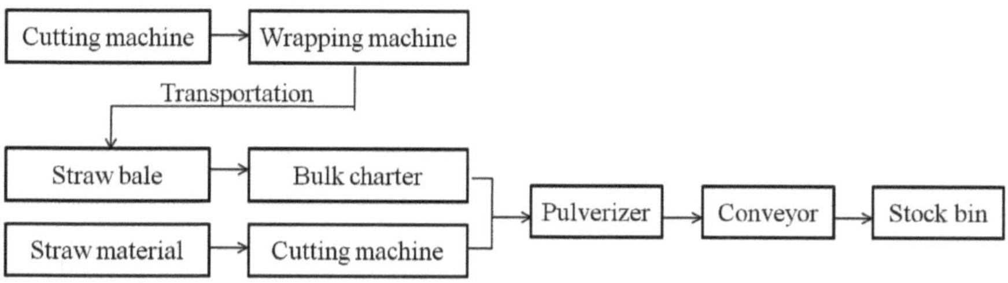

3.1.1 Knife-Rall Straw Cutter

Cutting equipment for straw, which is non-wood cellulose materials, mainly uses a knife-rall straw cutter. There are two types of knife-rall straw cutters, which are given in Table 3.1 [1].

The three-knife blade roll machine consists of feeding grass knife roller, pressure roller, and bottom knife. Feedstock is fed to feed mouth by the feed belt and is pressed by the first feed roller and then rotates with the feed roller. The feedstock was then continued to feed to a second and three feed rollers. Relying on the weight of the feed rollers, spring pressure compresses the raw material into middle of the knife and the bottom knife. As a result, the feedstock was cut into grass pieces.

H. Chen, *Gas Explosion Technology and Biomass Refinery*,
DOI 10.1007/978-94-017-7414-7_3

Table 3.1 The technical characteristics of straw cutter machine

		Unit	Type	
			ZCQ1	ZCQ2
Production capacity		Ton/hour	2–3	4–5
Length of materials		Millimeter	20–23	16–20
Size of knife roll		Millimeter	Φ400 × 390	Φ425 × 770
Revolving speed of knife roll		Rotate/minute	306	300
Fly cutter		Bundle	3	3
Dead knife		Bundle	1	1
Linear speed of first and second roller		Meter/minute	20.1	16.83
Linear speed of third roller		Meter/minute	21.7	19.24
Motor	Power	Kilowatt	13	30
	Rotate speed	Rotate/minute	970	970

In order to make the raw material cut by shear force, blade and knife roll axis should have an angle of 4°–7°, and it is fixed on the blade roll by bolt fixing. Its back has several silk tops for avoiding the retreat of blade. Meanwhile, the distance of the knife and the bottom knife can be adjusted. The angle of the knife blade is 40°–45°. Bed knife is horizontally fixed on the rack, and its position can be adjusted. Bottom knife is very thick, and its blade angle is in 80°–85°.

Raw materials are at the end of the knife, and the knife cuts material into a certain length, and the material falls on the conveyor belt at the bottom of equipment and is then sent to filter cleaning system.

3.1.1.1 Gap of Knife-Rall Straw Cutter

The fly cutter and bottom knife of knife-rall straw cutter should be replaced termly [2]. When replacing the blade on the knife, you will find that fly cutter just contact with bottom knife on both ends of knife roller, and there is always a gap in the middle section. That is to say, the clearance at the ends of section is different from the clearance at the middle section, as shown in Fig. 3.1. Theoretically, when straw cutter is at work, straw is cut by fly blade and bottom blade at C or D firstly, and then, the cutting section gradually shifts from one end to the other end with the rotation of knife roller. As shown in Fig. 3.1, in order to illustrate the gap of knife-rall straw cutter, fly cutter and bottom knife were drawn on a plan, while there is a difference in meshing time in fact. In order to illustrate the gap distributions of fly cutter and bottom knife at the full length, Fig. 3.2 is given (Fig. 3.3 is the three sides projection of Fig. 3.2). Assume that fly blade and bottom blade are both in ideal straight line, and the angle between the blade and the MN axis of knife roller rotation is α (this angle usually takes 4°–7°), and we suppose a piece of fly blade

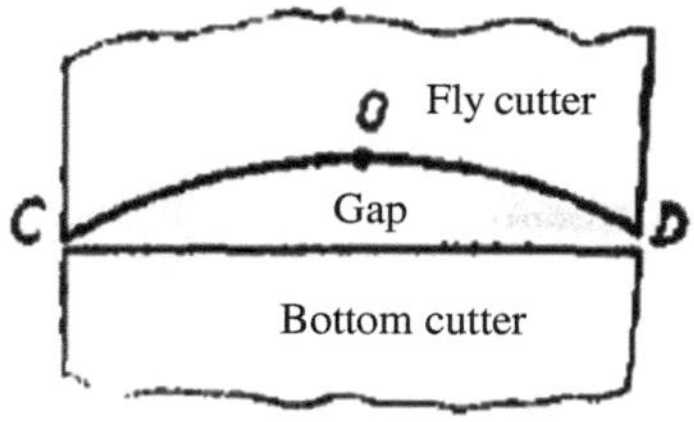

Fig. 3.1 Fly cutter, bottom cutter, and gap of knife-rall straw cutter

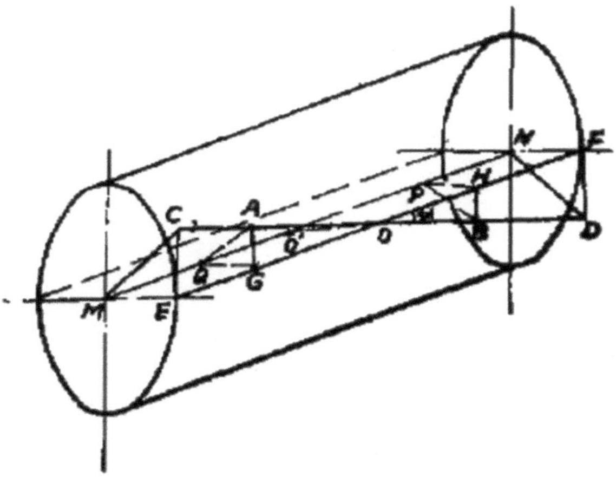

Fig. 3.2 Illustration of the gap distributions of fly cutter and bottom knife at the full length

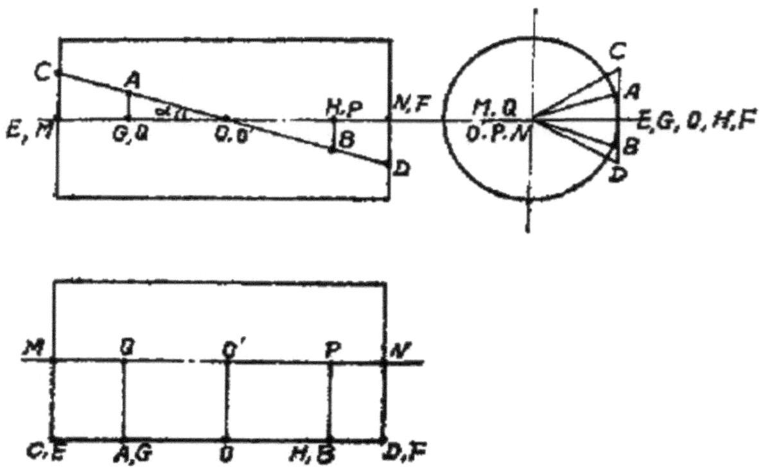

Fig. 3.3 The three sides projection of Fig. 3.2

(CD) is in the vertical plane. So, when the knife roller of the straw cutter rotates around the axis of MN, the circle radius of C, D points and midpoint O is different. Taking MN as the axis through the blade midpoint O, we can draw a cylindrical surface using the distance O and MN as the radius; circular M and N are the two cross sections, which are vertical to the axis of MN.

In △CEM中, ∠CEM = 90°,

$$\therefore MC = \sqrt{ME^2 + EC^2} \tag{3.1}$$

In △CEO中, ∠CEO = 90°, ∠COE = α,

$$\therefore CE = EO \tan\alpha \tag{3.2}$$

Take (3.2) into (3.1):

$$MC = \sqrt{ME^2 + (EO \tan\alpha)^2} \tag{3.3}$$

Take A and B in CD randomly, so:

$$QA = \sqrt{QC^2 + (GO\,tg\alpha)^2} \tag{3.4}$$

QA is the distance of A to MN, and QG is the radius of the cylinder surface, so QG = OO′ = ME,

$$\because AG < EC,$$

$$\therefore MC > QA > OO' \tag{3.5}$$

$$\text{In the same way, } ND > PB > OO' \tag{3.6}$$

We can get the following conclusions from the above discussion.

① As shown in Eqs. (3.5) and (3.6), although fly blade and bottom blade are both in the straight line, the radius of circling motion of each point on fly blade around the axis of MN is different when the knife-rall straw cutter rotate. If the central point of fly blade O contacts with the bottom blade, the point of fly blade except O will also contact with the bottom of blade and then stop rotation.

② As shown in Eqs. (3.5) and (3.6), we can obtain the following relations: MC–ME > QA–QG > OO′–OO′, ND–NF > PB–PH > OO′–OO′, ME = QG = NF = PH = OO′. These results showed that the gas distribution of fly blade and bottom blade on the full length is bigger in central point and smaller in end point.

③ The relations of interference amount and blade length:

$$C = \sqrt{R^2 + (X \tan \alpha)^2} - R \quad (3.7)$$

where

C is the interference amount;

R is the radius of fly blade;

A is the angle between the blade and the MN axis of knife roller rotation, $\alpha = 4°–7°$;

X is a variable value in the half length of blade, $X = 0–\frac{L}{2}$;

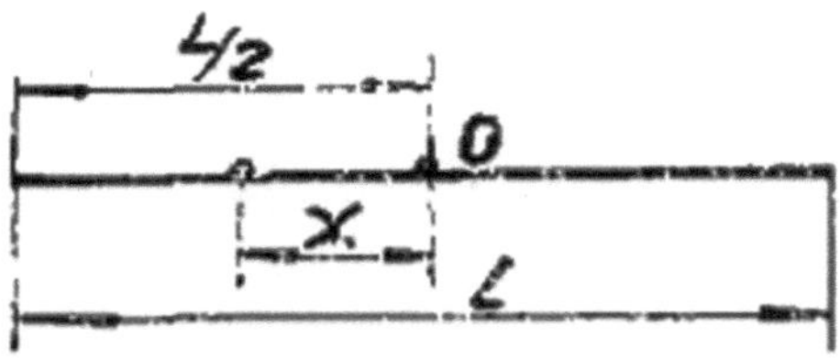

When $X = 0$, so $C = 0$; when $X = \frac{L}{2}$, so $C = \sqrt{R^2 + \left(\frac{L}{2} \times \tan \alpha\right)^2} - R$

If the gas distribution is same on the full length, then the shape of blade should be the bulge in the center of fly blade or bottom blade.

④ As shown in Eqs. (3.3) and (3.4), the length of knife roller should be suitable in order to avoid the increase in the different values of gas on the full length.

⑤ The angle between the blade and the MN axis of knife roller rotation should be suitable. As shown in Eqs. (3.3) and (3.4), the increase of α leads to the increase of $GO \cdot \tan\alpha$ and $EO \cdot \tan\alpha$, and the increase of EC and GA. So, the value of MC–OO′ and QA–OO′ increases, and hence the difference value of gas on the full length increases. We take ZCQ1 and ZCQ2 as examples to illustrate the gas distribution.

ZCQ1: The diameter of knife roller is Φ400, which is OO′ = 400/2 = 200 mm, and the length of knife roller is 399 mm. If we set $\alpha = 4°$ and take these data into (3.3), then we obtain the following equations:

$$\begin{aligned} MC &= \sqrt{ME^2 + (EOtg\alpha)^2} \\ &= \sqrt{200^2 + \left(\frac{390}{2}\tan 4°\right)^2} \\ &= \sqrt{200^2 + (195 \times 0.0699)^2} \\ &= \sqrt{40{,}185.93} = 200.46(\text{mm}) \end{aligned}$$

That is, the radius of C and D of fly blade around the MN axis is 200.46 mm, while the radius of central point O is 200 mm. The largest difference value of gas is 0.46 mm.

If $\alpha = 7°$,

$$\begin{aligned}\text{so MC} &= \sqrt{\text{ME}^2 + (\text{EO}\tan\alpha)^2}\\ &= \sqrt{200^2 + (195 \times 0.1228)^2}\\ &= \sqrt{40{,}573.27} = 201.43(\text{mm})\end{aligned}$$

The largest gas difference value of CD and O is 201.43 − 200 = 1.43 (mm).

ZCQ2: The diameter of knife roller is Φ430, which is OO′ = 430/2 = 215 mm, and the length of knife roller is 690 mm. Set $\alpha = 4°$ and take these data into (3.3), we obtain the following equations:

$$\begin{aligned}\text{MC} &= \sqrt{\text{ME}^2 + (\text{EO}\tan\alpha)^2}\\ &= \sqrt{215^2 + \left(\frac{690}{2}\tan 4°\right)^2}\\ &= \sqrt{46{,}807} = 216.35(\text{mm})\end{aligned}$$

That is, the largest difference value of gas between fly blade and bottom blade is 216.35 − 215 = 1.35 (mm).

If $\alpha = 7°$,

$$\begin{aligned}\text{MC} &= \sqrt{\text{ME}^2 + (\text{EO}\tan\alpha)^2}\\ &= \sqrt{215^2 + \left(\frac{690}{2}\tan 7°\right)^2}\\ &= \sqrt{48{,}019.427} = 219.13(\text{mm})\end{aligned}$$

In this condition, the largest difference value of gas between fly blade and bottom blade is 219.3 − 215 = 4.13 (mm).

From the above discussion, it clearly shows that the largest difference value of gas between fly blade and bottom blade increases with the increase of α and the length of knife roller.

3.1.1.2 Mechanical Property of Main Bearing of Knife-Rall Straw Cutter

Knife-rall straw cutter is still special equipment for cutting the grass in small and medium-sized papermaking enterprises. Although some improvement was done, the mechanical failure occurs frequently [3]. Main bearing of knife-rall straw cutter and journal of bearing are easily broken, which lead to the damage of fly knife and

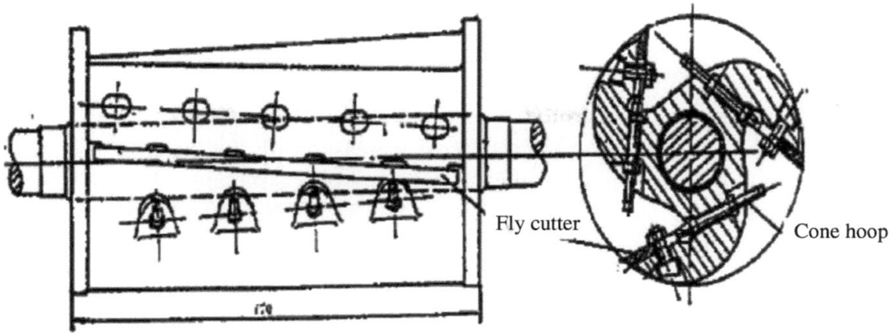

Fig. 3.4 Fly blade roller

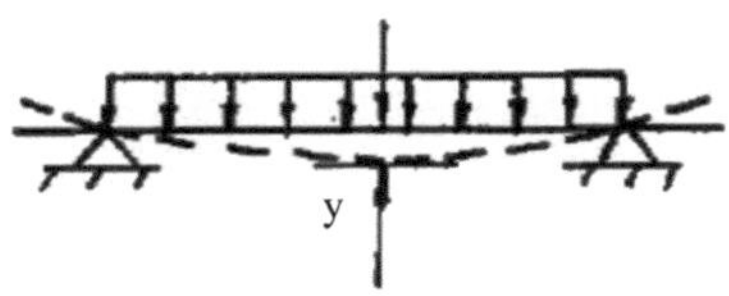

Fig. 3.5 Main bearing

other parts, and hence the stop of machine. Therefore, improving stiffness, vibration resistance, and wear resistance of main bearing of knife-rall straw cutter is essential to ensure that knife-rall straw cutter can work effectively for a long time.

(1) Stiffness analysis of main bearing of fly blade roller

Figure 3.4 shows the fly blade roller, and Fig. 3.5 is the force diagram of main bearing. The displacement of the middle piece of main bearing is *y*, so the stiffness of main bearing is F/y. Apparently, the increase in stiffness should lead to the decrease in main bearing deformation after the stress.

The small stiffness of main bearing should lead the big deformation when it is at work, which leads to the abrasion of bearing and journal. This also causes the resonance and the breakdown of machine. The main factor affecting the stiffness analysis of main bearing is the structure and size of main bearing and the stiffness of the supporting bearing.

① The structure and size of main bearing. The structrue and size of main bearing affecting the stiffness include the average diameter *D* and the bearing span *L*.

a. average diameter *D*. The effect of average diameter *D* on the stiffness is significant. According to the equation of moment of inertia $J = \frac{\pi}{64}D^4$, if the diameter of main bearing increases, the deformation of main bearing decreases as the inverse ratio of average diameter *D*. Additionally, the stiffness of bearing increases with the increase in diameter, which means that the displacement of main bearing caused by the deformation of supporting bearing will decrease.

b. bearing span L. The effect of bearing span L on the stiffness is complex. According to the equation $y = \frac{5gL^4}{384EI}$, the displacement (y) of main bearing caused by the bend of main bearing increases with the increase in bearing span (L). When the parameters of the supporting structure and main bearing are certain, y increased with the increase in L. Therefore, it should reduce the L as far as possible when it does not affect the efficiency of knife roller.

② Supporting stiffness. The stiffness of bearing using rolling bearing as support depends on the stiffness of the bearing itself, the contacted stiffness of the inner and outer part of the bearing and the supporting hole of the main bearing journal, and the stiffness of the supporting seat. The elastic displacement of rolling bearing produced by external force mainly causes a contact deformation between the rolling element and the raceway sleeve weeks of bearing. The elastic displacement is closely related to the type, size, and the adjusted status of bearing. Usually, the stiffness of line-contacted roller bearing is higher than that of point-contacted ball bearing, while the stiffness of double rolling bearing is higher than that of single bearing. The increase in bearing size and the bigger number of rolling element lead to the higher stiffness of bearing. When the rolling bearing is preloaded appropriately, the force of rolling bearing will be uniform. The stiffness of bearing will increase due to the facts that the deformation of the rolling element and the contacted raceway and the increase of contacted area.

③ Strategy of the improvement of main bearing stiffness

a. Determination of size of main bearing

As by the above discussion, the increase in diameter of main bearing should increase the stiffness obviously. However, the size of main bearing and knife roller increases with the increase in the diameter of main bearing, which affects the structure and size of fly blade roller and limits the rotate speed of bearing. This is due to the rotate speed of rolling bearing that is affected by the d, n_{max} (d is the diameter of bearing and n_{max} is the largest rotate speed of bearing). Therefore, the increase in diameter of main bearing should be suitable.

When the requirement of structure is met, the best supporting span should be adopted. When the larger or smaller support span has to adopt due to the reasons of structural requirement, bearing stiffness should be improved to make up the influence of the span.

b. adoption of high stiffness of rolling bearing and suitably preloaded

In order to improve the stiffness of main bearing, the parts of main bearing can not only adopt the general rolling bearing, but also it can adopt various special structures of rolling bearing. Additionally, the interface between the journal of main bearing and the supporting bracket connected with bearing should meet the requirement of geometrical shape and surface roughness.

(2) Vibration resistance and abrasive resistance of the main bearing

① Vibration resistance. The vibration resistance of main bearing is that the parts of main bearing can work and do not vibrate. The low vibration resistance of main bearing should easily lead to the vibration when it is at work. This also results in the decrease of the durability of knife roller. Therefore, the vibration resistance should be the key metric of the property of main bearing.

Theoretical analysis and experimental results show that the main factors influencing the vibration resistance of main bearing are its structure stiffness and damping characteristics. The large ratio of stiffness to damping leads to more difficulty of self-excited vibration and the smaller forced vibration. Therefore, the main way to improve the vibration resistance of main bearing includes (a) the increase in stiffness of main bearing; (b) the increase in parts resistance of main bearing.

The damping performance of main bearing using sliding bearing is much better than that of using rolling bearing, and the tapered roller bearing in roller bearing is better than that of ball bearing. Preloading the rolling bearing suitably not only can improve the stiffness of the parts of main bearing, but also it can increase the damping ratio. Adopting high precision rolling bearing can help improve the vibration resistance of the parts of main bearing due to the decreased shape error of bearing raceway and rolling body and the even force of rolling element bearing. In addition, improving the main bearing journal and the gas between rolling bearing and bearing seat hole may also improve the damping ratio of the parts of main bearing, so as to reduce the vibration.

② Abrasive resistance

The good abrasive resistance is the main factor affecting the work efficiency of fly blade. The poor abrasive resistance leads to the quicker abrasion of axle and bearing, which affects the working life of the fly knife roller and the straw cutter. The measures to increase the abrasive resistance include the following:

(1) Adjust bearing clearance reasonably and ensure the good lubrication and seal.
(2) The correct selection of the materials of main bearing and sliding bearing and the heat treatment methods. The bearing must be able to adjust to compensate for enlarged gap after abrasion. In addition, the rational use and maintenance is also very important to improve the abrasive resistance of main bearing of knife roller.

3.1.1.3 Notes on the Operation and Maintenance of Straw Cutter

In order to improve the qualified rate and ensure the normal operation of equipment, attention should be paid to the following notes:

(1) When the forage is fed to tape, clods, stone, wood, iron, and other sundry must be checked and removed from the forage, in order to avoid the collapse or damage of machine by accident.
(2) Fly blade must be installed before the machine running, and a suitable gap between fly blade and bottom knife is made, which is generally between 0.3 and 0.5 mm. Adjusting the blade has greater influence on the performance of the straw cutter.
(3) Fly blade and bottom blade must be sharp, and a blunt knife has the poor shear effect, and the qualified rate of the cut grass is low. Therefore, blades must be regularly changed and reshaped.
(4) When feeding the materials, the thickness of material should be uniform and smooth, in order to avoid the accident of blade collapse. If blade is nipped, the machine should be stopped immediately. The knife roller should be removed, and the raw material is withdrawn. After the defects are checked and corrected, feeding process may continue.

In order to make the normal operation and safety production of straw cutter, attention is paid to the following maintenance work:

(1) Newly changed fly blade or bottom blade after a certain time should be tightened again.
(2) When loading the knife, deformed or sliding tooth screw and nut should not be used.
(3) Straw cutter should be repaired every three months. The deformation and damage of rotary bearing, gear, and knife roller should be checked and adjusted timely.
(4) Knife roller may be damaged after a long-term utilization, and the following points should be paid attention to when knife roller is repaired:

   a. knife roller bearing has two diameters of rollers in the roll, which is that the end of v-belt point is greater than that of fly wheel. Therefore, the end of v-belt point should be pressured out when the bearing is opened.
   b. Ensure the appropriate interference tolerance when the knife roller is replaced.

3.1.1.4 Productivity of Knife-Rall Straw Cutter

The productivity of straw cutter is generally calculated as follows:

$$Q = 60\,KbHVr$$

where
Q is the productivity, (kg/h);
K is the unbalanced coefficient of feeding materials, which is 0.8 generally;
b is the length of feeding roller, (m);

Fig. 3.6 Straw cutter

H is the thickness of feeding layer, which is 0.2–0.3 m;
V is the feeding speed (m/min);
r is the bulk density of material (kg/m^3).

r values of several material: rice straw 55–65 kg/m^3; sweet sorghum 60–65 kg/m^3; wheat straw 65–75 kg/m^3; corn stover 60–65 kg/m^3; awn straw 70–75 kg/m^3; and reed straw 70–75 kg/m^3. The straw cutter is shown in Fig. 3.6.

3.1.2 Straw Baler

In China, the traditional methods of handing straw in paper mill is that the scattered grass is transported to the factory, and then cut, dedusted, transmitted, and presoaked. The disadvantage of this approach includes the high cost of transportation, the big area covers of the storage, the high risk of fire, the serious air pollution of cutting, and the dedusting operation of the straw. "Straw baler" improved these shortcomings by handling the original process in the rural areas generally for cutting, dedusting, and packaging of straw. After transmitting to the factory, the straw is dispersed and presoaked. At present, there are many types of straw baler;

Fig. 3.7 Screw baler

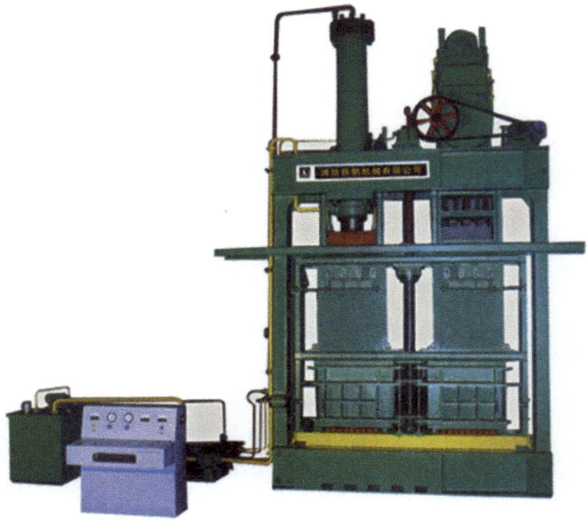

the following straw baler, including screw baler (Fig. 3.7) and hydraulic baler, is mainly introduced.

3.1.2.1 Screw Baler

Figure 3.8 shows the drive system diagram and transmission principle of the screw baler [4]. The rotation movement speed of the motor is first reduced by the belt, and then reduced by the two-stage gear. Finally, the movement is spread to nut which is connected with the big gear. Nut rotates while the screw which is combined with the nut does not. So, the extrusion force will be generated by the up-down movement of screw.

As shown in Fig. 3.8, the main component of the main drive system should be a deputy campaign of nut screw. It is the main strength member. The incorrect design or parameter of deputy campaign will not produce the desired working pressure or

Fig. 3.8 Drive system diagram and transmission principle of screw baler

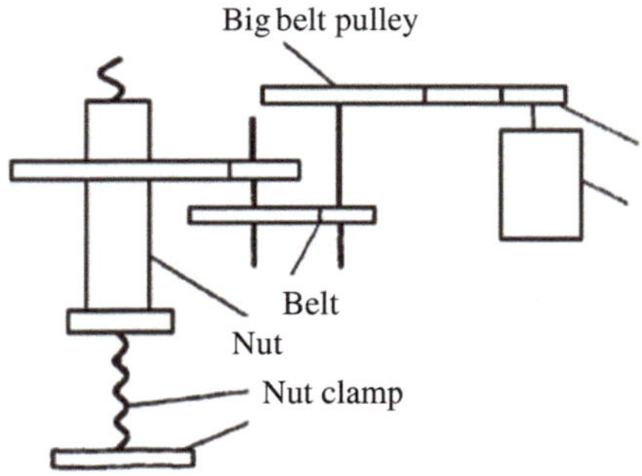

will short the utilization life. A brief summary about the design process of nut screw deputy campaign will be introduced as follows:

(1) The choice of materials and shape of screw

① Selection of screw material
According to the actual work of the machine, #45 steel is selected as the material of screw from the perspective of utilization life and cost of the machine. Stiffness and abrasive resistance of this material are better.

② Selection of nut material
Because the good abrasive resistance and low coefficient between screw and nut are required and thread will bear a greater load when the machine is at work, suitable materials should be selected. The suitable materials include ductile iron and cast bronze (ZQSn6-6-3). Taking all aspects into consideration, ZQSn6-6-3 is used as the material of nut.
If two radial rolling bearing, plane bearing, and a big gear are installed on the nut and nut also cross a bearing housing, the dimension of nut is larger. If ZQSn6-6-3 is selected as the material of nut, the cost of the product will increase. Therefore, according to the actual need, nut is divided into two parts including inner sleeve and outer sleeve. The cast steel is used as the material of the outer sleeve, and the required length of outer sleeve is made. The ZQSn6-6-3 is used as the material of the inner sleeve, on which internal thread is added. Length of internal thread is around ten pitches. The interference fit is used for inner and outer sleeves, and bolt is used for connection at the end and to convey torque. This will not only satisfy the work requirements and but also reduce the production cost.

③ The selection of thread type
There are three kinds of force transmission thread tooth type in generally, including rectangular thread, trapezoidal thread, and sawtooth thread. The tooth angle of rectangular thread is $\beta = 0°$. Transmission efficiency of rectangular thread is higher, but the root is weak. The tooth shape angle of trapezoidal thread is $\beta > 0°$. Friction of trapezoidal thread is high, transmission efficiency is low, but its root is its strength, which can work under high load. The machine will bear the big force under the working conditions, which requires the strength of the root. Therefore, choose the trapezoidal thread as the optimal thread.

(2) The main parameter selection and calculation
A sliding screw drive is used on the machine. Its structure is simple and the processing is convenient, but transmission efficiency is low. Therefore, the selection of main working parameters is very important. If the parameter selection is improper, on the one hand, it can reduce the transmission efficiency and does not produce the design working pressure; on the other hand, although the design of work pressure is reached, it greatly reduces the service life of the screw vice. In order to make the packaging products to meet the size

requirements after measurement by experiment, required working stress is about 25,000 kg. Additionally, according to the stipulated time requirements per pack products by users, preliminary selection of thread numbers is $n = 1$ and pitch is $S = 20$ mm taking the nut rotation speed requirements into consideration.

① The selection and calculation of the screw size is as follows:

$$d_1 = \sqrt{\frac{4F}{\pi[\sigma]}}$$

where

d_1 is the inner diameter of screw;
F is the force bore by screw, $F = 25{,}000$ kg;
$[\sigma]$ is the allowable stress of screw, which is 80 MPa in this condition

$$d_1 = \sqrt{\frac{4F}{\pi[\sigma]}} = \sqrt{\frac{4 \times 25{,}000 \times 9.8}{3.1415 \times 80}} = 62.4(\text{mm})$$

According to the GB784-65, the parameters of trapezoidal thread ($S = 20$ m) are as follows:

The outer diameter of screw thread is $d = 90$ mm;
The inner diameter of screw thread is $d_1 = 68$ mm;
The outer diameter of nut thread is $d' = 92$ mm; and
The inner diameter of nut thread is $d_1' = 70$ mm;

② the calculation of thread angle and self-locking conditions

$$\lambda = \arctan\frac{L}{\pi d_1} = \arctan\frac{ns}{\pi d_1}$$

where

λ is the thread angle;
L is the lead of screw thread;
n is the number of screw thread;
S is the thread pitch; and
d_1 is the inner diameter of screw thread;

$$\lambda = \arctan\frac{ns}{\pi d_1} = \arctan\frac{20 \times 1}{3.14 \times 68} = 5^\circ\ 21'$$

Considering the materials of screw and nut and the surface roughness and the lubrication of machine, we initially identified the friction coefficient of deputy thread is $f' = 0.12$, and friction angle of deputy thread is $\theta = \arctan f' = \arctan 0.12 = 6^\circ\ 50'$.

Because $\lambda = 5° 21' < 6° 50' = \theta$, deputy thread meets the condition requirements of self-locking.

(3) Thread strength check

For the screw drive, the wear and damage occurs mainly in the nut section. Therefore, we only check the nut portion.

① Thread shear strength check

If the thread shear strength meets the requirement, it should follow the equation:

$$F/(\pi \times d' \times t \times Z) \leq [\tau]$$

where

F is the pure pressure, $F = 245{,}000$ N;

d' is the inner diameter of screw, $d' = 92$ mm;

t_1 is the width of thread root, $t_1 = 0.65 \times S = 13$ mm;

Z is the number of screw thread, $Z = 9$; and

$[\tau]$ is the allowable stress, which is 40 MPa in this condition.

$$\frac{F}{\pi \times d_1 \times t_1 \times Z} = \frac{24{,}500}{3.14 \times 92 \times 13 \times 9} = 7125\ \text{MPa} < 40\ \text{MPa}$$

Therefore, the screw thread meets the requirements of shear strength.

② Bending strength check of thread

If the thread shear strength meets the bending strength conditions, it should follow the equation:

$$\frac{3F \times h}{\pi \times d_1 \times t_1^2 \times Z} \leq [\sigma_b]$$

where

F is the pure pressure, $F = 245{,}000$ N;

h is the height of thread, $S = 0.5 \times S = 10$ mm;

t_1 is the width of thread root, $t_1 = 0.65 \times S = 13$ mm;

Z is the number of screw thread, $Z = 9$; and

$[\sigma_b]$ is the allowable stress, which is 60 MPa in this condition

$$\frac{3 \times 245{,}000}{3.14 \times 92 \times 13^2 \times 9} = 18.7\ \text{MP} < 60\ \text{MP}$$

Therefore, the screw thread meets the requirements of bending strength.

(4) Screw stability calculation
If screw meets the requirements of stability, the ratio of length to diameter should be among a certain value.

$$\gamma = \frac{4 \times \mu \times l}{d_1}$$

where

- γ is the ratio of length to diameter of screw;
- μ is the convert coefficient of screw length;
- l is the actual stress length of screw, which is l = 1550 mm in this condition; and
- d_1 is the inner diameter of screw thread.

Screw, which is made of non-hardened steel, meets requirements of stability when the ratio of length to diameter γ is less than 90. Take these data into the following equation:

$$\gamma = \frac{4 \times \mu \times l}{d_1} = \frac{4 \times 0.7 \times 1550}{68} = 63.8 < 90$$

So, the critical pressure of screw stability is calculated as follows:

$$F_{cr} = \frac{334}{1 + 1.3 \times 10^4 \times \gamma^2} = \frac{\pi \times d^4}{4}$$
$$= 792{,}833(\mathrm{N})$$

So, $\frac{F_{cr}}{F} = \frac{792{,}833}{24{,}500}$ = 3.24 (F is the actual load of screw), which meets the requirement of screw stability ($\frac{F_{cr}}{F}$ is less than 2.5–4).

Therefore, the normal operation of screw can meet the requirements of stability. The screw drive mechanism designed by the above-described methods can show the good performance in actual operation, which can achieve the desired goal.

3.1.2.2 Hydraulic Baler

In China, Wang et al. [5] developed a straw baler using a hydraulic drive system in 1991, which is named DBJ-1 hydraulic baler. After identifying and commissioning, all the performance parameters of DBJ-1 hydraulic baler meet the design requirements. It consists of four major components: (1) packing box; (2) power section; (3) Energy section; and (4) control section (Fig. 3.9).

Packing box consists of box, cover, front door, and other components. Box has four channels in anterior and posterior wall for wire penetration. Power section consists of cylinder and big pusher. Cylinder stroke is 800 mm with 100 t thrust. Hydraulic cylinder bracket is welded directly to the frame chassis. The back of the

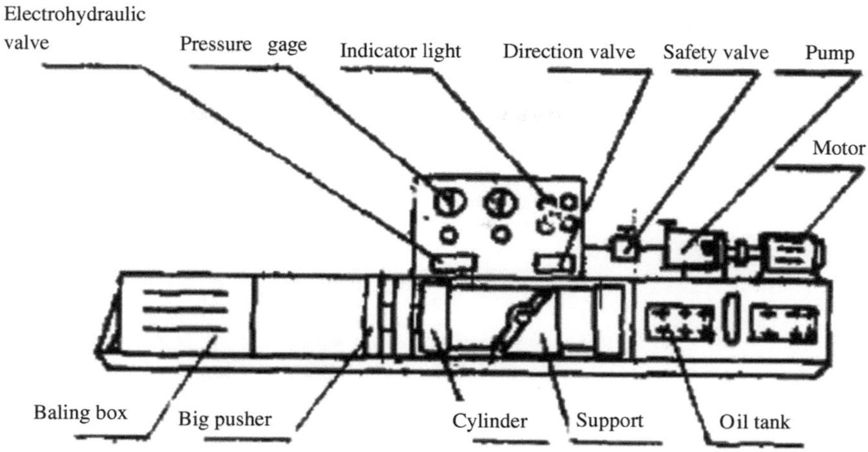

Fig. 3.9 DBJ-1 hydraulic baler

big pusher has four guide wheels. Rear side of guide wheel is equipped with front and rear apron and trip switches. Front and rear apron and the trip switch control the movement position of hydraulic cylinder. Control section consists of electronic control and hydraulic control, which is used to control the work program of panel.

Hydraulic system of this equipment includes main power part; fuel supplied part of hydraulic pressure control valve (Fig. 3.10). Working of the hydraulic system is as follows:

① Driven process. After the main motor start, the SCY-14-1B hydraulic pump (15) begins to work. Hydraulic oil in hydraulic pump tank (12) is filtered into the electrohydraulic valve (21) (hereinafter referred to as electric valve) by the suction filter. The solenoid is turned on, so that the valve is in the working state at the right position, and the hydraulic oil flows from the electrohydraulic valve to the right side of the cylinder (22), pushing the piston to the left and pushing the big pusher from "1" to the "2." The forage straw then molded and compacted (Fig. 3.10).

② Baler process. After the molding and compaction of forage straw, big pusher touches the limit switch (3). Tie off solenoid at the right side of the electrohydraulic, which is in the neutral position, and then the hydraulic oil is directly returned to the tank through the oil filter (20). At this time, bale wire penetrates its passage, and the forage straw is packaged tightly (Fig. 3.10).

③ Return process. After packaging, turn left the solenoid valve of electrohydraulic, which is in the left position working condition. Hydraulic oil flows from the electrohydraulic valve to the left side of cylinder. When the big pusher is turn to "1" from "2," and touches the limit switch (4) and cut off the magnet, then the machine stops.

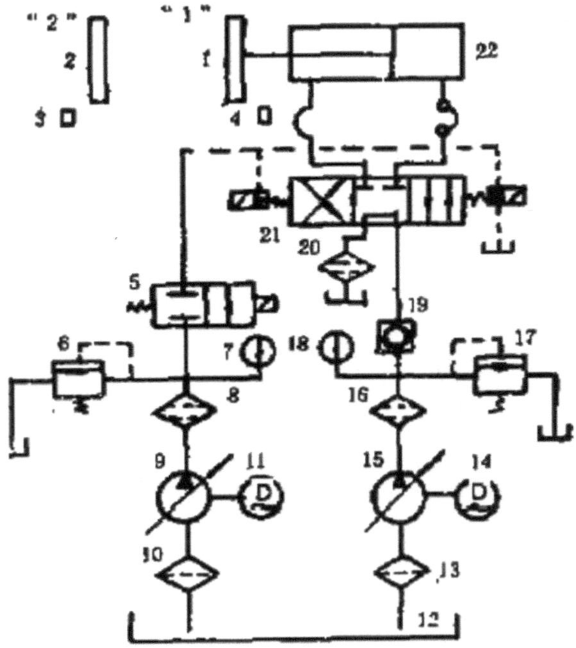

Fig. 3.10 The hydraulic system of DBJ-1 hydraulic baler

The maximum flow of pump Q is 100 L/min, the hydraulic cylinder stroke l is 800 mm, and the output force F is 100 kgf. The machine has the advantages of low cost, low energy consumption, and high efficiency. Compared with the traditional screw baler machine, the benefits of DBJ-1 hydraulic baler are good (Table 3.2).

Results show that the working efficiency of DBJ-l hydraulic baler is two times as screw baler, while the energy consumption is reduced by 50 % and the volume of a single bundle is reduced by 50 %, which is helpful for handling and transportation.

Table 3.2 Two baler benefits comparison

Types	Cost ($\times 10^4$ yuan)	Electricity consumption (kW)	Packaging time (min)	Equivalent volume (m^3)	Deposit amount (bundle)	Deadweight tonnage (t)
Screw-type	6	15	10	0.133	8	4000
Hydraulic type	4.5	11	5	0.066	16	8000

3.1.3 Straw Baler Loosing Machine

After the straw bag is transferred into the treatment site, it needs to be processed. The efficiency artificial bulk package is low, and the labor intensity is high. Generally, straw bulk charter is used in the larger treatment field. The machine can not only improve the work efficiency and reduce labor intensity, but also can evacuate the bulk package into a loose piece of grass. This machinery is briefly introduced in the following section (Figs. 3.11, 3.12, and 3.13).

Four-charter roll scattered vertically arranged guide roller right, at the bottom of the guide roller conveyor for material on the output side of the guide roller to squeeze rollers are provided at the output side of the squeeze roller pair provided with a bulk package rolls, guide roller right, squeeze rollers, bulk bag rolls are connected with the corresponding drive motor. Squeeze rollers, including the pressure roller and the transition roller, were the horizontal layout. Bulk package has two rollers, namely a bulk package rolls, the second bulk package rolls, bulk package is more than twice the radius of the roller rolls bulk packages, two times roll bulk package provided to the transition roller and a bulk package rolls surrounded output area, a bulk package rolls and consistent direction of rotation of the second bulk package roll.

Straw package delivery conveyor 11 to guide roller for a guide roller pair will be involved on a straw bag to the pressure roller 2 and the transition roller 3, by the pressure rollers 2 and 3 to achieve the transition roller straw bag decentralized, semi-dispersed state in a bulk package straw bag squeeze roller 4 output, part of the material through a bulk package rolls between 4 and 5 secondary bulk packages run

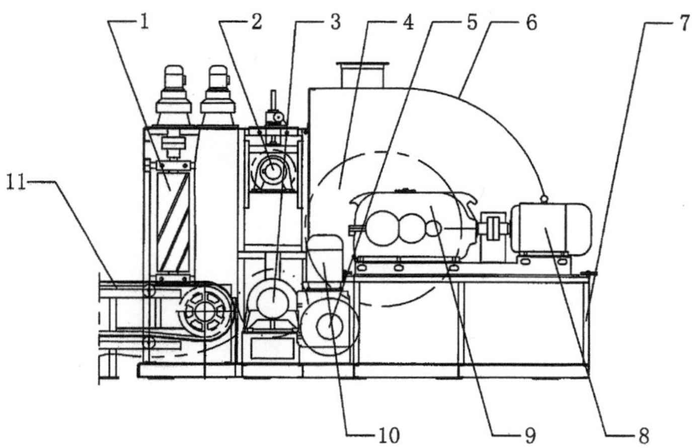

Fig. 3.11 Front view of straw baler loosing machine. *1* Feed roller; *2* upper roll; *3* transitional roller; *4* package material roller 1; *5* package material roller 2; *6* cover; *7* rack; *8* motor 1; *9* reduction drive; *10* motor 2; *11* conveyor

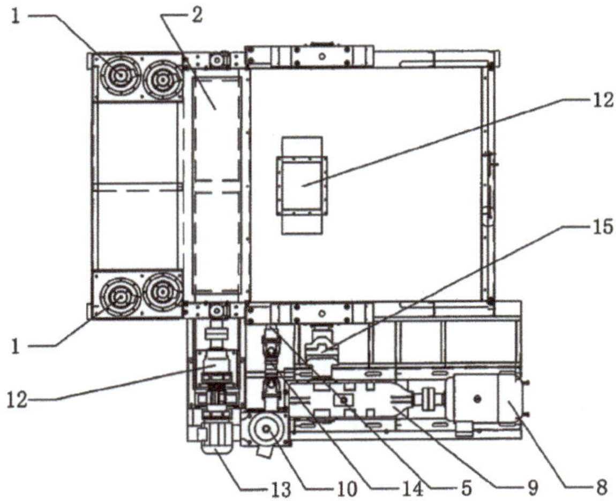

Fig. 3.12 Aerial view of straw baler loosing machine. *1* Feed roller; *2* upper roll; *3* transitional roller; *4* package material roller 1; *5* package material roller 2; *6* cover; *7* rack; *8* motor 1; *9* reduction drive; *10* motor 2; *11* conveyor; *12* drive motor 1; *13* drive motor 2; *14* Cardan joint; *15* cross-linked coupling

Fig. 3.13 Bale loosing machine

over rollers, rolling to achieve the second part of the material from bulk package the output side of the secondary roller 5 is discharged [6].

3.1.4 Conveyor

Screw conveyor is generally divided into two kinds. One kind is one-stage and another kind is multistage. One-stage large span screw conveyor has a wide range application in conveying forage, such as grasses screw blanks presoak equipment and large volume screw discharging device in pulping and papermaking company. Diameter of spiral leaves is mainly in 400–800 mm, and span is between 6 and 13 m. Compared with the multistage, it has no suspension helical bearing in the middle, and it is more adaptable to a variety of materials. Thus, it shows a broad application prospect.

Large span screw conveyor [7] is mainly used for material prepreg process. That is, it is used after cutting and before entering the digester, making forage sheet uniformly mixed with the liquid. It also increases the density of material, improves pot loading and harvest rates, and reduces air pollution and dust during transportation. Screw conveyor structure is shown in Fig. 3.14. Rotating spiral blade pushes the material transportation, and material such as the nut without rotation moves axially. So, the force that the material does not rotate together with the spiral leaf material is the weight of the material and the friction of the material and shell.

Normal life of helical axis is about 6–10 years. The screw shaft of screw conveyor may be get broken in a production run. The reason for the spiral shaft fracture may be that large span screw shaft is generally made by seamless steel pipes welded helical blades. It has bearing shaft at both ends, but it is vacant in the middle. Large span screw axis mainly bears bending moment and torque moment. The greatest danger force area is in the middle section of the shaft. As for the deformation of the big span screw axis, torque moment is smaller compared with bending moment, which means that torque moment may be not counted in the actual calculation. When you press a pure bending moment, the force of the screw shaft is as shown in Fig. 3.15.

Rotated screw shaft works under alternating stress conditions for a long-term, suffering a symmetric cycle alternating stress. Therefore, although the screw shaft is used as a good plastic material (such as A3 steel, 20 steel or 30 steel, etc.) is used,

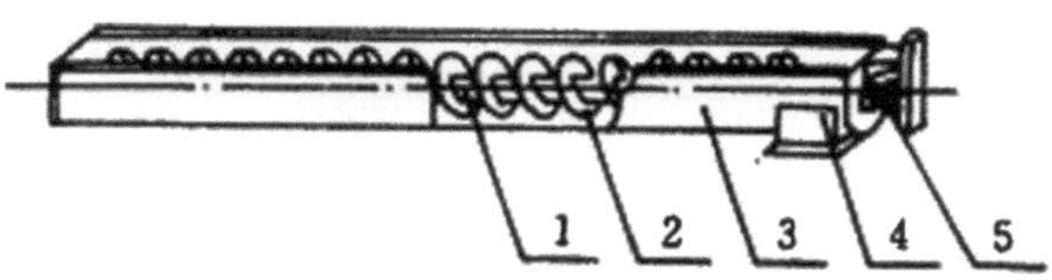

Fig. 3.14 Screw conveyor structure. *1* Screw shaft; *2* helical blade; *3* shell; *4* discharge hole; *5* bearing

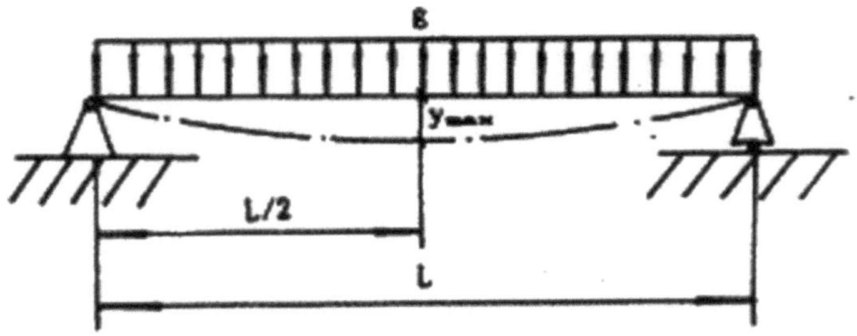

Fig. 3.15 Free-body diagram of screw shaft

the maximum working stresses are far below the ultimate strength of the material. The obvious fatigue fracture will often occur in the case of no plastic deformation. So, fatigue fracture is the main reason for the break of screw shaft. Damage factor of fatigue fracture is the limit value from the biggest line strain to the uniaxial stress state. Because the strain on project is similar to the line deflection rate, Song et al. [8] proposed the stiffness design of screw shaft using deflection rate. According to the stiffness of the screw shaft, axis diameter is selected with the deflection rate as an indicator. The number of rotations is used to predict the life of the screw shaft, which will bring a simple and satisfactory result. Large span screw shaft based on the design method of taking check stiffness as the core can not only carry out the calculation of the shaft diameter and span, but also it can predict the reliability and life [9]. Factors condition is variable, and material properties and manufacturing techniques have bias, and thus the calculated results have dispersed, but there is still a guiding role in the actual production. This calculation method is relatively simple and more intuitive and easy compared to the strength check screw shaft method, which is suitable for engineering applications.

3.2 Rehydration and Dehydration Equipments

3.2.1 Rehydration Equipment

Before gas explosion, materials need to be pretreated, which generally includes presoak pretreatment by water, acid, or alkali (liquid ammonia, sodium hydroxide, etc.). The equipments are generally the same for different pretreatments. As for large size materials, a pulverizer should be added before presoak. The aim of pretreatment was to increase the efficiency of the gas explosion.

Water presoak pretreatment can increase the moisture content of materials and hence improve the performance of gas explosion. Meanwhile, water presoak pretreatment can decrease the dust in materials, which purifies the materials. Acid presoak pretreatment can lead to the easy hydrolysis of hemicellulose, which facilitates the compositions fractionation in gas explosion. Alkali presoak

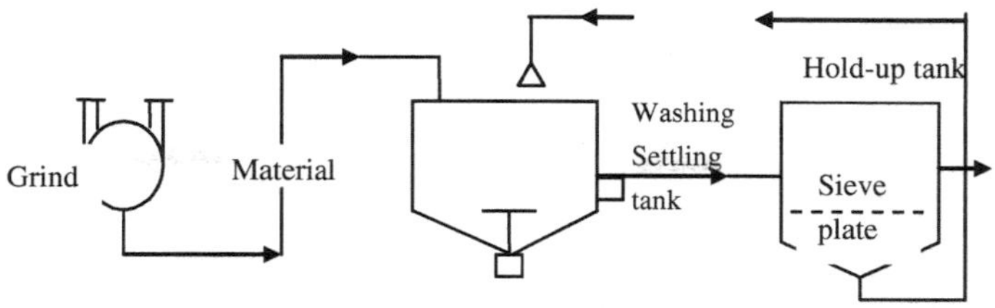

Fig. 3.16 Presoak pretreatment equipments

pretreatment can lead to the dissolution of lignin and dissolve the hemicellulose in gas explosion, and hence, it increases the efficiency of gas explosion. If ammonia is used for presoak pretreatment, the *N* content of materials can be increased, which should facilitate the digestibility of materials by microbes and ruminant. Presoak equipment is shown in Fig. 3.16.

Straw and other materials are firstly transported to the dip tank. If the material is relatively clean, the nozzle can be sued to evenly moist for the material based on the desired moisture content. If the material contains more impurities, such as dust, more water into the immersion tank by tap can be added and the blender at the bottom of immersion blender tank to clean materials is started. A larger proportion of sand, stones, and some metal debris will be deposited at the bottom of the immersion tank. Cleaned straw is discharged from discharge tube in the side portion of the tank dip, and then transferred into a stainless steel storage tank through a metal mesh filter, concomitantly removing most of the water. The water can be recycled. After the material is discharged, you can clear the impurities at the bottom of the presoak tank.

Acid and alkali presoak pretreatment is very different from water presoak pretreatment. If the material has been screened and impurities have been removed, acid or alkali on materials can be sprayed directly. Materials can be then sent directly to the gas explosion tank. If the impurity content of material is relatively high, the materials can be washed using a lot of acid or alkali, and then removed from the gas explosion tank, of which procedure is the same for water presoak pretreatment.

When materials are treated with large amounts of acid or alkali, the solid–liquid ratio, temperature, pressure, and time of presoak should be controlled generally. Such as straw, 4–8 % NaOH, 3–10 % $(NH_4)_2SO_4$, urea, 0.08–2 % H_2SO_4 (w/w) can be used, while a solid-liquid ratio of 1:3–10 can be used. Handling time can be from several minutes to several hours, while the pretreatment temperature can range from room temperature to 100 °C. Generally, pretreatment concentrations of acid or alkali are higher, processing temperature is higher, and the processing time is shorter. Required acid or alkali concentration is determined by the specific pretreatment effects after pretreatment. It is noteworthy that water presoak catalyzed hydrolysis without addition of acid and alkali is a promise pretreatment currently since the flooding.

3.2.2 *Dehydration Equipment*

If liquid added to the material is less in the presoak pretreatment, then dehydration equipment is not required. Materials can be transferred directly into the gas explosion tank. If more liquid is used in presoak pretreatment process, then dehydration equipment is required. If fully submerged stirring treatment approach is used, excess liquid need to be removed, and materials are then transferred into the gas explosion tank. Dehydration equipment of presoak pretreatment can be simple or complex, which is decided on the basis of the actual production situation.

3.2.2.1 Double Net Press Master

Double net press master consists of two vertical sideless wires and a number of rollers (Fig. 3.17). It is a dewatering device for the pulping, which is widely used in the papermaking industry. It can be also used for dewatering of fiber material. The principle of double net press master is shown in Fig. 3.18. Slurry flows from the feed tank online to net, via gravity dehydration of roller case, and then it is squeezed into intermediate of two networks. Finally, it is added to the mechanical pressure dehydration equipment. The slurry concentration can be increased to 30 %. This equipment has high production capacity and compact structure, which has high efficiency [1].

Fig. 3.17 Double net press master

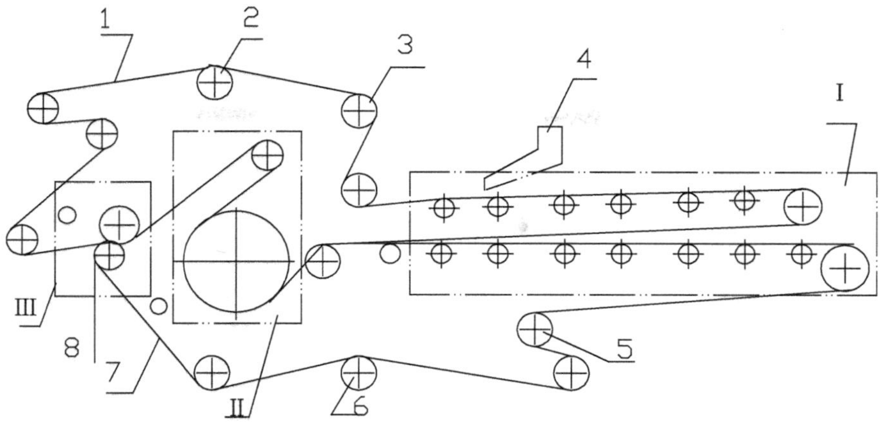

Fig. 3.18 Schematic diagram of double net press master. *I* Gravity-dehydration zone; *II* buffer pressure dehydration zone; *III* high-pressure dehydration zone. *1* Filter screen 1; *2* guide roll 1; *3* stretch roll 1; *4* flow box; *5* stretch roll 2; *6* guide roll 2; *7* filter screen 2; *8* discharge port

3.2.2.2 Drum Dehydration Equipment

Drum dehydration equipment [10] consists of a pair of roller, which is opposite movement, a pair of spring, a pair of regulating screws, a pair of rocker, feeding stations, discharging ramp, hopper, racks, and motor (Fig. 3.19).

In this dehydration equipment, roller is the main working parts, which is made of steel. The down roller is the capstan roller. In order to increase the friction coefficient of the working surface and fiber and decrease the slippage when the fiber is fed, the working surface of roller is often rough machining, or processed into a pattern. The up roller is a driven roller and pressed against the down roller, which is

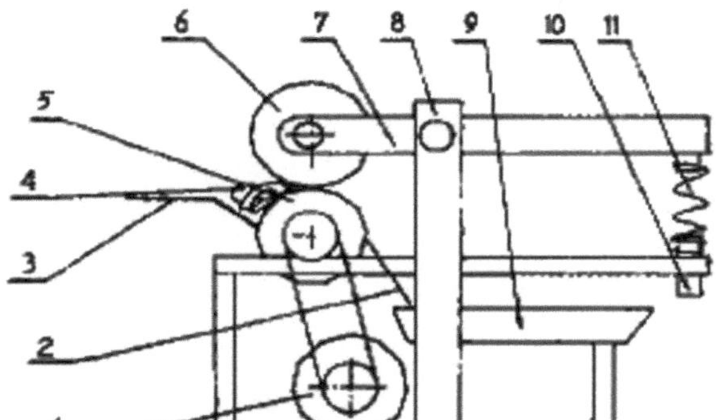

Fig. 3.19 Dehydration equipment. *1* Motor; *2* discharging inclined plate; *3* feeding plate; *4* material; *5* down roller; *6* up roller; *7* rocker; *8* rack; *9* aggregate bin; *10* regulator screw; *11* spring

rotated by relying on the friction with the down roller. The up roller bonds a thick steel cylindrical sleeve, whose role is to use pouches of elastic deformation. So that feed fibers can be squeezed at different thicknesses. The spring presses two rollers through the rocker arm based on the principle of leverage. Spring pressure within a certain range can be adjusted through the regulator screw to adapt to different fiber dehydration rates. The role of the discharged swash plate is to scrape the adhesive fiber from the down roller, on which it has a lot of opening holes. The role of opening hole is to isolate fiber and water.

In the present equipment, the rotation of up roller relies on the friction with the down roller. The rotation of the up roller uses a pair of meshing gears connected with the down roller. So, the structure is simplified, and the manufacturing cost and the consumption power are reduced.

When the roller is operated, presoaked material is fed from the feed plate into intermediate between two rollers. After squeezed by the rollers, the water flows from weep hole between the down roller and the swash plate and then fall into the ground drains. Materials slip from the swash plate and fall into the hopper. This equipment is suitable for small-volume batch production.

3.2.2.3 Press-Type Dehydration Equipment

This press-type dehydration equipment consists of a rack, a hydraulic cylinders mounted vertically above rack, a squeeze plate connected the hydraulic cylinder at the bottom, and a groove masonry, which is below ground and corresponds to the position of squeezed plant [11]. Groove contains accommodate waste, U-shaped steel corresponding to the squeeze plate steel. U-shaped steel wall distributes uniformly drainage holes. Both sides of the hinge plates have squeeze steel chain, which can connect with U-shaped steel (Fig. 3.20). The bottom surface of squeeze plate is polyhedron in shape with the raised intermediate and four surrounding rectangular chambers, drainage holes is placed between each plane. The upper end of U-shaped steel has ear hook attached to steel chain.

As shown in Fig. 3.20, when using this press-type dehydration equipment, the U-shaped steel mold (8) is firstly placed into the masonry cement groove (10). At this time, hydraulic cylinder (4) raises the pressure plate (5) to the highest position. In the work area, presoaked slurry is transported and poured into the U-shaped steel mold (8) by forklifts. Then squeeze plate (5) begins to decrease pushed by the hydraulic cylinder (4) until it contacts the slurry. With the gradual increase of oil pressure, the pressure of the squeeze plate (5) to the slurry increases, and the water in slurry begins to be squeezed and discharged. The bottom surface of the squeeze plate (5) is a polyhedron-truncated pyramid with intermediate projection and four peripheral chambered rectangular. There is a drain groove (11) between the plates of the truncated pyramids. Therefore, when the slurry is under pressure, the pressure on the middle portion is larger. The squeezed water is discharged from the U-shaped steel (8) of the peripheral wall and the bottom of the drainage holes (9). The discharged water flows into groove (10) and drain groove (15). Along the drain

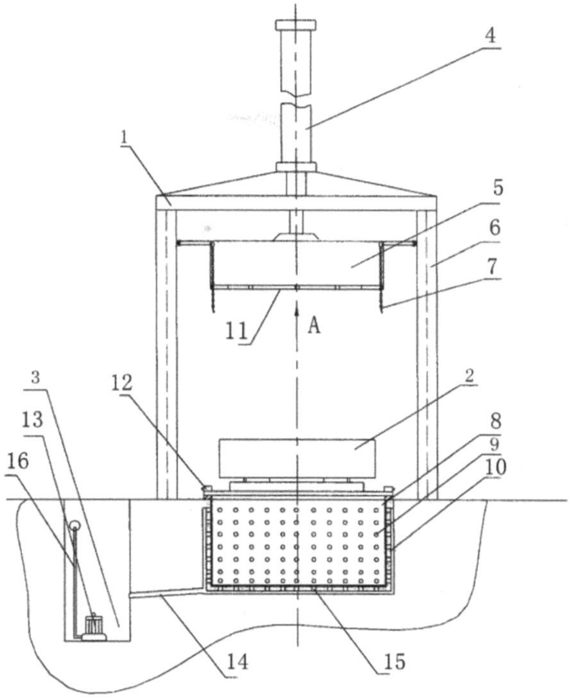

Fig. 3.20 Press-type dehydration equipment. *1*, *6* Rack; *2* material; *3* sump; *4* hydraulic cylinder; *5* squeeze plate; *7* steel chain; *8* U-shaped steel mold; *9* drainage holes; *10* groove; *11*, *15* drain groove; *12* hook; *13* pump; *14* input pipe; *16* output pipe

groove (15) connected with the diagonal arrangement of the input pipe (14), water flows into the sump (3) at the low position. The pump (13) of sump (3) conveys water by output pipe (16) to the pool, which can be recycled.

This press-type dehydration equipment can reduce the moisture content of the presoaked material to 45–48 %. This equipment has several advantages, including low investment cost, simple structure, easy to operate, small workload of maintenance, and high dehydration efficiency, which is suitable for larger plants.

3.3 Gas Explosion Equipments

3.3.1 Batch Gas Explosion Equipment

Chen Hongzhang invented gas explosion tanks with dual inlet and quick operating door, including tank, cover, feed valve, and slip valve (Fig. 3.21). In the product process, it not only can ensure the requirements of desired pressure, but also can control gas explosion temperature within a certain range. Using cylinder to control joystick can achieve quick open of the cap of gas explosion tank by pneumatic control, which ensures the production requirements of gas pressure and improves

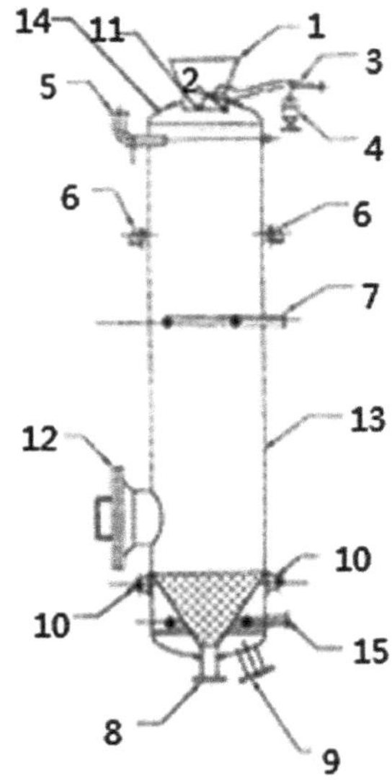

Fig. 3.21 Gas explosion tank with dual inlet and quick operating door. *1* Hopper; *2* feed valve; *3* lever rod; *4* differential double-acting cylinder; *5* pipe; *6* lug; *7* nozzle; *8* discharge port; *9* slagging port; *10* rings; *11* small wheel; *12* manhole; *13* tank; *14* top cover

the production efficiency. For the processing of Chinese herbal medicine, agricultural waste, and other products, it has several advantages, including high pressure and low temperature, the quick open of valve compared with traditional gas explosion tank.

Pipe 5 is welded with tank 13, on which a top cover 14 is placed. Two lugs 6 and rings 10 are welded with tank 13 for fixing the tank. The pressure of gas explosion tank is below 1.7 Mpa. The temperature of the gas inside the tank can be controlled within a range of 180–206 °C. Material is loaded into tank through a hopper 1, the feed valve 2 can be turned on or off by pushing the lever rod 3, small wheel 11, and differential double-acting cylinder 4. Differential double-acting cylinder 4 can push or pull lever rod 3. There is a small wheel 11 at the end of the lever, which can slip in the chute of feed valve 2 and make the valve open or close. The feed valve 2 has two sets of seals. Saturated steam enters into gas explosion tank through pipe 5 and nozzle 7. High-pressure mixture gas enters into the gas explosion tank through nozzle 7 to ensure the desired temperature and pressure. The resulting gas-exploded material is discharged through the discharge port 8, and wastes are discharged by slagging port 9. The tank can be inspected through the manhole 12.

Currently, gas explosion tank has been successfully amplified from laboratory scale to industrial scale applications, which have been amplified from 0.5 L to 1, 5, and 50 m^3 scale industrial applications. Considering the heat distribution, steam distribution pipe layout is optimized; gas explosion tanks with dual inlet and quick operating door is invented [1]. Based on the different temperature requirements of raw materials and gas explosion, gas explosion using mixed gas instead of steam only and in situ gas explosion are proposed.

Fig. 3.22 5.0-L gas explosion tank in laboratory scale

Figure 3.22 shows a 5-L gas explosion tank in laboratory scale designed by us, which consists mainly of a steam generator, a pressure maintenance tank, and a receiver. Operating pressure is among 0–2.5 MPa, while temperature is among 0–250 °C. Feed and outlet valve is in manual control, which can be connected with nitrogen bottles to achieve a mixed gas explosion. Figures 3.23, 3.24, and 3.25 are gas explosion tank in industrial scale.

3.3.2 Continuous Gas Explosion Equipments

Stake Technology Company has in-depth researched and developed gas explosion equipments and has a number of patents. Key equipments, such as feeding systems, prevented anti-spray devices, and discharge equipment, have unique advantages (as shown in Fig. 3.26).

Fig. 3.23 0.5 m^3 gas explosion tank in industrial scale

(1) Feeding systems
Currently, there are four kinds of feeding system in Stake Technology Company using for feeders (Co-Ax-Model) of continuous gas explosion of pulping process, which is shown in Table 3.3.
(2) Horizontal pipe continuous digester
Currently, there are four kinds of digester, which is used in industrial production as shown in Table 3.4 in Stake Technology Company.
(3) Discharge system
Discharge system is very critical in the pulping process. Stake Technology Company has successfully developed and designed the discharge system to adapt to the pulping process.

Sawada T. divided the gas explosion equipment into one-segment type and two-segment type (Figs. 3.27 and 3.28). The highest steam pressure can reach 6 Mpa, and the maximum steam temperature is 275 °C. Muffler mounted on the bottom of the reactor can partially cut huge crashing sound when the material is exploded. The specific operation procedure is as follows: The amount of wood chips is added into the tank, and the steam is injected into tank. Materials are cooked at high pressure for a certain residence time, and then ball valve at the bottom of the tank is instantly opened. Due to the drastic changes of pressure inside

Fig. 3.24 5 m^3 gas explosion tank in industrial scale

Fig. 3.25 20–50 m^3 gas explosion tank in industrial scale

and outside the wood chips, material is exploded into fibroblasts or fibrillar substrate, falling within the cyclone receiver. The reactor systems are separated into gas, liquid, and solid substances. Gas phase is condensed and recovered, while liquid and solid phase material is saccharification material. Two-segment gas

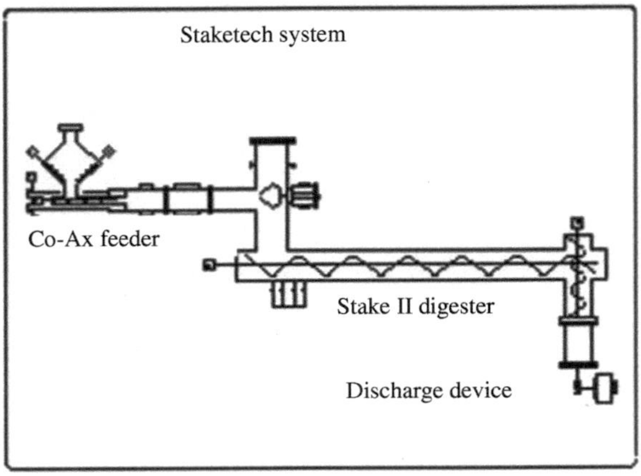

Fig. 3.26 Steam-explosion systems in Stake Technology Company

Table 3.3 Feeders technical properties of continuous gas explosion of pulping process

Standard	Production capacity of wood (ODT/h)	Production capacity of straw (ODT/h)	Transport concentration (%)	Transport pressure (kg/cm^2)
6″ (Φ150)	0.75	0.45	35–90	~45
8″ (Φ200)	2.0	1.2		
10″ (Φ250)	5.0	3.0		
14″ (Φ300)	15.0	9.0		

Note 1 kg/cm^2 is equaled to 98.0665 kPa

Table 3.4 Digester technical properties of continuous gas explosion in industrial production process

Standard	Production capacity of wood (ODT/h)	Production capacity of straw (ODT/h)	Transport concentration (%)	Transport pressure (kg/cm^2)
12″ (Φ150)	0.75	0.45	~45	~233
24″ (Φ200)	2.0	1.2		
36″ (Φ250)	5.0	3.0		
96″ (Φ300)	15.0	9.0		

explosion equipment is the improved type of one-segment gas equipment. Its purpose is to prevent heat loss in one-segment type and to reduce power consumption.

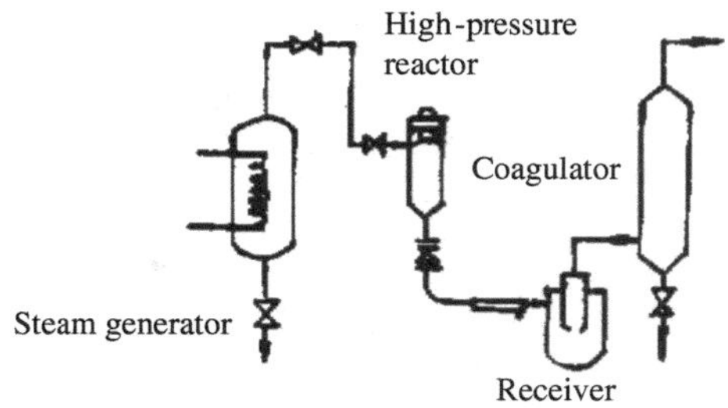

Fig. 3.27 One-segment gas explosion equipment

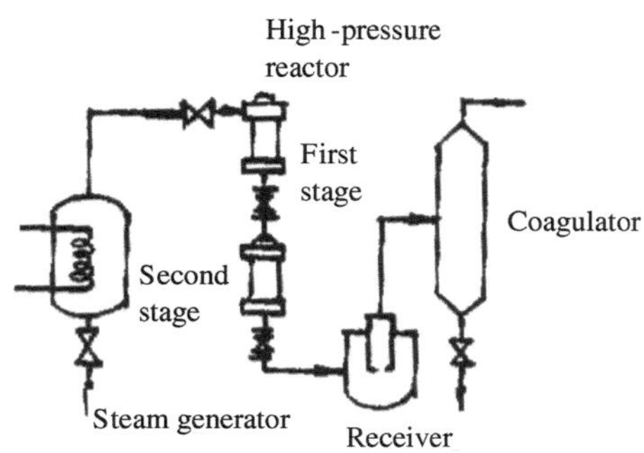

Fig. 3.28 Two-segment gas explosion equipment

3.3.3 In Situ Gas Explosion Equipment

The prospects and advantages of gas explosion technology are obvious, but there are several problems based on the current structure of gas explosion equipment. Pretreated raw materials will intertwine with each other when gas explosion reactor uses the cyclone type as open door, which obviously affects the subsequent separation and carding. The spout style of open door has also led to the difficult recovery and loss of pretreated raw materials.

To solve the above problems, based on the non-polluting low pressure gas explosion equipment, author proposed new ideas of gas explosion technology [12]: The material was packed in the material car, which divided into box-type material car and cage-type material car. The wall of box-type material car is of mesh structure, and the steam can be directly injected into the material car through the mesh; the wall of cage-type material car is also of network structure, and the top wall has a hook. Material can be hanged on the hook. At the instantaneous pressure of gas explosion, steam is escaped from the material car's mesh, and then escape through the steel plate holes, while the material remains in the material car. The pretreated material can be obtained from the discharge port of the material car. Escaping gas can be recovered from the gas recovery system, which facilitates the qualitative and quantitative analysis and the secondary energy use.

In situ gas explosion equipment is shown in Fig. 3.29. The main structure of in situ gas explosion equipment is horizontal tanks 9, which connected with

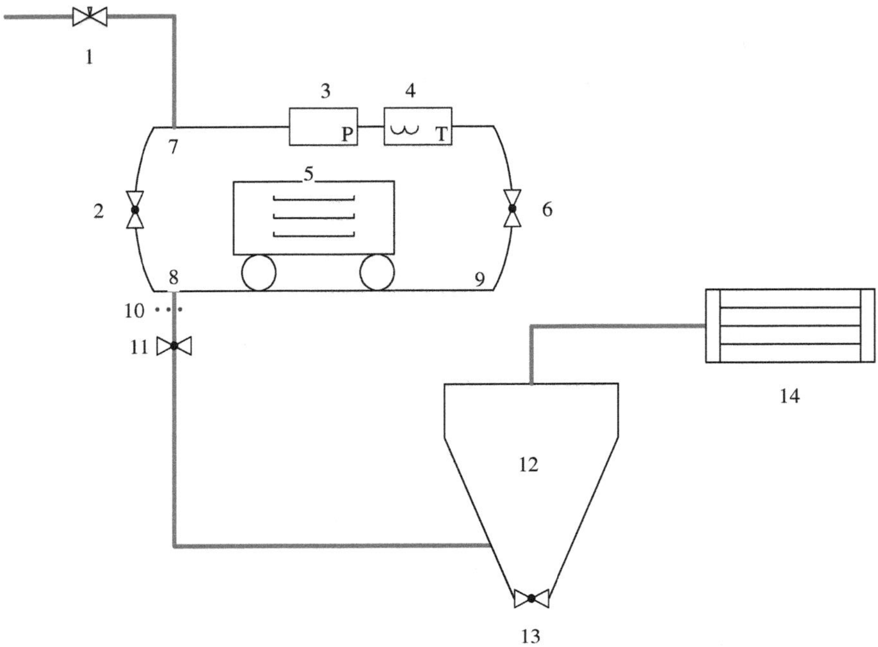

Fig. 3.29 In situ gas explosion equipment

pressure gage 3, thermometer 4, steam inlet 7, and steam outlet 8. Ball valves 2 and 6 for the inlet and outlet of materials are installed on both sides of the horizontal tanks 9, respectively. The steam inlet valve is controlled by a motorized valve, while the steam outlet valve is controlled by a pneumatic valve control. Steel plate 10 is set before the pneumatic valve of the steam outlet valve, which played a role of intercepting the material. There is an axial-fixed rail at the bottom of the tank with, skip track 5 can move on the tank through the wheel. According to the material requirements, material feed box is divided into box-type material car and cage-type material car. The wall of box-type material car is a mesh structure, and the steam can be directly injected into the material car through the mesh; the wall of cage-type material car is also a network structure, and the top wall has a hook. Material can be hanged on the hook. For chopped straw, box-type material car with mesh is selected. The diameter ratio of mesh to material particles is about 1:(1–5); for the long fibrous materials, cage-type material car is selected; for meat or food raw materials, box-type material car with mesh partitions in the interior is used, which is similar to drawer. The inside track is connected to the outside track, and the other end of movable track is connected to the track fixed on the tank. A mechanical tractor pulls material track into the gas explosion tank. After a certain residence time, open the pneumatic valve 11, and then the steam entrances into the buffer tank 12 through material car 5 and the feed plate 10. Finally, the steam enters into the recovery system 13. The analysis of condensable gases can be done by obtaining the gas from the recovery system 13. The pore size ratio of steel stencil 10 to material car is about 1:(2–1.5), which plays a major role in the secondary interception. Gas condensing and recovery system 14 uses cooled water, and the heat transfer area is about 0.1 m^2/200 g material with 50 % initial moisture content. The material can be cooled at room temperature within 1 min. After the discharge of steam, open the valve 6, and pull out the material car. Pretreated material is obtained.

In addition, based on the existing in situ gas explosion equipment, the discharge port can be changed to the outlet with a filter device, which results in that material can be in situ during gas explosion vapor. By changing the pressure and residence time, simultaneously the flash and gas explosion on one device can be achieved. Gas explosion with flash technique can play a role of drying the material. On the one hand, it can pretreat material; on the other hand, it can achieve the purpose of dry, digestion, and sterilization. So, it has a wide range of applications, which is suitable for handling a variety of materials, such as dried manure, sludge, and other activity.

3.4 Steam Generator

Steam generator has a wide range of application. In addition to the surface transport and the power plant, steam generator is used for heating, evaporation, and drying in the manufacturing process in manufacturing industry. In the process of gas explosion, steam is the force and the media for straw infiltration and catalytic reaction.

3.4.1 Overview of Steam Generator

The steam generator transfers the chemical latent heat in the fuel into the sensible heat in the flue gas by combustion. After heat propagation, high-pressure steam stores the sensible heat in the steam equipment.

The steam from the steam generator—mostly water steam—often has overheated. There are various purposes introducing the steam into a variety of mechanical devices which are as follows: (1) steam engine to generate mechanical power (reciprocating steam engine and steam output machine); (2) the heating device to increase room temperature; (3) the gas generator to assist power gas or water gas occurs; and (4) a variety of industrial equipment for heating, evaporation, and drying.

Generally, the steam generator refers to the following types of equipment:

(1) Stove

Stove is the device that is used to complete the combustion and generate flue. The grate of stove is used for solid fuel burning, while burner of stove is used for burning liquid, gas, or powder furnace fuel. The former can be called grate stove, the latter can be called burner stove.

Burning is carried out and completed in a fire house which is built by brick (also known as the combustion chamber or stove). The task of fire house is to make the fuel to burn completely before leaving the fire house and lead to the escape of flue gas which is nonflammable components.

After the escape of flue gas from fire house, most of the heat is transferred into the equipment from flue gas, such as boiler body, superheater, and preheater. Flue is the connecting or amplification channel, which is built with bricks and forces the flue to flow along with a certain path. The second task of the fire house and flue is to isolate the connection of the inside and outside of the oven and reduce the heat loss by conduction and external radiation.

Making the flue gas flow at a certain direction is called ventilation. The temperature of chimney column is higher than that of the outside air, while the density is lower than that of the outside air. The exhaust gas rises out of the furnace by certain buoyancy, which constitutes major natural ventilation. Using a blower or a suction machine can result in high pressure (above atmospheric pressure) or low (below atmospheric pressure) in stove, which can help increase of natural ventilation. It is called artificial ventilation.

Fuel for burner-type stove must be first pretreated. For example, pulverized coal must be prepared by milling equipment, gas equipment must have ash equipment, and the oil must have filtered and preheating equipment.

In addition, the remaining ash after combustion of the fuel must be discharged by ash discharging equipment frequently.

(2) Boiler body

Boiler body can make water filled therein the body evaporate under high pressure, so the boiler body must be sustained at a high-temperature high-pressure tolerance. The boiler body must be made of steel parts of cylinder, tube, or other similar forms. In order to facilitate the clean work of the entire interior, ministries manholes and hand holes often locate on it. The former can accommodate a body out, while the latter can accommodate manpower into.

Boiler body must have a maximum water surface and a minimum water surface. When working at the maximum water surface, steam-containing water moisture should not exceed the stipulation. When working at the minimum water surface, there should be no risk of explosion. The most important thing is to maintain the actual water surface between the maximum water surface and the minimum water surface. Surface area of water is called the evaporation area. According to experience, greater evaporation area leads to the less moisture content of steam.

Water storage capacity of boiler is known as boiler water content. The larger water capacity results in a smaller pressure change when output power is subject to change; on the contrary, the smaller water capacity results in a larger pressure change when output power is subject to change. So, a big storage capacity of the boiler has a large thermal storage effect. That is, it has a good power load elasticity or flexibility.

Output per hour of steam weight can be used to compare the size of the boiler power; the size of the heated area can be used to compare relatively large size of the boiler. Heated area has two sides: one side is in contact with the flue gas, and the other side is in contact with water.

(3) Superheater

The steam outputted by boiler body generally contains 1–3 % of moisture content; the moisture is heated and transferred into steam through the superheater, which is more than 450 °C. Superheater installed in the chimney is called conduction superheater. Superheater mounted on the front walls of the fire stove is called radiation superheater.

(4) Preheater

Boiler water is usually preheated in a preheater, which is made by special steel. High-pressure boiler has the role of partial evaporation, which is also called as evaporator preheater. Large steam boiler uses steam or waste steam from steam engine to replace gas flue for heating.

The device for preheating air is called an air preheater. Larger boiler equipment usually has two preheaters in flue: Water preheater is in front and the air preheater is in back.

(5) Ventilation equipment

The chimney of natural ventilation and the fan or blower of artificial ventilation belong to ventilation equipment. Artificial ventilation devices can reduce the height of the chimney, but the chimney cannot be canceled. However, the exhaust gas must be scattered at high altitude or it pollutes air and hazards health.

(6) Water supply facilities

Water supply facilities used to the boiler water supply can also be included in the boiler. Accordance with the provisions, more than two water supply facilities should be equipped for the boiler. It should be dragged by different driving forces to ensure safety.

(7) Water purification equipment

Many chemicals in water may corrode the inner wall of the boiler, affecting heat transfer and even causing disasters. Most boilers have water purification equipment. Water is pretreated to a certain clarity, and it is then supplied by the water supply facilities to the boiler.

Straw, wood, municipal solid waste, and other wastes are most organic matter. Gas steam is used to break the structure of these matters. Cellulose, hemicellulose, and lignin are readily degradable through thermal and mechanical expansion, which result in the porous structure of these matters. Temperatures in the process cannot be too high, which is generally between 150 and 250 °C. In this process, the fermentation inhibitor should not be produced from cellulose, hemicellulose, lignin, and other positions. The presence of water can act as a catalyst to accelerate the reaction and improve the treatment effect. Steam generator generally used in gas explosion is without superheater.

The amount of steam required for gas explosion pretreatment is not high. In addition, gas explosion pretreatment has very short processing cycle. The small industrial boilers can meet generally production needs of gas explosion pretreatment, while electric steam generator in the test is used mostly as a steam source.

3.4.2 Electric Steam Generator

Electric steam generator is powered by an electrical heating element and gets the steam pressure by the heating aqueous medium. It is widely used in industries and field of laundry, clothing, food, leather, chemical fiber, and textile. Electric steam generator has the advantages of simple maintenance, no noise, no flames, no smoke, no pollution, small floor area, safe and easy to operate, high degree of automation, and nice appearance.

(1) Structure and electrical control principle [13]

The main structure of automatic electric steam generator is composed of 3 parts, i.e., steam production unit, water supply equipment, and electrical control systems. Steam generator and water supply equipment are shown in Fig. 3.30. Steam generators consist of shell, water lever regulator, steam pipes, electric heater, and other components. Water supply equipment is composed of water tanks, water pump, and inlet pipe. The shell of steam generator is the steel pressure vessel and installed an electric heater. The shell equips with pressure gauge, safety valve, water level regulators, and other accessories. The role of the regulator is to regulate and control the water level in the steam generator, which can be set in high water level and low water level. High water level setting is to maintain sufficient space for steam and the low one is to ensure safe performance of the heater.

Control theory of the electrical system [14] is shown in Fig. 3.31. The system has seven functions of automatic control of water level, automatic alarming for extremely low and high water level, automatic power off for extremely low water level and overpressure, and automatic start in low voltage. Manual and automatic operation states can be chosen in the operation control system. When the control system is in automatic operation, water supply and heating of the automatic steam generator are performed automatically. If the water level is under or beyond the limit setting of the generator, then the control system will raise the sound and light alarm and cut off the power of the electric heater. This can ensure the steam generator to perform safely.

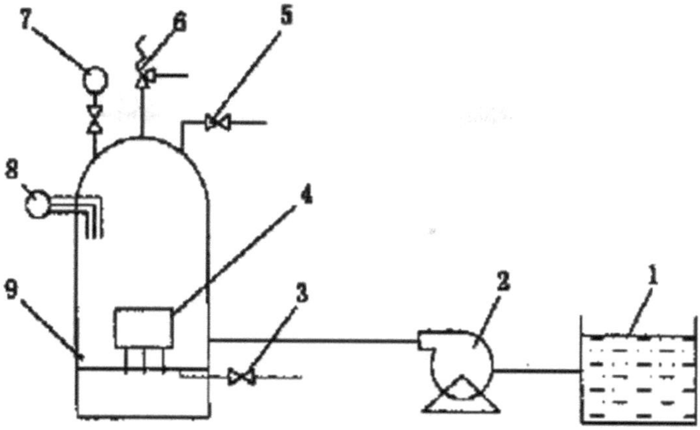

Fig. 3.30 Structure of electric steam generator. *1* Water tank; *2* water supply pump; *3* sludge discharge valve; *4* heater; *5* outlet valve; *6* safety valve; *7* pressure gage; *8* water level regulator; *9* shell

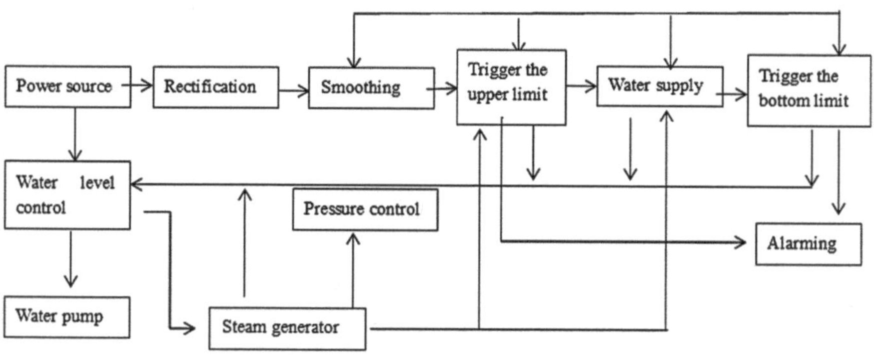

Fig. 3.31 Control theory of the electrical system

(2) Calculation of heating power and steam outlet diameter

Parameters of automatic electric steam generator include evaporation capacity, vapor pressure, heating power, and steam outlet pipe diameter. Particularly, evaporation and vapor pressure are set according to demand. The heating power and steam outlet diameter are obtained based on calculation.

① Calculation of heating power

According to the first law of thermodynamics, apart from the loss, the supply of electrical energy is converted into the heat carried off by the steam, which is

$$\mathrm{Wp} = \mathrm{Qo}, \tag{3.8}$$

or

$$\mathrm{Wp} = AP\eta(1 - q) \tag{3.9}$$

Wp is the effective energy, kJ/h; P is the heating power, kW; A is the mechanical equivalent of heat, 3600 kJ/kW h; q is the energy loss of the shell, %; η is the transfer efficiency, %.

$$\mathrm{Qo} = D[h'(1 - X) + Xh'' - h_o], \tag{3.10}$$

Qo is the energy carried off by the vapor, kJ/h; D is evaporation capacity, kg/h; h_o is specific enthalpy of the water, kJ/kg; h' is the specific enthalpy of the saturated water when the pressure is p, kJ/kg; h'' is the specific enthalpy of the saturated steam when the pressure is p, kJ/kg; X is the steam dryness, %.

By substituting Eqs. (3.9) and (3.10) into Eq. (3.8), the following equation can be obtained:

$$P = \frac{D[h'(1 - X) + Xh'' - h_o]}{A\eta(1 - q)} \tag{3.11}$$

when p is 0.4 MPa, evaporation capacity is 100 kg/h, team dryness is 0.6, water temperature t_o is 10 °C; according to the handbook of water vapor, we know that h' is 604.67 kJ/kg, h'' is 2737.6 kJ/kg, $h_o(t_o c)$ is 41.868 kJ/kg; when η is 95 %, q is 5 %, then the value of P can be calculated as 56.7 kW. While at the case of practical design, P can be set as 60 kW.

② Calculation of steam outlet diameter

When outlet is given, the steam outlet diameter can be calculated by specific heat capacity of the vapor.

Specific heat capacity of the vapor in outlet is as follows:

$$\gamma = (1 - X)\gamma' + X\gamma''. \tag{3.12}$$

When p is 0.4 MPa, X is 0.6, we can get

$$\gamma' = 0.001084\ \mathrm{m^3/kg},$$
$$\gamma'' = 0.4662\ \mathrm{m^3/kg}.$$
$$\gamma = 0.2778\ \mathrm{m^3/kg}.$$

When outlet velocity is set as 15 m/s, the vapor volume in one unit is

$$A_o v = D\gamma,$$

A_o is cross-sectional area of the pipe, m^2.
Diameter of the outlet pipe is

$$d = 2\sqrt{D\gamma/(v\pi)}$$

$d = 2\sqrt{D\gamma/(v\pi)} = 25.6$ mm, which can be set at 25 mm in practical design.
The design of automatic electric steam generator is based on the principle of meeting the demand of the vapor in the process of steam explosion. Heating power is balanced with evaporation capacity, while the power load capacity is taken into consideration. Basic technical parameters are shown as follows:

Evaporation capacity: 50–150 kg/h;
Pressure: 0.3–0.8 MPa;
Heating power: 30–90 kW;
Voltage: 380 V;
Working current: 50–150 A; and
Supply frequency: 50 Hz.

(3) Selection of the water supply equipment
The water supply equipment of an automatic electric steam generator mainly refers to the water tank and supply pump. Tank specifications can be selected according to the demand. The water level should not be less than the minimum amount of water (0.6 m^3). The bottom of the tank should be 10 cm lower than the pump inlet, and the sewage valve should be installed. Precipitation at the bottom should be discharged timely according to the water quality. Water supply pump is one of the key equipments of automatic electric steam generator. Its main function is to provide water for the generator. This requires that the pump outlet pressure (head) should be higher than the design pressure of steam generator. Otherwise, it is impossible to supply the running generator with water. In order to stabilize steam pressure during the supply process, the requirements of filling water should not exceed 0.01 m^3. Supply rate of waters should be modest, and the pump flow should be less than 0.5 m^3/h. Check valve should be installed in the outlet pipes so as to prevent the backflow of high-temperature water under the high-pressure steam. The bottom of water supply pump should be designed with an outlet hole. Water in the pump and pipes should be discharged when the steam generator stops running for a long period to prevent the cracking or corrosion.
Water in the automatic electric vapor generator should be of the same quality with that in the oil-fired boiler, and if permitted, deionized water should be used. This can prevent the generation of scale on the surface of electric heater.

In the absence of deionized water, domestic water will be a good choice. In order to guarantee the heating performance of the electric heater, scale on the surface should be cleaned at least once a year.

(4) Usage and maintenance
The following procedure should be followed in order to ensure the safe and normal operation of generators and prolong the life span of the equipment:

A. The aqueous medium should be clean, non-corrosive, and without water impurities. Usually, soft water or filtered water through the filter should be used.
B. To ensure that the safety valve is in good condition, class work should be finished before manually exhausting the steam for 3–5 times. Once delayed or stuck valve is found, the valve must be repaired or replaced.
C. Water level controller electrode should be cleaned regularly to prevent electric control failure caused by electrode fouling. No. 00 emery cloth is used to clean the electrode fouling. This work cannot be carried out until the power is cut off and no steam is in the device.
D. Cylinder must be washed once for each class work to ensure that the barrel is not or slightly contaminated.
E. In order to ensure the normal operation of the generator, the electrode, electric components, and cylinder wall should be cleaned every 300 h.
F. To ensure the safe operation of the generator, the generator must be checked regularly for periodic inspection. The project includes water level controller, electrical lines, seal all valves and connecting pipes, all kinds of instruments of reliability and accuracy of the gauge, pressure switch, and safety valve. They should be sent to the high inspection institutes for verification and sealed before using at least once a year.
G. Safety inspection of the generator should be carried out once a year. Security check should be reported to the local labor department under its supervision. Generator's common faults and solutions are concluded as follows:

   a. Causes for not generating steam: The fuse is switched off; heating pipe burned; contactor trouble; and control board failure. Solutions: replacing with appropriate current fuse; replacing the heating pipe; replacing the contactor; and repairing or replacing the control board. Based on our experience in the maintenance, the most common fault element of the control panel is poor contact of the two transistors and two relay. In addition, a variety of switches on the control panel are very prone to failure.
   b. Causes for water pump failure: open circuit of the fuse; pump motor burned; contactor failure; control panel trouble; and damage of water pump parts. Solutions: replacing the fuse; repairing or replacing the motor; replacing the contactor; and replacing the damaged parts.

c. Causes for disorders level controller: electrode fouling; control panel trouble; and failure of intermediate relay. Solutions: removing electrode fouling; repairing or replacing the control panel components; and replacing intermediate relay.
d. Causes for pressure deviation from the given pressure range: pressure relays deviation and pressure switch failure. Solutions: readjusting the given pressure of pressure switch and replacing the pressure relay.

3.4.3 *Fuel Steam Generator*

Fuel steam generators are divided into vertical and horizontal ones according to types of boiler. LSS-type steam boiler (commonly known as tubular boilers) is mainly introduced in this section. This is a small-volume (0.1–2 t/h)-packaged boiler with return two vertical pipes combustion chamber. The boiler is mainly composed of a ring header and the inner and outer rings (both ends closed) water wall tubes. Combustion chamber (furnace) is consists of compact dense water wall tubes. And, the inner tube and outer tube form the convection pass. Inflame is set on top of boiler, and white flame is injected into the furnace from bottom to up, and later goes into the annular flue and the chimney connected with the atmosphere (Fig. 3.32).

(1) Design of ring header
The upper and bottom ring headers are both constructed with two 180° bend (Φ219 mm × 8 mm, $R = 330$ mm). 88 mm × 102 mm hand spike is set in weld joint of the bend, which is convenient for wielding and X picture shooting. In addition, this also tackles the problems of inner debris, sludge, and other issues. The upper and bottom ring headers are arranged 2000 mm from each other.

(2) Arrangement of water wall tube
Water wall is made by Φ51 × 3 tube ends by necking to Φ38, and the necking length is 170 mm. Inner water wall tubes are densely arranged, namely the hole pitch is 51 mm (diameter), which constitutes the combustion chamber (chamber), and aside from a tube pitch as the furnace exit. Outer water wall tubes are loosely arranged and fins ($\delta = 4$) are welded between the pipes. And the inner tube and outer tube form the convection pass. The outer water wall, upper ring header, and the bottom ring header constitute the closed boiler body.

(3) Water recycling and steam–water separation
No downcomer is set in LSS boiler and its water circulation is more like that in a once-through boiler, but not the forced circulation of the once-through boiler. Therefore, it is called tubular boilers. Boiler water enters the upper header from the bottom header first and then enters the upper ring header passing through

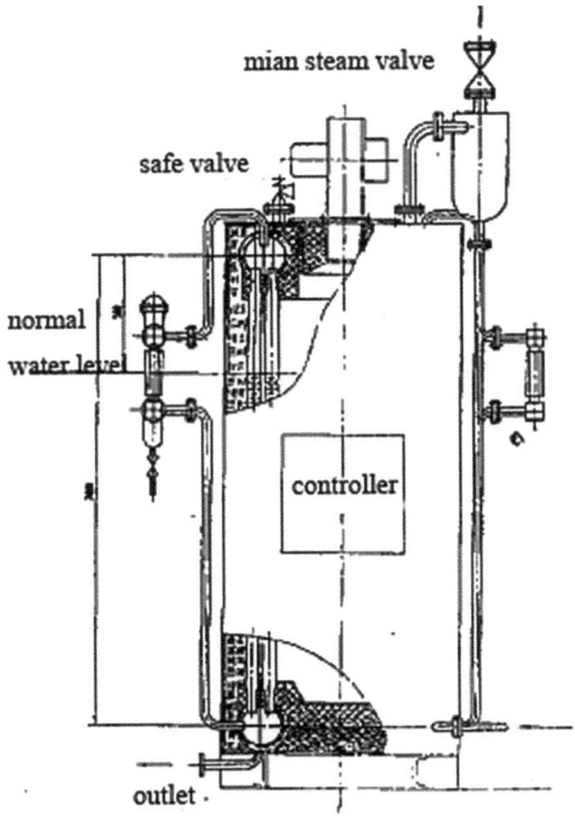

Fig. 3.32 Structure of fuel steam generator

the water wall pipes. Mixture of water and steam is sent to the external steam separator guided by effuse in the header, and then the separated steam supplies the steam consumption equipment.

(4) Setting of the boiler water level
According to the provisions of Article 149 of the "steam boiler safety technology supervision order," two independent boiler water gauges are set. The setting of water level is critical to the quality of humidity for boiler steam of LSS-type. By trial and error, the final design level is set at 500 mm from the center line of the upper header. This will get further evaporated mixture of steam and water, thus reducing the burden of external separate separator and guaranteeing the quality of steam-less 3 % for humidity.

(5) Others
Boiler combustion system is made of imported automatic fuel burner and equipped with ancillary control box. In order to facilitate cleaning and replacement of fuel flexible tips, the burner is designed disassembly.

Refractory concrete pouring is used in furnace wall, in which the necessary nail grip is equipped.

Insulation material consists of 8 layers of phenolic resin bonded rock wool of $\delta = 15$ mm, which is compacted with cooling wall to the thickness of 100 mm. Colorful steel plate and aluminum are used in the fireback, which is connected with the blind rivet. Therefore, the appearance of boiler is beautiful and generous.

3.4.4 Coal-Fired Steam Generator

Coal-fired steam generator is the most widely used industrial steam generators. Compared with electric and fuel steam generators, coal is used in coal-fired steam generator for heating. And then, we will introduce coal-fired steam boilers briefly. Horizontal coal-fired steam boiler is applied most widely. For example, DZG-type coal-fired boiler is fast-loading horizontal steam boiler with the single drum and three-pass fire tube, and the fixed grate is used as combustion equipment. Both sides of the furnace are equipped with water wall tubes; burnout chamber is set behind; the drum is equipped with two internal return pipe tobacco and all of those will provide a large soda space, which can effectively reduce the steam with water, and therefore, the quality of steam is guaranteed. However, chain grate combustion equipment is used in the coal-fired boiler of DZL series. The produced flue gas passes through the hearth composed of the drum and its sides, and then goes into the two-pass convection smoke pipe of the drum; then the flue gas passes into the rear of the boiler economize after the heat exchange; finally, the flue gas is discharged after dedusting. Mechanical grate boiler is used in such series of coal-fired boiler, which makes the main operations items of coaling, slag remove, and dusting mechanized. It has the advantages of stability and reliability, high degree of boiler automation, and low labor intensity.

3.5 Receiver

Cyclone collector (Fig. 3.33) is used to collect steam-exploded feedstock safely.

3.6 Parameters Detection

Special requirement for the construction of test system is demanded in the process of explosion test in a closed tank, which can be concluded as follows: choice of transducer, respondent amplifier, rapid synchronized data collector, and installation of the different parts of the test system.

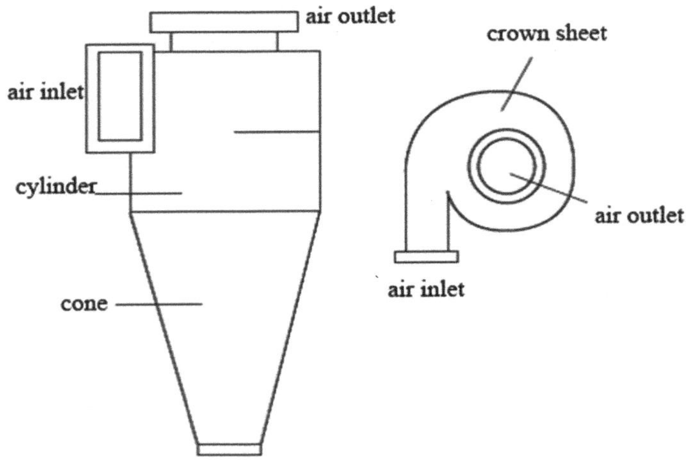

Fig. 3.33 Cyclone collector

3.6.1 System for Dynamic Data Test

Dynamic test and analysis system TST6000 is developed by Chengdu Test Company. It is the modern networked test equipment which combines multiple technologies including collection of dynamic data, embedded trunk, network communication, and analog signal processing and computes. TST6000 combines signal adjustment and processing, power the transducers, data collection and data storage and communicates with host computer through TCP/IP. It connects strain transducer, piezoelectric transducer, and ICP transducer. In addition, it adopts embedded data collection which can avoid the problems brought by hardware upgrading of computers and prolong the life of equipment.

Dynamic test and analysis system TST6000 (Fig. 3.34) equips 8/16 parallel collection channels with the highest values of 200 K. It combines signal amplification, smoothing, power the transducers, data collection, and data storage which enables this system to detect parameters through program and receive millivolt voltage signal. Data establish communication with host computer through Ethernet or USB.

TST6300 connects with strain transducer or piezoelectric transducer through DAP6.X program in host computer and constructs the dynamic test system. It collects signals of physical parameters such as velocity, accelerated velocity, displacement, force, and pressure conveniently. This system is small and exquisite and has compact structure and the convenience of connection. It provides high-quality test solution method for field laboratory testers.

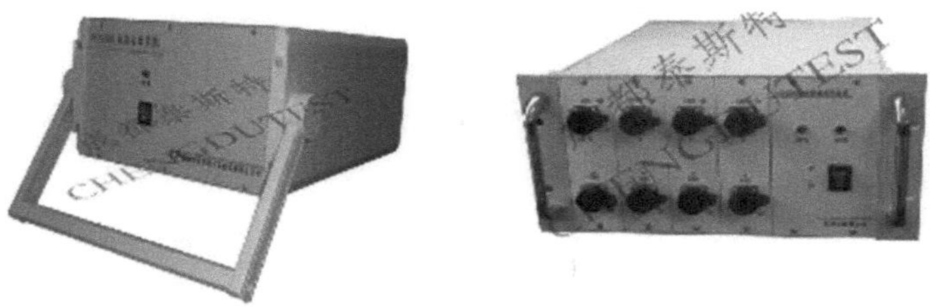

Fig. 3.34 Dynamic test and analysis system

3.6.2 Pressure Transducers

Indexes of high frequency pressure transducer are concluded as follows:

Measurement range: 0–5 MPa
Non linearity: <±0.5 %
Natural frequency: >400 kHz
Working temperature: −40 to 80 °C
Overload capacity: 150 %
Installation method: M20 × 1.5

In explosion test, high frequency pressure transducer should be adopted. In current explosion test, piezoelectric or piezoresistive transducer is usually used. From our viewpoint, piezoresistive transducer is better than piezoelectric transducer.

Piezoelectric transducer can detect larger pressure with the peak of 1000 MPa. Current domestic product has the smallest measurement range of 15 MPa, and it is very difficult to produce transducer with further smaller measurement range. Therefore, it is inappropriate to use piezoelectric transducer in domestic. Piezoelectric transducer has a more serious problem of temperature sensitivity when used to detect pressure in explosion process in the pipeline. Negative signal appears due to high temperature. Figure 3.35 shows the work curve of piezoelectric transducer heated with lighter.

It was usually thought that piezoelectric transducer had high-frequency response previously. In fact, piezoresistive transducer can do a better work currently. The natural vibration frequency of piezoelectric transducer is 150–500 kHz while that of piezoresistive transducer is 800 kHz–1 MHz.

3.6.3 Temperature Transducers

Platinum resistor is usually used to produce temperature probe for its high precision and fine stability. In addition, it also has the advantages of assembled abilities of

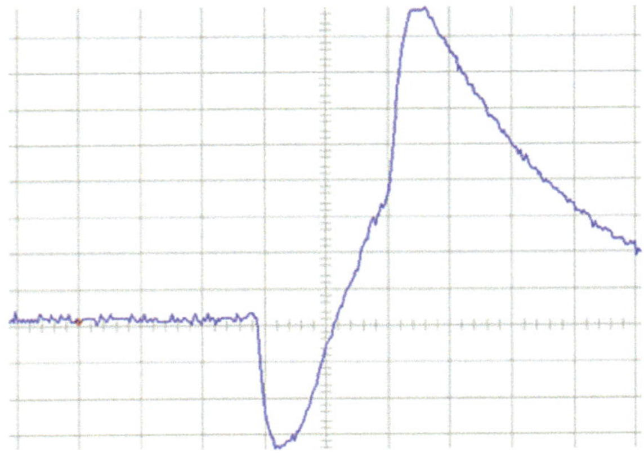

Fig. 3.35 Work curve of piezoelectric transducer

sensing and transduce, compact structure, convenience of installation, and low power consumption. Current output-type platinum resistor is suitable for long distance transmission due to its anti-interference of electromagnetism. It is used in environment with serious pollution of electromagnetism.

Main technical indexes of temperature transducers are concluded as follows:

Measurement range: −50 to 300 °C
Output signal: 0–5 V
Loading resistance: ≤500 Ω
Power source: 24 V DC
Power consumption: ≤1 W
Basic error: 0.2–0.5 % FS
Installation size: M20 × 1.5

3.6.4 Solid Flowmeter

Mass flowmeter DMF-1 (Beijing Sincerity Automatic Equipment Co., Ltd) is composed of two units: mass flowmeter transducer and associative cell (transmitter). Flowmeter transducer is composed of shell, micro-vibration measuring tube, vibration drive, signal detectors, temperature compensation components, and other units.

The measuring tube will obtain additional Coriolis force, which is proportional to the flow mass under the force of flow push and imposed vibrating force when the fluid flows through the micro-vibrating measuring tube. This will change the phase difference caused by Coriolis minute distortions into linear electrical signal and get output. And finally, the flow mass is obtained by the indicator.

Associative cell of the mass flow adopts disk loading structure and integrates the signal converter and flow digital indicator into one. This simplifies the instrument structure and is convenient for use and connection. The electoral unit can output the standard current signal of 4–20 Ma, frequency single of 0–10 kHz, and 485 communication signals. They coordinate with transducer to complete the signal process and output. In addition, it has the functions of multi-parameters display, configuration, communication, and query. It can display the instantaneous mass flow (Qm), accumulated mass (M), density (ρ), temperature (T), and water/oil ratio for the mixed flow of oil and water.

Electric units are equipped with safety barrier and linked with flowmeter transducer through skim core three-shielded cable when consisting of the explosion protection system. The total length of cable is 0–300 m.

Figure 3.36 shows the outline of large-scale flowmeter transducer. This instrument is based on Coriolis force principle and can directly measure the fluid mass flow, without any pressure, temperature, viscosity, density conversion values, or modification. The measured flow rate is reflected with the unit of mass flow (kg/h, t/h or g/s), which can be directly displayed on the electronic unit panel with the standard signal output of 0–10 kHz, 4–20 mA and 1–5 V. This flowmeter equips with immobile parts and has the advantages of wider range, high accuracy (±0.2 %) and pressure, and wide temperature range. In addition, it can be used for the measurement of high-viscosity and non-Newtonian fluid. These characteristics make the instrument widely used in oil fields, refineries, chemical industry, building

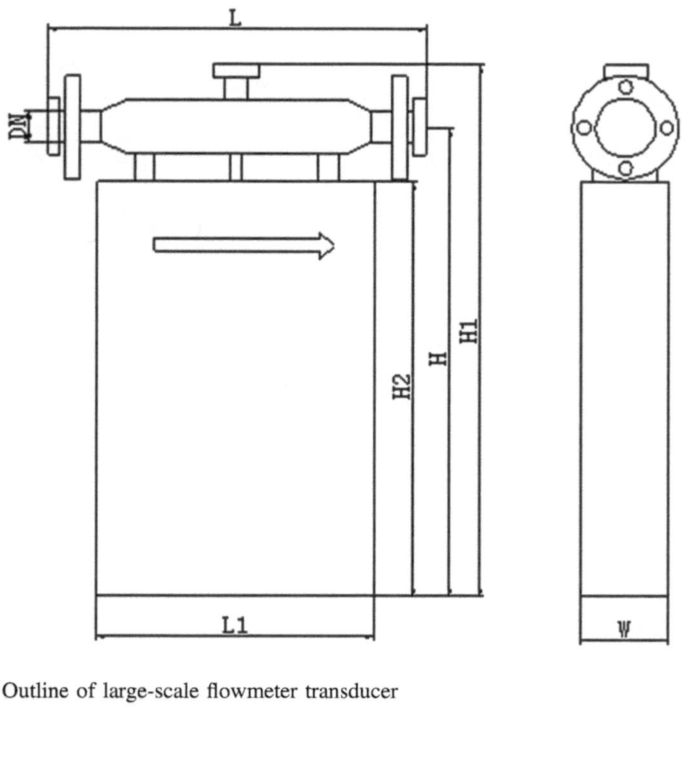

Fig. 3.36 Outline of large-scale flowmeter transducer

materials, food, medicine, leather, paper, paints, dyes, nuclear energy, metallurgy, aerospace, and other fields. Flow transducer is made of stainless steel (1Cr18Ni9Ti or 36L) and the sensor unit keeps clear of the media, making it have the quality of good corrosion resistance.

Figure 3.37 shows the laboratory-made experimental steam-explosion equipment. The vertical tank is the experimental explosion equipment while horizontal tank is the in situ steam-explosion equipment. The device is equipped with pressure transducer, temperature transducer and sight glass window on the pressure-holding tank, solid flow meter on the discharge port, and dynamic data acquisition and analysis system as well as a computer for external devices. Data provided by the device can be easily calculated for the balance of transfer and reaction, and thus the dynamic model among the main parameters and explosion effect is obtained. This is beneficial to the engineering enlargement and the broadening of application fields of the steam-explosion equipment.

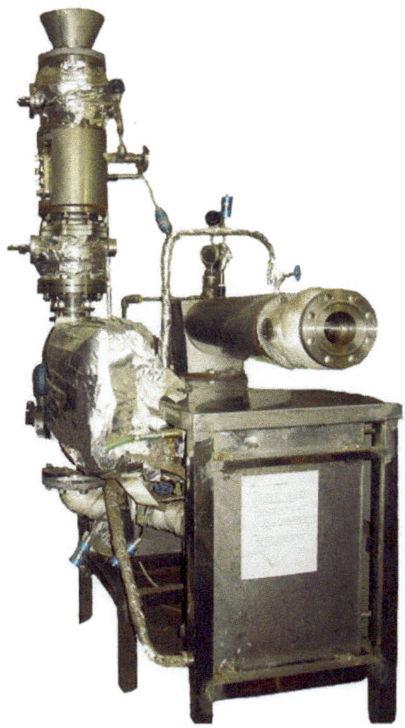

Fig. 3.37 Laboratory-made experimental steam-explosion equipment

3.7 Carding Device

3.7.1 Hydraulic Carding Device (Paul Fractionator)

Paul fractionator (produced by Xingping Zhongtong Test Equipment Company) can divide any fiber stack into different groups, each of which is equipped with four screens with different sizes. Those screens can analyze and detect the samples after obtaining the feedstock. This equipment is also used for quality control in the process of industrial material production such as glass fiber and synthesized fiber.

Paul fractionator ZT10-00 is shown in Fig. 3.38. It is equipped with four ladder-disposed elliptical tanks. The feedstock passes through the lower tanks after putting onto the highest tank because of gravity. All the tanks are equipped with different-size screens which can capture fiber with different sizes. Fine result can be obtained if the size of the latter screen is half of that of the former one. Each tank keeps different parts of different weight. The material weight on the smallest screen can be calculated by minus total fiber weight from the initial fiber weight. Main technical parameters are concluded as follows:

Stirrer speed: 650 n/m
Screen sizes: 14, 24, 40, 60, 100, 200 meshes
Main materials: stainless steel (0Cr18Ni9)
Overall dimension: 1780 mm × 520 mm × 1680 mm

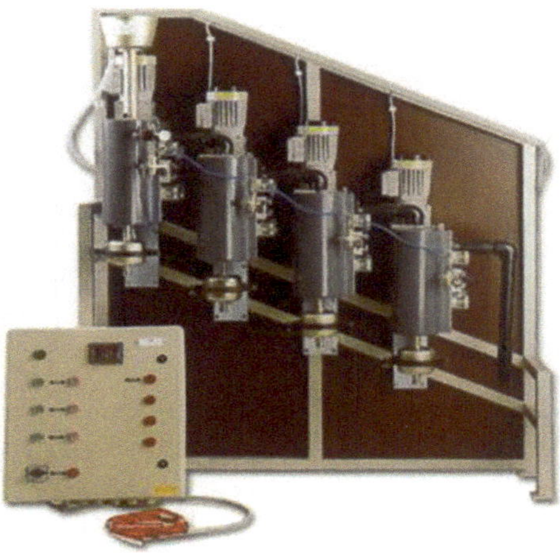

Fig. 3.38 Paul fractionator ZT10-00

3.7.2 Airflow Grading Device

Airflow grading is a common method for material separation according to the particle size, which is mainly based on the centrifugal force. Particle will be set in the force field composed of centrifugal force from impeller, air friction and gravity after the mix of particle and air with certain ratio passes into the grading room at certain speed. Different particles are graded by adjusting grading point through changing parameters such as turbine and wind speed [15].

Figure 3.39 shows the schematic diagram of airflow grading device for small feedstock which is composed of input pump, adjust pump, adjust ring, grading turbine, transmission device, closed-air aspirator, middle tank, and lower con.

Multi-level separation system (composed of several tandem air-flow grading equipment) can be used for the separation of multi-level product. Figure 3.40 shows

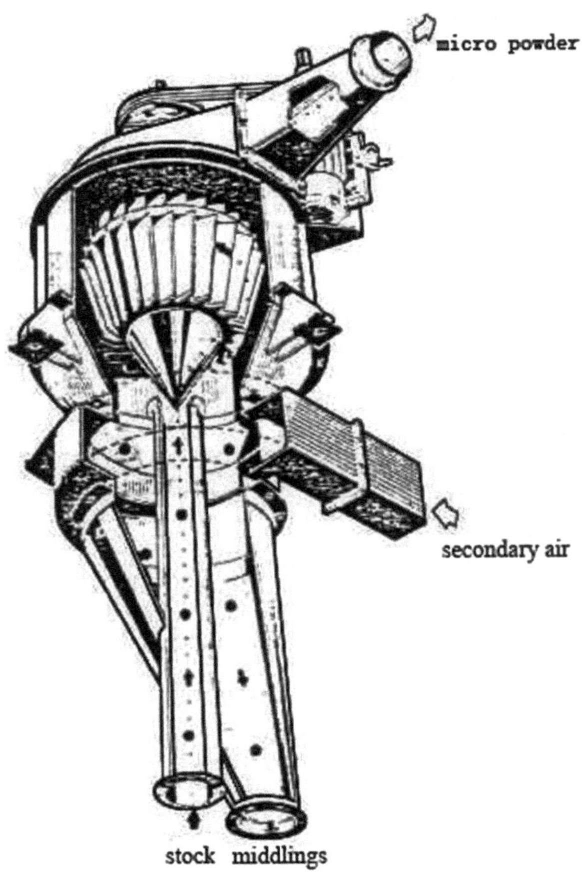

Fig. 3.39 Airflow grading device

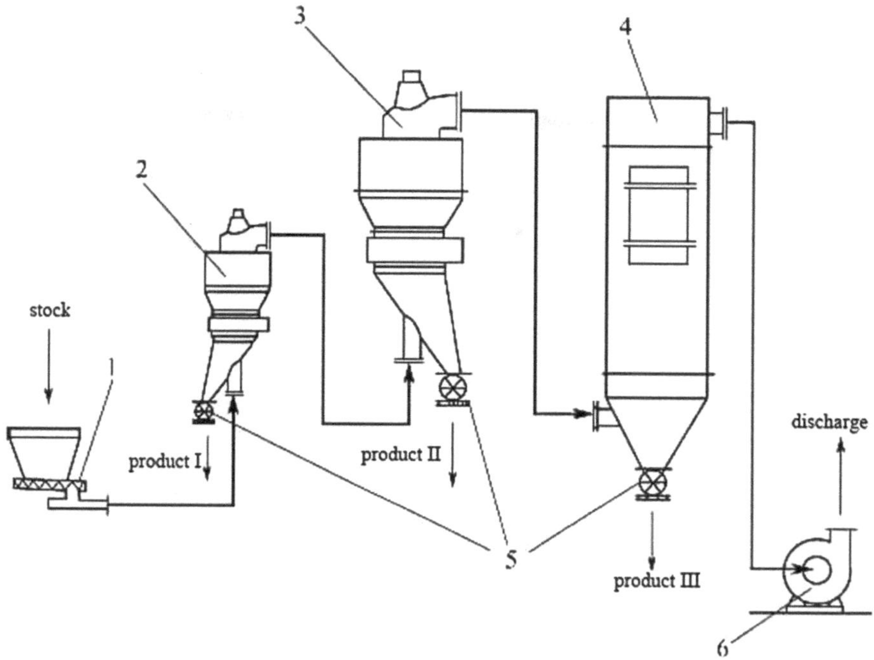

Fig. 3.40 Multi-level separation systems. *1* Feeder; *2*, *3* air-flow grading equipment; *4* collector; *5* rotary ejector; *6* fan

the multi-level separation system composed of air-flow grading equipment, collector, and fanes [16].

Scholars both at home and aboard have done well in the theoretical researches of feedstock separation using air as medium under dilute phase conditions. In the later 1990s, Johansen and Silva carried out theoretical research on air-flow grading hydrocyclone based on centrifugal force field theory [17]. Through several air cyclone modeling and flow field analysis coupling with computational fluid dynamics software for numerical simulations (Fig. 3.41), the result showed that the factors were complex when carding the particles of a few hundred microns to less than 1 μm, and the centrifugal flow field caused by rotor was quite different from the traditional theory. Particles in air classifier cyclone trajectory was also very different from the previous assumptions, which provided basis for parameter optimization of classifying cyclone flow centrifugal force field and lowered the minimum size of grade to less than 1 μm [17]. Wang et al. also had done theoretical research on the separation mechanism and centrifugal separation of particles under the countercurrent flow field. They derived particle size separation formulas under different flow field velocities by establishing mathematical models of the flow field based on two-phase flow model. Their theoretical models are consistent with laboratorial results [18]. Wang et al. [19] carried out laboratorial tests on horizontal

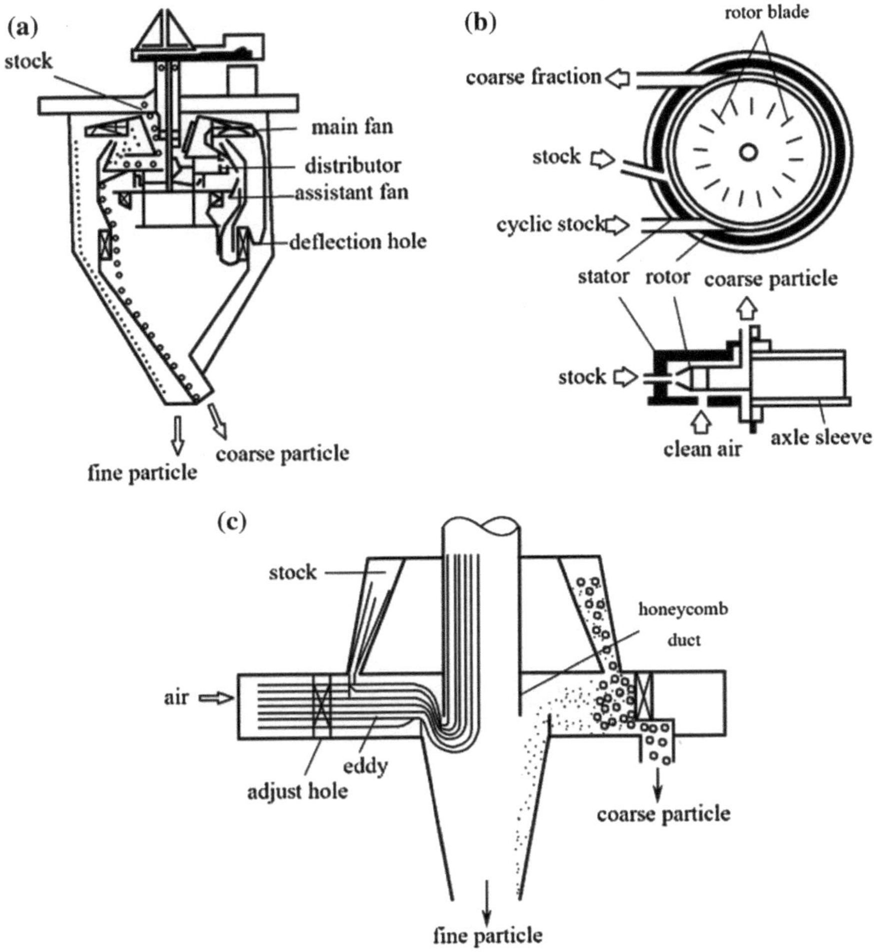

Fig. 3.41 Air-flow grading device

transverse airflow grading equipment and computer numerical simulation. The results explained the reason of the efficiency and accuracy difference between the actual results and the theoretical derivation. And then, they optimized the structure parameters and technical parameters of the equipment for further steps. They obtained a two-dimensional computational fluid dynamics models based on Doppler laser particle size analysis system and HELOS laser method for flow characteristics under different boundary conditions and sorting parameters. Optimization of technical parameters and structural parameters improved grading efficiency of the lateral flow grading equipment greatly.

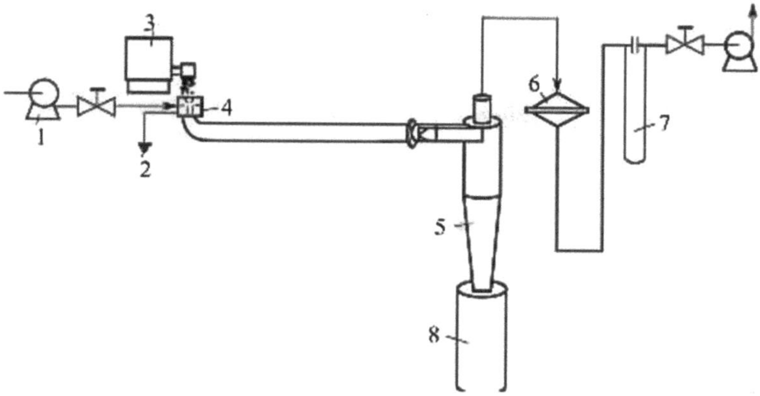

Fig. 3.42 Double cone structure-type air classifier cyclone laboratory test system. *1* Compressor; *2* grounding; *3* screw feeder; *4* disperser; *5* cyclone; *6* filter; *7* outlet; *8* dust box

The double cone structure-type air classifier cyclone laboratory test system is shown in Fig. 3.42. Yashida et al. [20] carried out theoretical research and laboratory test on the swirling air classification equipment. The results show that head loss of Iinoya-type air classifier cyclone fluid was reduced by 10 % compared with that of conventional air classifier cyclone. Particles were generally concentrated in the lower end of the top of cone due to the smallest cross-sectional area of the pipe. Simulation results also confirmed the conclusion. To avoid mismatches coarse particles into the fine-grained level, a Iinoya double cone-type air classifier cyclone with structural parameter optimization got good efficiency of separation.

3.7.3 Mechanical Carding Device

Mechanical carding device is composed of high-speed roller and arc-shaped board. Feedstock passes though roller and arc-shaped board and then is impacted, rubbed, grinded, and carded. Feedstock is put in from one side of the roller and casted from the other side after its movement along the roller axes. This device is called axial-flow type carding device. One axial-flow roller and sieve plate can realize functions of loosening and separation for axial-flow device and can separate short and long fibers based on centrifugal force. Therefore, the device structure can be simplified.

Factors that influence carding efficiency include water content of steam-exploded feedstock and roller speed. The device is shown in Fig. 3.43.

Fig. 3.43 Mechanical carding equipment

References

1. Chen HZ, Liu LY. Technology of steam explosion: principles and applications. Beijing: Chemical Industry Press; 2007.
2. Li QZ. Straw cutter knife gap. Light Ind Mach. 1990;4:51–3.
3. Chen G. The mechanical properties and failure analysis of spindle assembly of knife roll cutting grass machine. Huibei Paper. 2001;3:23–5.
4. Yang ZQ. Spiral cinnamon balers. Pack Food Mach. 2002;18(3):31–3.
5. Wang GH. The development of hydraulic forage balers. Energy-Sav Technol. 1991;6:26–7.
6. Yuan SS, Wang YN, You W. A modified four-roll style casual charter. China Patent, 200810244526.9.
7. Song CS. The size design of large span screw conveyor. Xinan Paper. 2002;1:16–7.
8. Song CS, Wang HS. The design and application of large span screw conveyor. Light Ind Mach. 1999;4:34–7.
9. Song CS, Huang YD, Li YF, Zhao H. The design and life analysis of the screw shaft of screw conveyor. China Mech Eng. 2003;14:1049–52.
10. Ou ZQ, Zhang J, Li MF, Deng GR, Yao XM. The equipment development of cleaning dewatering in pineapple leaf fiber extraction process. Trop Agric Eng. 2001;2:19–21.
11. Li SQ, Le GM, Xiao HT, Wei W, Liu HY, Xiang GM, Yao Q. One dewatering system for high moisture waste slag press. China Patent, 200410009136.5. 2004.
12. Chen HZ, Zhang YZ. Method and apparatus for in situ steam explosion. China Patent, 01110068899.7. 2001.
13. Chen QC, Wang JW, Gao GF, Yuan H, Zhao JH, Zhang YF. Automatic electric steam generator structure and electric control principle. Oil Field Equip. 2011;31:26–8.
14. Li ZS. The use, maintenance and common fault analysis of electric steam generator. Meas Technol. 2004;10:54–5.
15. Zeng F, Hu YP, Yang Y. Mineral processing particuology. Beijing: China University of Mining and Technology Press; 2001.
16. He YQ, Zhao YM. Pulsing air classification. Beijing: Chemical Industry Press; 2009.
17. Johansen ST, de Silva SR. Some considerations regarding optimum flow fields for centrifugal air classification. Int J Miner Process. 1996;44–45.

18. Wang X, Ge X, Zhao X, Wang Z. A model for performance of the centrifugal countercurrent air classifier. Powder Technol. 1998;98(2):171–6.
19. Wang Q, Melaaen MC, De Silva SR. Investigation and simulation of a cross-flow air classifier. Powder Technol. 2001;120(3):273–80.
20. Yoshida H, Fukui K, Yoshida K, Shinoda E. Particle separation by Iinoya's type gas cyclone. Powder Technol. 2001;118(1):16–23.

Chapter 4
Process Development of Gas Explosion

4.1 Process Development of Gas Explosion Technology

4.1.1 Overview of Gas Explosion Technology

The technology of gas explosion commonly consists of pretreatment of raw materials, gas explosion process of materials, and the post-treatment of materials after gas explosion [1].

The purpose of pretreatment is to enhance the explosion performance, resulting in ideal properties of materials for the successive treatment. Generally, the pre-treatment methods include smashing, screening, dedusting, soaking, and dehydration. The particle size of materials decreases after smashing, which can increase the charge coefficient; moreover, the surface area increases, which is conducive to the permeation of explosion medium. Screening improves the uniformity of materials, making the condition of gas explosion stable and being well controlled to get homogeneous gas-exploded materials. Dedusting avoids the dust in the surroundings to reduce the impurities of raw materials for the ease of purification. The aim of soaking is to enhance the explosion performance and improve the properties of exploded materials. The choice of soaking agents differs according to different purposes and various materials, including water [2], dilute acid (sulfuric acid [3, 4]), dilute alkali (NaOH [5]), antioxidants (Na_2SO_3 [6]). Dehydration is needed after soaking in order to adjust the moisture content. Metal screen is usually used for filtration, and the filtrate can be recycled, while the solid materials are transferred to the hopper of reactor by a screw or ribbon conveyor. A belt weigher is usually located in front of the hopper or the conveyor to control the mass of materials transferred into the reactor.

In a gas explosion process it is important to control the charge amount, heating up time, gas digesting time and temperature, and the explosion pressure, in order to make full use of the chemical reactions during digesting and the physical tearing effect during decompression. After steam explosion, the materials enter the collector

H. Chen, *Gas Explosion Technology and Biomass Refinery*,
DOI 10.1007/978-94-017-7414-7_4

with a screen through the bottom of the discharge gate while the waste steam drains from the top of the gate, making it easy for the separation of steam from solid. Liquid in the solid materials will flow into the bottom of the collector through the screen and then flow out of the bleeder tube for reuse; solid portion in the exploded materials can be transferred out of the upper part of the collector by a conveyor for utilization, realizing the separation of liquid from solid in the exploded materials. Saturated steam [7, 8], superheated steam [9], mixture of air and steam [10, 11], inert gases [12], CO_2 [13], and NH_3 [14] can be used as the medium of gas explosion.

Post-treatment of exploded materials is aimed to satisfy the demand for successive operations. For example, lignocelluloses can be fermented to produce ethanol, but due to the fermentation inhibitors produced in the steam explosion process including organic acids (formic acid, acetic acid), furan compounds (furfural, 5-HMF), phenolic compounds (ferulic acid, p-coumaric acid) and soluble lignin, washing is usually needed to remove these inhibitors. At the same time, there are many degradation products of hemicellulose in the hydrolysate which can be used to extract xylose and xylooligosaccharide, or to produce chemicals by fermentation [15].

4.1.2 Iogen Steam Explosion Technology

Iogen was set up in 1974, which was named Iotech then. The earliest study of Iotech was to use steam-exploded straw and wood to produce animal feed and then test whether the feed could improve the digestibility [16]. Due to the rising worries of shortage of oil resources worldwide, Iotech changes its directions in 1978 to convert lignocelluloses into fuel ethanol through steam explosion technology and carry out the research of cellulase system to degrade the exploded lignocelluloses for the fuel ethanol production. In 1983, Iotech got the governmental fund and established a pilot plant in Ottawato to produce fuel ethanol. In this plant, Iotech pretreated lignocelluloses using its own patent technology of steam explosion and then used cellulase produced by their own to convert exploded lignocelluloses into sugars, finally the sugars were fermented by yeasts and the ethanol was derived by distillation. Moreover, Iotech cooperated with Petro-Canada and Hoffman-Laroche to improve the technologies of cellulase production and enzymatic hydrolysis, aiming to solve to energy problem of Canada. In 1986, Iotech was renamed as Iogen. In 2003, the pilot factory of fuel ethanol gained success, which could deal with 25 t wheat straw and produce 320,000 L cellulosic ethanol. We will introduce the steam explosion technologies combined with the pretreatment technology for raw materials dated from that of Iogen Corporation. The explosion device of Iogen made an improvement based on that of Masonite Corporation, belonging to intermittent technology as shown in Fig. 4.1.

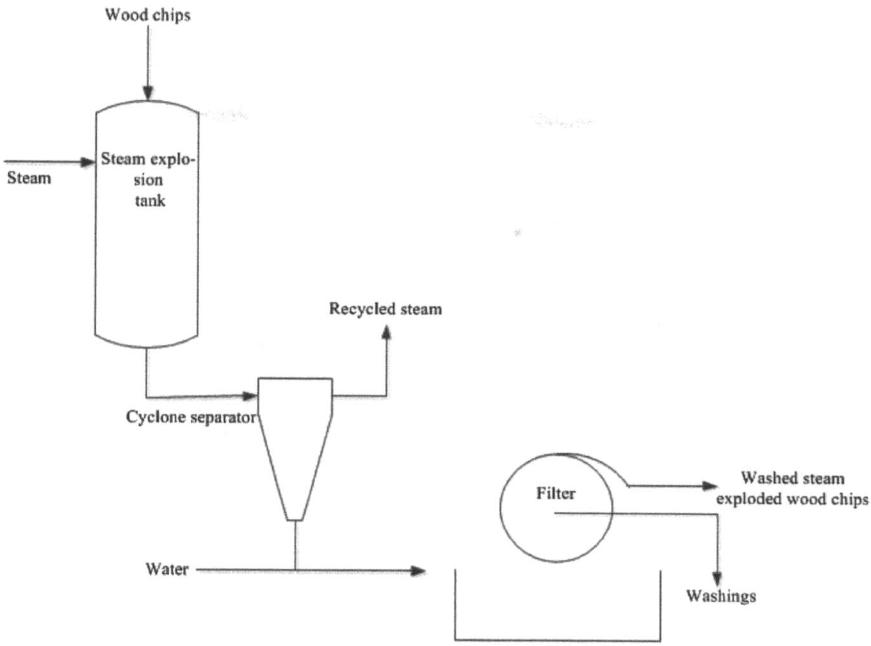

Fig. 4.1 Process flowchart of Iogen steam explosion technology

In this technology, hardwood was smashed into slices of 1 in. (1 in. = 0.0245 m) in length and 1/8 in. in width, and then, the slices were put into the reactor loosely after spraying 0.01–1 % H_2SO_4 solution. Then, saturated steam was inlet into the reactor to heat the reactor to 200–250 °C and the pressure reached 500–750 psi (1 psi = 6894.76 Pa) (which would take about 15 s). Finally, the pressure was discharged instantaneously (<100 psi in 10 s) and the materials was discharged from the reactor. Organic acids in wood could control the pH value of reaction, while the volatile substances such as acetic acid could be recycled through washing and concentration. The steam-exploded wood was adjusted to neutral using alkali and then used for enzymatic hydrolysis and fermentation or the production of livestock feed. Lignin produced from steam-exploded aspen using this technology could be dissolved in ethanol which was used to produce resin, plastics, detergent, and chemicals or used as wood adhesives. By this technology, 90 % cellulose and 80 % hemicellulose in aspen was hydrolyzed into sugar which could be used for ethanol conversion via fermentation with 95 % conversion ratio of the theoretical yield. Generally, 1 t wood could produce 65 gal (1 gal = 3.78541 L) ethanol. Moreover, the yield could be increased to 90 gal if an efficient method to use xylose was discovered. The flow chart of ethanol fermentation after enzymatic hydrolysis using steam-exploded wood was shown in Fig. 4.2.

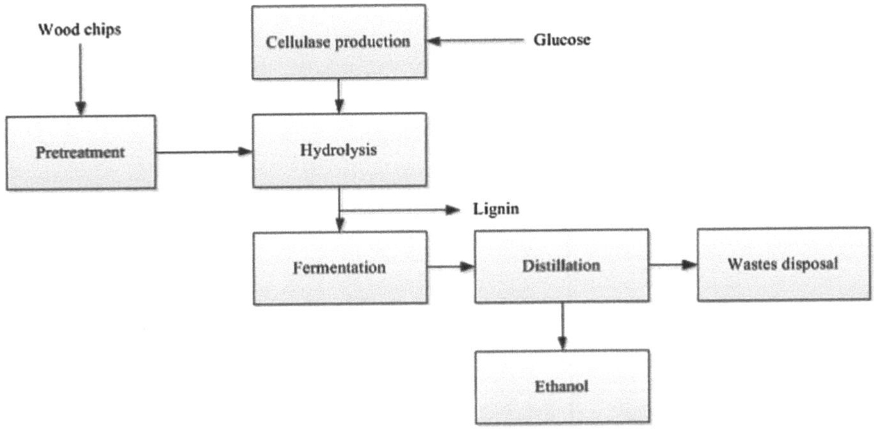

Fig. 4.2 Process flowchart of ethanol production from wood using enzymatic hydrolysis and fermentation with steam explosion pretreatment for wood

Iogen was one of the earliest companies to produce cellulase using glucose fermentation instead of lactose fermentation. Most of the sugars derived from steam-exploded materials were used to produce cellulase, while a small amount was used for ethanol, guaranteeing the profit of the company. Such technology was applicable for hardwood as well as wheat straw, cornstalk, but not for softwood [17].

4.1.3 Stake Steam Explosion Technology

Registered in 1973 in Toronto, Canada, Stake was the largest supplier of organic food who also developed continuous steam explosion technology for ruminant feed preparation and clean pulping [12, 18, 19]. In 2003, Stake was renamed as SunOpta. In 2010, Mascoma Company bought SunOpta BioProcess Inc (SBI) belonging to SunOpta and combined the steam explosion technology with its integrated bioprocessing technology to produce low-cost fuel ethanol and high-valued products by lignocelluloses. Stake Technology had deep researches of devices related to steam explosion and owned many patents. For example, their key feeding system, antispraying devices, and charging devices were all unique, of which the technology and devices of continuous steam explosion are still most widely used worldwide. Stake Technology applied this technology into pulping and gradually developed to straw pretreatment and production of animal feed using pulping waste.

In 1992, Stake Technology set up a set of continuous steam explosion pilot technology in Trisaia, ENEA (Italian National Agency for New Technology, Energy and Environment), Italy. Such technology could deal 175 kg straw and wood slices per hour to get cellulose, hemicellulose, and lignin, as shown in Fig. 4.3.

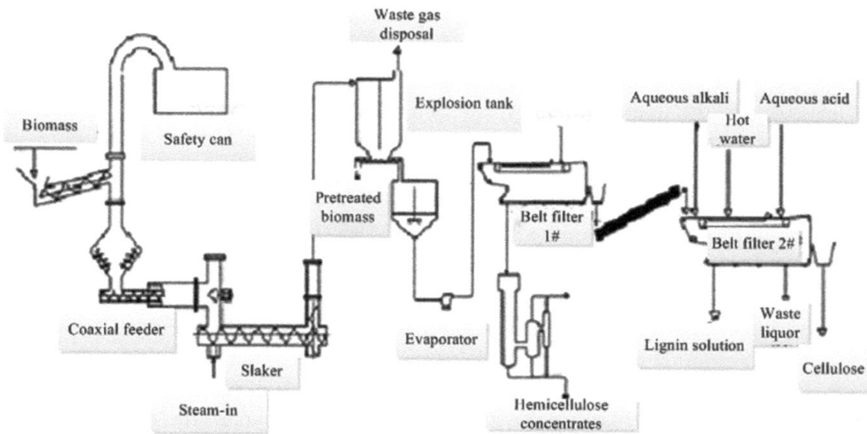

Fig. 4.3 Technical flowchart of Stak Tech steam explosion [20]

The technology concluded 5 parts: biomass storage and processing devices, Stake Tech system, water extraction system, alkali extraction system, and waste processing devices.

(1) Biomass storage and processing devices

In this part, well-piled wood slices or minced straw were transferred to the top of storage tanks and then separated from the transfer gas flow by a whirlcone. The materials fell into the storage tanks from whirlcones and then they were transferred to the belt weigher with cover which was used to measure the materials' flow. Then, the moisture content of materials was manually adjusted to 50 % and the pretreated materials were transferred to the Stake Tech system by inclined plate feeding tanks.

(2) Stak Tech system [21, 22]

Stak Tech system was consisted of a coaxial feeder and a slaker. A big hopper was set on the bottom of the inclined plate feeding tank. Biomass falling from the inclined plate feeding tank was transferred to the big hopper by a reversible two-way screw conveyor. The materials were compressed into plug lumps and sealed the high-pressure slaker.

Compressed materials would be smashed by the adjustable valves after entering the slaker and quickly exposed to the operating temperature and pressure of slaker and then transferred to the outlet of slaker by a variable speed screw conveyor set in the vertical section of slaker. The handling time of materials in the reactor could be adjusted through the transfer speed of screw conveyor.

Saturated steam was inlet from the intake tubes set near the entrance. The operating temperature and pressure were set at 200 °C/1.55–238 °C/3.2 MPa and the holding time was set as 1–5 min.

The discharge port was set at the rear of the slaker. Through a right–left crossed screw conveyor, the materials were squeezed to the ball valve which could discharge regularly and brought the materials to the atmosphere from the high-pressure environment of the tank. Generally, the ball valve was opened every 5–10 s, each lasting for 0.1–1 s.

Steam-exploded materials were collected in the impacted recycling tanks in which steam and solid materials were separated. Steam was recycled by the steam collector, while solid materials were transferred to the receiving tanks by a reversible screw conveyor. If materials without extraction were demanded, solid materials on the bottom of the tanks were transferred to the receiving tanks directly; if extracted materials were demanded, solid materials would be transferred to the size pots for extraction. Size pots had two functions: storage tanks for steam-exploded materials and commingler for circulation fluid. Steam-exploded materials were presoaked in water to dissolve the pentosan and then recycled the filtrate through belt filters. Secondary vacuum extraction filtrate was used as circulation fluid, entering the commingler.

(3) Water extraction system

Multistage countercurrent extraction was used for the extraction process of steam-exploded materials using belt filters interlinked with outside equipped with cover plates. Steam-exploded materials in the impacted recycling tanks were soaked into pulp by the secondary vacuum extraction filtrate and the concentration was condensed to 6 % from 50 %. Then, the pulp was pumped to the belt filters in which solid materials were mixed with the reversing hot water (80 °C) along the belt and the pentosan was extracted here. Extraction liquid was concentrated by a 60 °C falling-film evaporator and the condensed water was recycled, while the concentrated pentosan syrup was obtained with the ultimate temperature of 80 °C. In order to reserve the fibers before evaporation, pulp was sieved by 20-mesh sieves (two in parallel). After a vacuum extraction, the pentosan concentration was 6 %. Then, the filtrates were transferred to the falling-film evaporator in the vertical tube, in which the pentosan syrup was condensed to 50 %.

The concentrated pentosan syrup was collected and stored in cans for further analysis. Such syrup had similar properties and viscosity with sugarcane molasses, shown in Table 4.1.

Table 4.1 Properties of pentosan syrup

Raw material	Straw	Wood
Mass of syrup/kg	104.1	60.7
Moisture content/%	50	50
Hemicellulose/%	41.2	47.8
Pentosan in hemicellulose/%	26.6	39.5
Ash (minerals)/%	7.4	1.6
Protein/%	1.4	0.6

(4) Alkali extraction system

The materials filtered from the first belt filter was transferred to the pulp tanks and mixed with water and alkali solution vacuum extracted from secondary filter. The alkali extraction was feed to the secondary belt filter at 73 °C, adding fresh alkali solution to dissolve lignin and then washed with 90 °C water and adjusted to neutral with H_2SO_4. The final lignin content was about 3 %. Such solution was stored in two tanks and then concentrated to 50 % of lignin content with falling-film evaporator. Features of condensed black lignin solution were shown in Table 4.2.

Solid residue filtered from secondary filter was cellulose without bleaching, with moisture content of 65 % and the properties of semi-refined pulping, showing in Table 4.3.

(5) Waste processing devices

Gaseous waste and steam mainly contained acetic acid, furfural, and light solvents that could be washed and/or concentrated by gas scrubber (Fig. 4.4). Solution was cooled to 35 °C through a cooling tower and recycled to the gas scrubber; solution that could not be concentrated was burned in the incinerator. Rotary incinerator was used for the disposal of gaseous and solid waste with the handling capacity of 160 kg/h for solid and 6 kg/h for gaseous waste. Burned gases were discharged into air after purification, while the ash was remained for further disposal. Waste water produced from every stage was collected to the drainage for emission after anaerobic digestion to meet the drainage standard.

The steam explosion technology of Stake Tech was applied for the stripping and recycled with the use of waste paper, wood, and straw pulping and the production of fiberboard. Additionally, Stake Tech also used such technology to pretreat cellulose for ethanol production through enzymatic hydrolysis.

Table 4.2 Properties of lignin solution

Raw material	Straw	Wood
Mass of liquor/kg	60.8	78.8
Moisture content/%	50	50
Lignin/%	31.6	37.3
Hemicellulose/%	9.0	5.7
Minerals and salts/%	9.3	6.8

Table 4.3 Properties of unbleached cellulose

Raw material	Straw	Wood
Mass of wet cellulose/kg	255.7	294.9
Moisture cont/%	65	65
Cellulose/%	26.7	30.3
Hemicellulose/%	2.1	1.5
Lignin/%	1.9	2.5
Protein/%	2.2	0.5
Minerals and salts/%	2.3	0.2

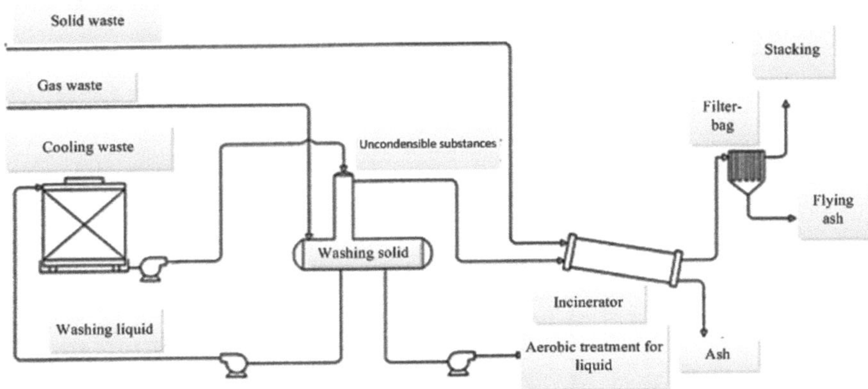

Fig. 4.4 Disposal flowchart of gaseous and solid waste

4.1.4 Low-Pressure and Non-pollution Steam Explosion Technology

Based on the difference of chemical components and structures of straw and wood, Prof. Chen, from Institute of Processing Engineering, Chinese Academy of Sciences, improved the previous steam explosion technology and proposed a low-pressure technology without addition of chemicals to the straw. They also developed 3- and 5-m^3 steam explosion vessels with quick operating valve and applied for many national patents [23].The pollution sources were eliminated without addition of chemicals; furthermore, the resource utilization of lignocelluloses was obtained due to the use of degraded hemicellulose during steam explosion. Therefore, this technology solved the pollution problem of steam explosion and substantially decreased the cost. Till now, the low-pressure and non-pollution steam explosion technology has broad prospects in the integrated utilization of straw processing, tobacco processing, pulping industry, herbal extraction, and clean degumming technology of fibrilia [24].

This technology belongs to batch operation and the steam explosion device is shown in Fig. 4.5, which is consisted of a steam generator, a discharge valve, and a receiving tank. The detailed operation flowchart of using this technology to separate the components of wheat straw is shown in Fig. 4.6.

Dedusted wheat straw was out into the explosion workshop for presoaking treatment firstly due to the different moisture content of materials would affect the speed to reach the highest cooking temperature and influenced the explosion performance. Previous studies validated that 34 % moisture content encountered better explosion performance and the highest hemicellulose recovery (Fig. 4.7) as well as the improvement of defibrination and the properties of pulping. Presoaked straw was transferred to the explosion tank, inletting high-pressure steam with certain pressure and temperature, discharging the pressure instantaneously after holding for

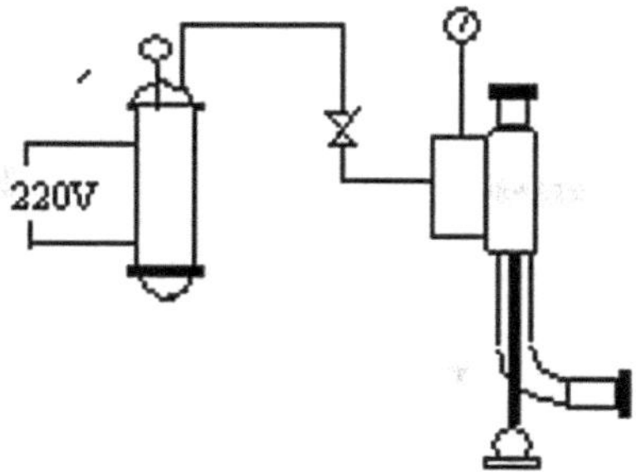

Fig. 4.5 Setup diagram of steam explosion

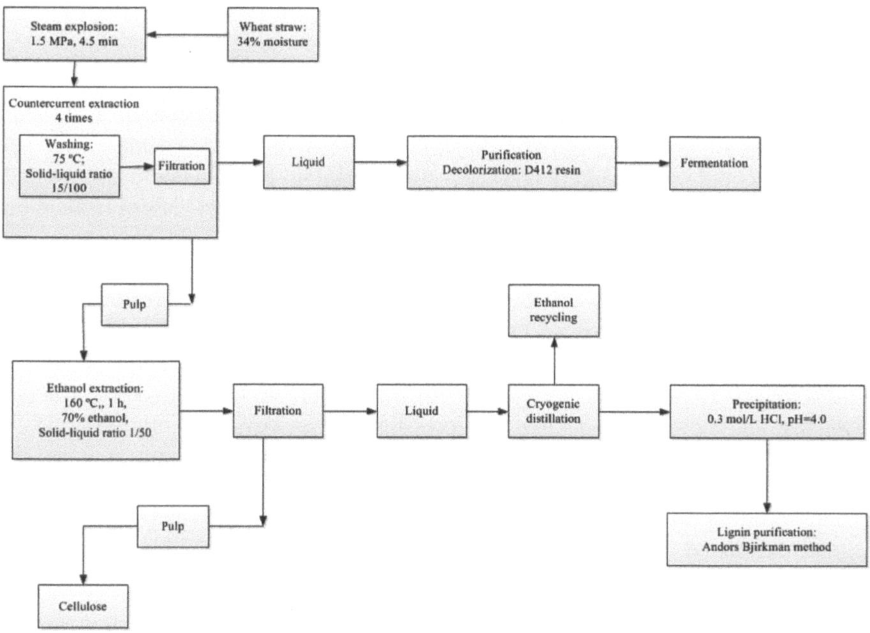

Fig. 4.6 Flowchart of the separation and utilization of steam-exploded wheat straw [25]

a certain time. Under virtual circumstances, those parameters could be adjusted according to the properties of materials, the use of exploded materials and the devices of steam explosion to satisfy the demand.

Wheat straw with 34 % moisture content was steam exploded after cooking 4.5 min at 1.5 MPa. Then, the degraded sugars from hemicellulose were extracted under the following conditions: liquid–solid ratio 15/100 (w/w), temperature 75 °C, and countercurrent extraction for 3 times, obtaining at least 80 % recovery of hemicellulose. The recovered monosaccharides and polysaccharides can be

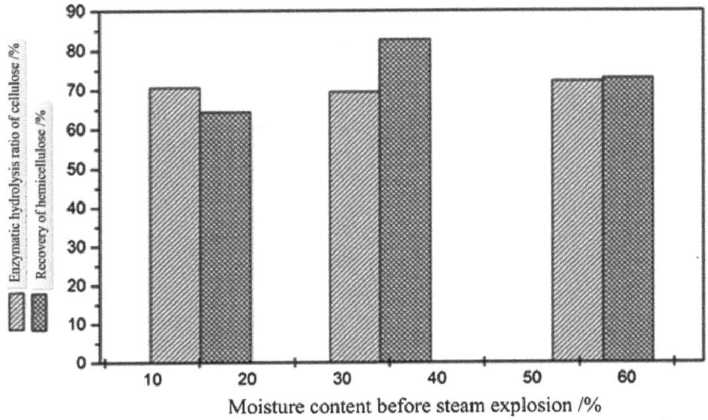

Fig. 4.7 Effects of moisture on the steam explosion performance (1.5 MPa, 10 min)

fermented or sold as products after further purification. The solid residue after extraction was reacted with 70 % ethanol at 160 °C (liquid–solid ratio was 50), obtaining alcohol soluble lignin and high-purity pulping. Ethanol could be recycled, while lignin could be used for the synthesis of chemical products after purification. Under this condition, the lignin recovery could reach 75 %. At the same time, the pulping could be used to make high-quality paper after blanching and papermaking. Besides, the pulping could also be used for enzymatic hydrolysis to obtain sugars with 90 % conversion ratio and then fermented to produce fuel ethanol.

This technology, which has been successfully magnified to industrial scale, has good adaptability to straw materials with low lignin content and high acetyl content. Also, without chemicals' soaking, low pressure and energy consumption radically solved the problems of pollution of steam explosion, which not only realized the integrated utilization of straw without pollution but also applied in tobacco processing, pulping, herbal extraction, and degumming of fibrilia, realizing the green upgrade of related industries.

4.1.5 In Situ Gas Explosion Technology

For certain materials, the chemical actions are preferred while the physical tearing effects should be limited to reduce the damage to raw materials. For example, during the degumming process of fibrilia using steam explosion, the fibrilia is easy to crack due to the rubbing and tearing of pipes when draining from the pipes; the fibrilia is also readily to wind and tie due to the airflow in the pipe, resulting in the trouble for successive separation and carding. Prof. Chen proposed a novel gas explosion technology based on these problems, i.e., in situ gas explosion technology and the operations were listed as follows. Materials were put onto a tailor-made trolley which had two categories of box-type and cage-type; box-type trolley had a netlike wall from which the steam could enter the inside of the trolley; cage-type also had a netlike wall and a pothook on the top of the wall on which the long stripped materials could be attached and a steel sheet was set near the steam entrance valve. The steam went through the meshes and flew from the steel sheet meshes during instantaneous discharge, but the materials could stay in the trolley. Thus, the steam-exploded materials could be obtained when taking the trolley out of the tank [26].

4.1.6 In Situ Multistage Flashing and Steam Explosion Drying Technology

Traditional drying equipment has problems of low efficiency, high energy consumption, high cost, and long working time. Based on these problems, Prof. Chen suggested a combination of steam explosion and steam drying technology and proposed the in situ multistage flashing and steam explosion drying technology which was fit for those materials with fair hygroscopic, realizing the dual functions of pretreatment and drying.

Based on the principle of removing moisture content through steam explosion and flashing, this technology could dry the materials besides pretreatment. During flashing, the moisture within the materials was heated to evaporate, leading to continuous water loss; in particular at the moment of discharge, materials were dried due to the water loss through flash evaporation. Flashing evaporation was proceeded continuously, while the materials stayed in the tank. Thus, without discharge, the technology was simplified, with the avoidance of pollution due to multiple discharge processes. Multi-flashing attained the goal of multi-drying; thus, the drying efficiency was sharply improved. During steam explosion, the instantaneous discharge of steam within the materials smashed them, which was more entirely and thoroughly, saving the mechanical smashing operation besides drying and improving the production efficiency as well as saving the cost. This technology was suited for the pretreatment and drying of cow dung, pig dung, and activated sludge.

4.1.7 Steam Explosion and Carding Technology

Biomass, especially agricultural straws, has uneven structures, which leads to dramatic difference of physical and chemical effects during steam explosion. For example, cornstalk contains leaf, pith, and cortex. Leaf and pith have weak mechanical properties and are easy to crack, while the cortex mainly contains mechanical tissues with strong mechanical properties. Additionally, leaf and pith consist of many non-fiber cells containing considerable cellular contents which are easy to generate inhibitors during the drastic explosion process. Therefore, a two-step technology of steam explosion and carding was proposed by Chen according to the differences of mechanical properties of various organs and stability tolerance encountering the high-temperature and high-pressure acid environment of different tissues. In the first step, the steam explosion condition was moderate, and thus, the tissues with weak mechanical properties were smashed, while those with strong mechanical properties kept their features. Then, the separation was achieved by mechanical carding equipment according to the various features of materials after steam explosion. At the same time, materials were evenly soaked in the first step and the porosity of materials increased due to the mechanical tearing effect, presenting to be fluffy. Materials that encountered unobvious explosion effects were transferred to the second section which was also carried out at relatively low explosion strength. Thanks to the evenly soaking and mechanical tearing effects, the materials were fluffy and contained even moisture which could be exploded under moderate steam explosion condition. Next, we will demonstrate the two-step technology by the pretreatment of cornstalk [27].

4.1.7.1 Feasibility Analysis of the Two-Step Technology

The uneven structures of cellulosic materials lead to the difference of pretreatment and utilization path of various tissues [28]. During steam explosion, the extent of steam penetrating into the cells and the resistance to tearing strength of cells influences the performance of steam explosion. Without considering the external factors of particle size and packing coefficient, the thickness of cell walls became the main factor affecting the tearing resistance of cells; the cell wall thickness of materials and size of cell cavity were the main factors affecting the penetration of steam. Given that the fibrocytes have thick wall and small cavity while parenchyma cells have thin cavity and large cavity, the penetration performance of steam into these two kinds of cells will show difference.

As shown in Fig. 4.8a, the water reabsorbing capacity of fibrocytes and parenchyma cells was different during pressure maintenance. Parenchyma cells showed better water reabsorbing capacity than fibrocytes with a larger amount of reabsorption and a shorter time to reach the balance. In Fig. 4.8b, the moisture contents varied in these two kinds of cells after steam explosion and the parenchyma cells had higher moisture content than those of fibrocytes. We may conclude that due to the structural difference of cells and penetration difference of steam into these two kinds of cells, the degradation and tearing extent of fibrocytes and parenchyma cells were different as steam working as the heat carrier and power source during steam explosion process. Therefore, when the structural difference and fraction were not involved, the steam explosion conditions will become drastic in order to pursue high degradation of hemicellulose, high increasing rate of specific surface area and low entrainment rate of raw materials, which leads to the overdegradation of parenchyma cells, resulting in higher possibility to generate inhibitors.

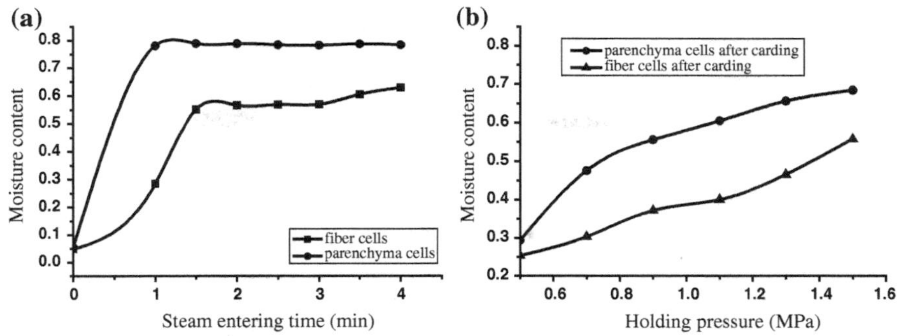

Fig. 4.8 Comparison of the rehydration performance of steam-exploded fibrocytes and parenchyma cells. **a** Moisture content of steam-exploded fibrocytes and parenchyma cells under different steam-inlet time. **b** Moisture content of steam-exploded fibrocytes and parenchyma cells after mechanical carding

Therefore, we may choose different steam explosion conditions for fibrocytes and parenchyma cells in order to reach separate optimum performance.

As shown in Fig. 4.8, steam explosion was conducive to the evenly water reabsorption for fibrocytes and parenchyma cells. Prof. Chen also concluded that steam explosion could help improve the separation degree of fibrocytes and parenchyma cells from raw materials [29]. The two-step steam explosion and carding technology adopted moderate conditions in steam explosion stage for even rehydration and separated parenchyma cells with high moisture and fibrocytes with low moisture based on the principle of weight grading of centrifugal air classifier, and then, the separated fibrocytes were steam exploded for another time under moderate condition. Thus, this technology was feasible and reasonable.

4.1.7.2 Effects of Two-Step Steam Explosion and Carding Technology on Inhibitors

Figure 4.9 shows that the inhibitor contents in parenchyma cells were higher than those of fibrocytes after carding, while the inhibitor content in one-step steam-exploded materials without carding was in between, implying that under the same steam explosion conditions, the degradation extent of parenchyma cells was higher than those of fibrocytes. Hence, it indicated that the heterogeneity of lignin structure determined the difference and selectivity of pretreatment condition, which also implied the necessity of fraction and choosing pretreatment methods.

Considering the second-step steam-exploded materials, the inhibitor contents in experimental groups were lower than those in the control group (1.2 MPa with 8-min duration time) except for the group of 1.5 MPa and the lowest one was the group of 1.1 MPa. The results may be explained by that the best separation performance of fibrocytes and parenchyma cells (Fig. 4.10) was reached under

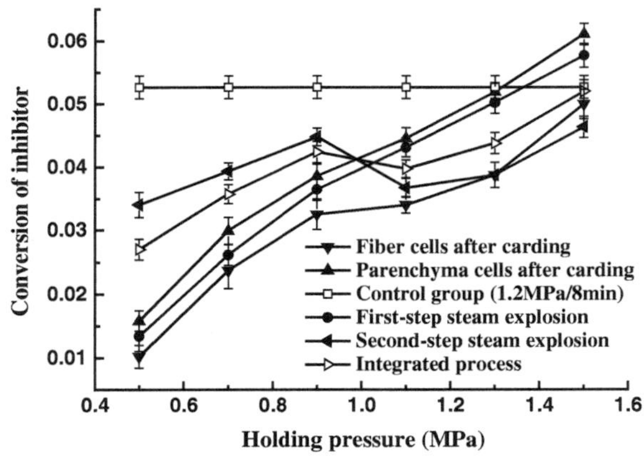

Fig. 4.9 Effects of the steam explosion and mechanical carding methods on the inhibitor content

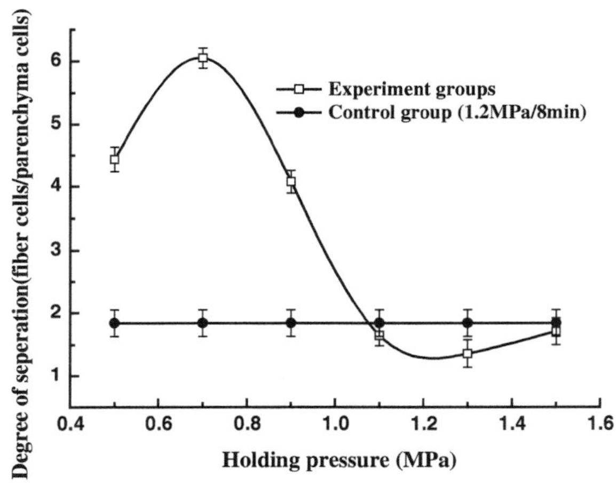

Fig. 4.10 Separation degrees of fibers under different steam explosion conditions

1.1 MPa condition; thus, the parenchyma cell content was the lowest when coming to the second-step steam explosion after carding, generating the lowest content of inhibitors. The inhibitor contents increased during 0.5–0.9 MPa. For one thing, the intensity of steam explosion and the degradation degree both increased, leading to the increase of by-products. For another, the separation degree of materials was poor among the 0.5–0.9 MPa range; thus, the fibrocytes and parenchyma cells could not be separated fully. Among 1.3–1.5 MPa, despite the fair separation of fibrocytes and parenchyma cells, the inhibitor content increased due to the drastic explosion condition. Combining Figs. 4.9 and 4.10, when the condition was 1.1-MPa/4-min carding–1.2-MPa/4-min carding, the optimal separation degree of cornstalk was 1.6 with the lowest content of inhibitors.

4.1.7.3 Effects of Two-Step Steam Explosion and Carding Technology on Enzymatic Hydrolysis

As shown in Fig. 4.11, the enzymatic hydrolysis ratio of parenchyma cells was higher than that of fibrocytes after one-step carding while that of the one-step steam-exploded materials without carding was in between, indicating that the degradation degree of parenchyma cells was higher than that of fibrocytes under the same explosion conditions.

Compared with the control group, the enzymatic hydrolysis ratio of one-step-exploded materials was even higher from 1.1 MPa condition. For the second-step-exploded materials, the enzymatic hydrolysis ratios were higher than those of the control group except for the 0.5 MPa condition; furthermore, the enzymatic hydrolysis ratio increased with the increase of steam explosion strength.

Therefore, we may conclude that the optimal steam explosion and carding condition was 1.1 MPa/4-min carding–1.2 MPa/4-min carding according to Figs. 4.9, 4.10, and 4.11. Under such condition, the fibrotissues were moderately degraded while avoiding the excessive degradation of the parenchyma tissues, generating the lowest content of inhibitors during pretreatment.

4.1.7.4 Effects of Two-Step Steam Explosion and Carding Technology on 2,3-Butanediol (2,3-BD)

In Fig. 4.12, the experimental group contains the lowest content of inhibitors and the highest content of 2,3-BD. Compared with one-step steam-exploded materials (1.2 MPa/8 min), the content of inhibitors decreased by 33 % while that of 2,3-BD increased by 209 %. Compared with 2,3-BD fermentation only using sugar as the carbon source, the 2,3-BD content of the experimental group was higher than that of the control group while that of the other groups was lower, implying that the inhibitors generated during pretreatment conditions in the experimental group were

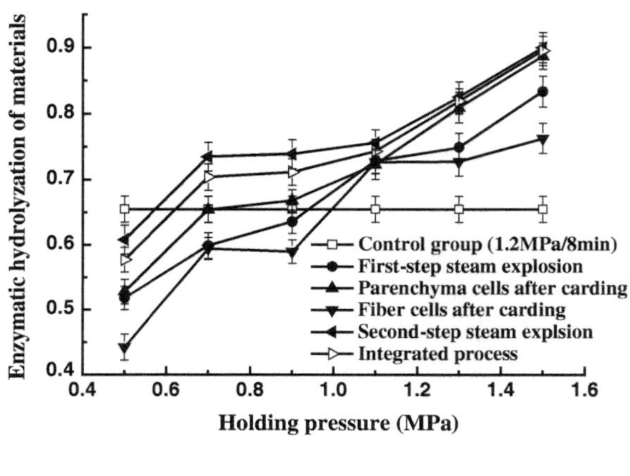

Fig. 4.11 Effects of the steam explosion and mechanical carding methods on the enzymatic hydrolysis performance

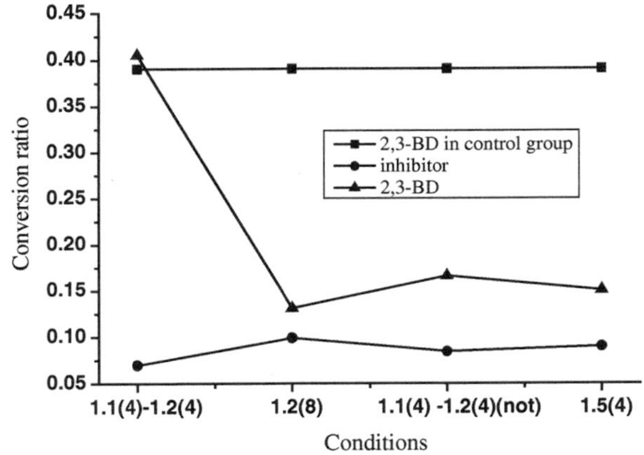

Fig. 4.12 Effects of two-stage steam explosion and mechanical carding technology on the production of 2,3-BD

conducive to the 2,3-BD conversion instead of inhibiting its generation and the inhibitors generated under other pretreatment conditions had an inhibition effect on the 2,3-BD generation.

4.2 Process Development of Eco-industrialization of Steam-Exploded Materials

4.2.1 Biomass Resource and Its Distribution

Biomass refers to the organisms directly or indirectly derived from photosynthesis, including all animals, plants, and microorganisms. Biomass owned the following characteristics.

① Renewability. As long as the solar energy exists, the photosynthesis of plants will not stop, thus the biomass resource will not be exhausted. That is to say, biomass resource is unlimited.

② Abundance. According to statistics, the total biomass generated every year is about 2×10^{11} t.

③ Substitutability. Biomass energy is different from other fossil resources, which is a kind of carbon resource that can replace fossil resources to convert into liquid or gaseous fuels and other chemical materials.

④ Cleanliness. Biomass replacing fossil resources could reduce the generation of SO_2 and CO_2, improving the environment. Without SO_2 emission, the combustion of biomass is clean. Moreover, the CO_2 emission during combustion of biomass is almost equal to the CO_2 absorption during photosynthesis, resulting in a zero carbon emission process.

⑤ Degradability. Originated from nature, biomass can be degraded by microorganisms, avoiding the solid waste pollution.

Biomass refers to the residual stems or leaves of rice, wheat, and corn after harvest during the process of agricultural production. Agricultural stalks have properties of abundance, variety, and wide distribution in China, which are estimated as 820 million tons (air-dried, 15 % moisture), of which rice straw accounts for 25 % (205 million tons), wheat straw 18.3 % (150 million tons), cornstalks 32.3 % (265 million tons), cotton stalks 3.2 % (25.84 million tons), oil crops stalks (mainly oilseed rape and peanuts) 4.6 % (37.37 million tons), beans stalks 3.3 % (27.26 million tons), and tuber crops stalks 2.7 % (22.43 million tons). The specific ratio was shown in Fig. 4.13.

Considering the distribution areas, the biomass resources of North China Region and Middle and lower Yangtze River Region are the most abundant, sharing about 233 and 193 million tons, accounting for 28.45 and 23.58 % of the total amount, respectively, followed by Northeast China Region, Southwest China Region and Mongo Xingjiang Region whose stalks resource are estimated as 141, 89.94, and 58.73 million tons, accounting for 17.2, 10.97 and 7.16 % of the total amount; Southern China Region and the Loess Plateau region share lower contents of stalks resource, which are 54.9 and 44.04 million tons, accounting for 6.7 and 5.37 % of the total amount separately; The Tibetan areas share the lowest content of stalks, which is 46.8 million tons, accounting for 0.57 % of the total.

Stubblemulchfarming is essential for many crops during harvest; meanwhile, part of the leaves will fall during collection and transportation of crops. Thus, considering the loss during collection, the available resource amount is not identical with the theoretical amount, which is affected by the kinds of crops, collection modes, and climates, relating to the collective techniques and radius. The available crop stalks in China are nearly 687 million tons, taking up 83.8 % of the theoretical yield [30].

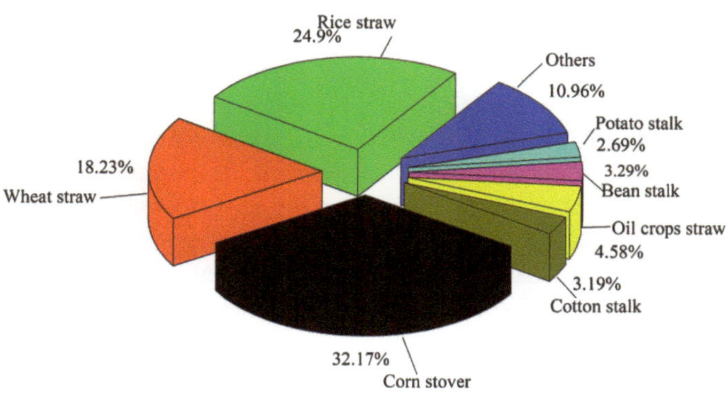

Fig. 4.13 Proportions of different agricultural straws of the total resources

4.2.2 *Collection and Transportation of Biomass*

4.2.2.1 Collection and Transportation Mode of Stalk

Botanical-based renewable materials have advantages of abundance, various sources, and renewability as well as the properties of lightweight, wide distribution, and harvest with seasons. Agriculture in China is mainly dominated by family contract, leading to the dispersed distribution due to small plantation area of each family. At the same time, due to the low density and large volume as well as seasonal harvest, industrial production of biomass encounters the problems of seasonal sources and poor production continuity. Therefore, the collection, storage, and transportation of stalk have become the bottleneck of the large-scale utilization of stalks. How to establish a system including collection, storage, and transportation of stalks is the first key to the development of biomass energy industry. Moreover, both quality and economic cost should be controlled for the material supply. At present, the representative modes of the system including collection, storage, and transportation in China can be divided into two categories: one is dispersed system mode with the stalk broker as the main part; the other is intensive system mode with the specialized collection and transportation companies as the main part [31].

(1) Dispersed system mode

① Mode operation characteristics

This mode takes the stalk broker as the main part, in which the broker organizes the farmers and provides stalk materials for enterprises all the year. Companies as CECEP (Suqian) and Baolixiexin (Baoying) have successfully established this mode through practice. Power generation companies choose some farmers with business sense and initial capital and train them as the stalk brokers in charge of the collection, drying, storage, and transportation of stalks. Some of the brokers are specialized in providing stalks for enterprises. Two ways are adopted to buy stalks by those brokers: brokers buy trucks themselves, set up simple storage sites, buy stalks from farmers, store the stalks in the sites, and provide then to the power generation enterprises at regular intervals; brokers train a batch of stalk buyers and pay them in advance at certain intervals as the working cash to purchase stalks and transportation tools such as tractors, and then the buyers wander in the villages to buy stalks all the year and transport the stalks to the enterprises directly. In the second way, the brokers take charge of settling accounts with the enterprises and make cash bonus with the buyers. The detailed modes are shown in Fig. 4.14.

② Advantages and disadvantages and prospects

Stalks are materials with large amount and light mass; thus, the drying and storage of stalks will take up a large place. In the dispersed mode, the problems of collection, storage, and transportation have transferred to the wide rural areas and the problems are solved in this way. Power generation enterprises do not invest to set up the collection, storage, and transportation system, decreasing the economic costs

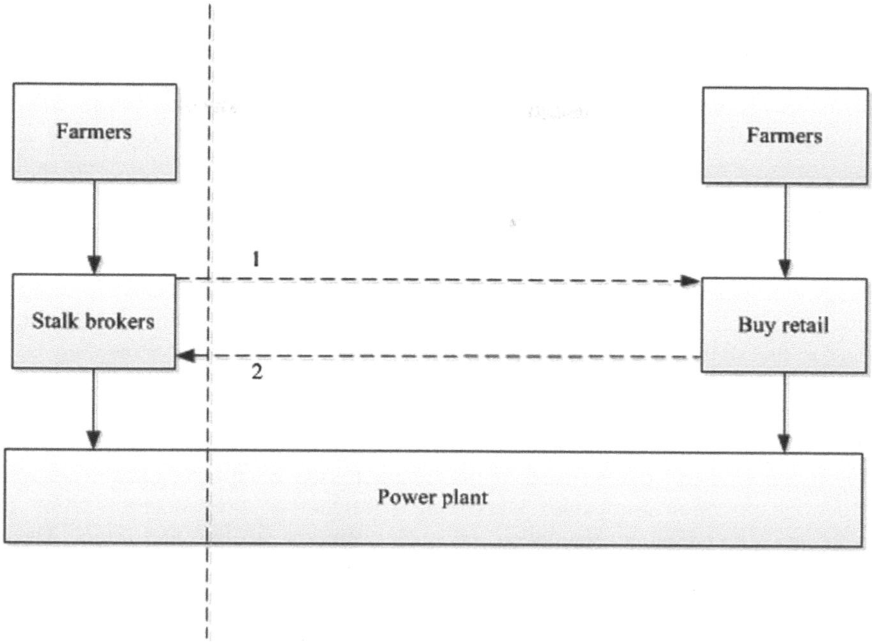

Fig. 4.14 Dispersive type of straws' collection–storage–transportation

of investment, management, and maintenance for the enterprises. One obvious weakness of this mode is that the material supply is largely limited to the brokers who belong to no organization and act relatively desultorily, with the increase of power generation enterprises and the expansion of these enterprises, the demand for stalks rises, leading to the raw materials competition among enterprises. In order to pursue maximum profit, the stalk brokers will increase the price randomly or just sell the stalks to other enterprises; at the same time, the enterprises have to put up the price to ensure the continuous supply of materials. As a result, the raw material cost increases substantially and some of the enterprises even face the crisis of stopping production due to the lack of raw materials. Looking at Suqian Biomass Power Generation Co. as an example, in Jun 2007, the average factory prices of rice straw, wheat stalk, and rice hull were 200, 250, and 300 y/t, respectively; while with the increasing demand of stalk materials, the prices of these raw materials increased to 250, 290 and 350 y/t, which was far beyond the budget. Therefore, the dispersed mode only goes for the areas with abundant sources, less competitive utilization, and sufficient supply of stalks.

(2) Intensive system mode

① Mode operation characteristics

Intensive system mode takes the specialized stalk collection and transportation company as the main part that is in charge of the collection, drying, storage and transportation and testing the moisture content and sandiness degree as well as the mildewing condition according to the universal standard rated by the power generation enterprises. Then, the stalks are weighed, paid, bundled, stacked, and stored keeping away from water and fire. Such companies focus on towns and set up one or several sites dispersedly within limits according to certain scales, forming a network of storage and transportation to adjust the storage amount of stalks and transfer the stalks to the power generation enterprises timely, guaranteeing both quality and quantity. Stalk storage and transportation companies collect stalks dispersedly while store and manage universally. Farmers or brokers as the main collectors, the stalks are preserved and stored in certain places after collection and drying according to the demand of the transportation companies. There are also some transportation companies who train a farmer cooperative organization of stalks and sign a contract regulating the buying amount, quality, and prices. These cooperative organizations organize farmers and take charge of material collection, pretreatment and small-scale storage, transferring to the storage stations periodically. Thus, a stalk collection and storage system from the farmer cooperative organization to stalk transportation companies till the power generation enterprises have been gradually established, guaranteeing the long-term effective supply of raw materials. The detailed operation path of intensive mode is listed in Fig. 4.15.

Enquiries revealed that the professional stalk collection and storage companies in China were usually established by the power generation enterprises themselves,

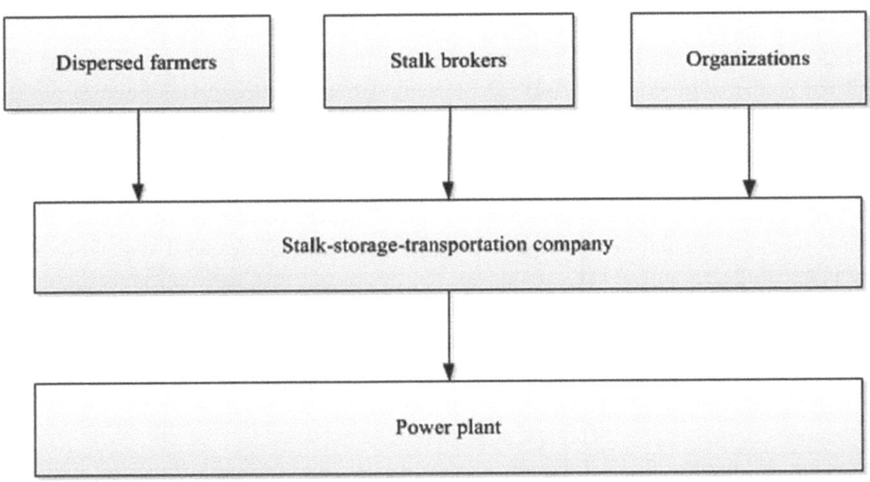

Fig. 4.15 Intensive type of straws' collection–storage–transportation

and the collection, storage, and transportation and the management issues were done all by themselves. For example, Sheyang Biomass Power Generation Company of National Energy Group has its own stalk collection and storage company, setting up 3 stations in the neighboring villages with the total capacity of 20,000 tons. There are special transportation teams in the stalk collection and storage companies which is responsible for the transportation of stalks to the power generation enterprises according to the utilization plan of raw materials.

② Advantages and disadvantages and prospects

In the intensive system, large-scale stalk collection and storage stations are essential. Besides, more land is needed as well as the establishment of rainproof, moisture-proof, fireproof, and thunder prevention facilities. Moreover, lots of manpower and materials should be invested for the daily maintenance and management, leading to higher one-time investment and higher fixed cost including depreciation expense and financial expense. However, on the other hand, the contract signed by the power generation enterprises and the stalk collection and storage companies, the supply of stalks has become the business activity within the legal persons of enterprises, which settles the randomness and risks of stalk supply, ensuring the long-term stable supply of raw materials. In addition, the stalk collection and storage companies adopt advanced devices and technologies for the quality check, smashing and bundling of stalks, ensuring the quality of stalks and improving the utilization efficiency. Therefore, with the development of large-scale utilization of stalks and the increase of market demand, intensive system will be the main mode in the future.

4.2.2.2 Cost Analysis of the Collection and Storage of Stalks

The cost of collection and storage of stalks involves the human power, materials, management expense, and reasonable profits in all links during the collection and storage of stalks. Prices of each link compose the factory price of stalks, mainly consisting of purchasing price, pretreatment price, storage price, and transportation price [31].

(1) Dispersed system mode

In this system, the costs of collection, drying, bundling, storage, and transportation of stalks in all links are shared by the stalk agents. Thus, the power generation enterprises could just set the factory price of stalks according to the stalk categories, moisture content, and grinding degree without considering the difference of collection radius, transportation distance, and the conditions of treatment and storage. For example, Suqian biomass power generation enterprise of CECEP sets the prices of stalks according to the calorific values of various stalks; the factory price of rice straw is about 250 y/t, wheat stalk 290 y/t, and rice hull 350 y/t. Based on the deep investigation of several stalk agents and power generation enterprises, the cost of each link in dispersed system is as follows with the wheat stalk as an example. The purchasing price refers to the costs of buying stalks from dispersed farmers, which is about 150 y/t. The smashing and bundling price refers to the costs of smashing and bundling of collected stalks, which is about 30 y/t (including labor cost 25 y/t and electricity cost 5 y/t). The storage price refers to the costs of field occupation, devices utilization, and manpower. At present, the storage price is often omitted because the storage volume is not large, the storage is ruleless and the field occupation fee is not high. The transportation price refers to the cost of transferring the collected stalks to the power generation enterprises by farmers or stalk brokers. The transportation price is directly related with the transportation radius which is usually controlled within 100 km and the cost is about 35 y/t. Labor price refers to the costs paid for manpower during the collection of stalks from dispersed farmers, which is about 60 y/t. The stalk brokers' price refers to costs of organization and timely communication with power generation enterprises of stalk brokers, which is about 15 y/t. Therefore, the total price is about 290 y/t. The above analysis showed that the raw materials cost accounted for a large proportion of the total cost (54 %). According to investigations, the predicted price of stalks by the enterprises is about 150 y/t. However, the situation is that the price reaches 150 y/t when farmers sell their stalks to the stalk brokers, and the factory price could reach 290 y/t after adding the necessary processing fees (including cutting or bundling fee and device depreciation fees), transportation fees, and labor costs. Moreover, stalks are seasonally harvested and larger land areas are needed for storage; thus, the fireproof facilities are necessary. In addition, the loss of mass and calorific values cannot be avoided during the processing, stacking, and handling of stalks, leading to the final price of 300 y/t and the price is still on the rise.

(2) Intensive system

In this system, the costs of each link are mainly paid by the stalk collection and storage companies and the factory price of stalks consists of purchasing price, storage price and transportation price. Here, we analyze the costs with Sheyang Biomass Power Generation Enterprises of CECEP as an example. Purchasing price refers to price of stalks delivered to the stalk collection and storage companies by the farmers based on the direct combustion quality standard. Stalk collection and storage companies set the prices according to the categories of stalks and the quality standards and the present purchasing price of cotton stalks is around 240 y/t. Storage price refers to the running expenses of stalk collection and storage companies include the venue rental fees, office facilities and labor costs, costs of quality checking, bundling, stacking, fireproof, rainproof and moisture-proof, necessary insurance fees, taxes, and the total reasonable profits, which is around 60 y/t. Transportation price refers to the cost transferring the collected stalks from storage sites to the power generation enterprises. Usually, the storage sites are distributed around the areas of power generation enterprises with the distance of about 10–15 km. Transportation price is around 10 y/t on average. The total fee of these above the three aspects is 310 y/t. Shown by the analysis, the purchasing cost of stalks accounts for about 77 % of the total cost, because purchasing price includes the fees of small-scale collection, drying, storage, and transportation of stalks by farmers and stalk brokers. Adopting intensive system mode, the raw material cost is stable because the factory price is set according to the contract signed by the power generation enterprises and stalk collection and storage companies. Moreover, stalk collection and storage companies own many storage sites and could ensure the long-term stable supply of stalk materials.

4.2.2.3 Current Problems of Collection and Storage of Stalks

The stalk storage and transportation system in China are still at their beginning. Though many places have established systems based on brokers or special collection and transportation companies, the foundation of such system is still on the initial stage and lacking in relative techniques and equipment. In addition, there are rarely regular and efficient collection and storage representatives. The existing problems are listed as below [31].

(1) Poor public awareness

Affected by traditional extensive farming and backward concepts, the agricultural stalks in China are usually deserted or burned. The farmers and primary-level organizations have not realized the economic values of stalks, leading to weak consciousness of selling stalks in rural areas. Besides, the purchasing price of stalks could not meet the expectations of farmers and the purchase of stalks is concentrated on the harvest time during which farmers are busy with harvest and cultivation; thus, farmers would rather abandon those stalks as wastes. Investigations also revealed that most farmers had little idea on the utilization of stalks as energy and that the situation of positive participation and supporting the resource utilization of stalks for the whole society.

(2) Backward techniques and equipment

The research of collection, storage, transportation, and pretreatment of stalks in China is very weak, lacking efficient and practical relevant equipment. On the one hand, the outdated collection technology of stalks becomes the main bottleneck of restricting the large-scale utilization of stalks. In China, the main methods for crops' harvest are either by hands or partially by machines. Thus, due to the absence of efficient harvester and packaging machine, the collection of stalks is difficult. Some of the stalks are smashed and scattered in the fields during harvest, while some other stalks harvested by hands have to be transferred by farmers, consuming lots of labor and time. On the other hand, due to the absence of efficient cutting and packaging machines, pretreated stalks present to be fluffy with low density. Under this condition, the transportation of stalks mainly relies on small tractors and agricultural vehicles, leading to small loading, poor security, and low transportation efficiency.

(3) High transportation cost and difficult to manage

Compared with developed countries, the purchasing targets of stalks in China are single farmers, making the collection, storage, and transportation more difficult and expensive and the price cannot compete with coal at the same calorific values because of small cultivation area of crops, various kinds of stalks, dispersed distribution of stalks as well as its fluffy volume and low energy density. In addition, with the increase of stalks demand, the competitive utilization ways of stalks have increased, resulting in higher price of stalks. While enterprises will expand the purchasing radius of stalks to get raw materials with the lowest price, leading to the disordered raise of operating cost. In particular in recent years, the density of some local biomass power generation enterprises has become bigger and bigger, resulting in an average purchasing radius of 100 km. Moreover, other industries such as agriculture, graziery, papermaking, and building materials are also struggling for raw materials; stalk brokers will corner stalks and raise prices, some of whom even add water or sand in stalks in order to get profits, making the collection, storage, and transportation of stalks more and more difficult.

(4) Lacking supporting systems and policies

Despite Chinese government pays much attention to the utilization of biomass resources, the supporting systems, and policies aiming at the collection, storage, and transportation of stalks are still on the way. For example, the purchasing of stalks is still disordered in market competition and the price can be randomly raised, lacking relevant regulations. Supporting policies on encouraging farmers to collect and sell stalks positively are rare, leading to the situation of "farmers burning and companies competing for stalks." Preferential policies for specific stalk transportation vehicles are absent. In addition, inadequate attention on the research of equipment as well as stalk collection and transportation has been paid besides the insufficient capital investment.

4.2.2.4 Advice on Promoting the Construction of Stalk Collection and Transportation System

(1) Setting up robust service systems

The supply of stalks has been the strong guarantee for the smooth operation of power generation enterprises; thus, it is necessary to set up a robust service system for stalk collection and transportation at first. The service system should be based on the existing autarkic economic mode in the vast countryside areas in China and make innovations on the mechanism. Taking use of the staff and sites of original collection organizations of grains and cottons to effectively organize the farmers, develop groups of stalk brokers, or set up a company, we can promote the construction of specific cooperation organization of stalk supply. In addition, through bringing the production and supply of stalk raw materials into the system, the service system can really increase the farmers' income and improve the organization extent of farmers.

(2) Reinforcing investment for research

The government should reinforce the key technologies of stalk collection and transportation and pretreatment to make breakthroughs on aspects of mechanized harvest, bundling, smashing, and packaging. Developing harvesting machines, pretreatment equipment, transportation vehicles, and supporting facilities that are fit for the small area farming situation in China, the stalk collection and transportation system will be efficient and adaptive and have potential to solve the problems of packaging, transportation and storage, bale breaking, and material breaking. The government should set up relevant standard and technical regulation to lead the large-scale use of stalks to the road of standardized development. Also, the government should set up a special fund for the collection and transportation technique and guide the self-funding of enterprises and the public for supporting the development of technologies and equipment, purchasing devices and facilities and constructing relevant systems and pilot projects.

(3) Strengthening the construction of systems and policies

In order to guarantee a steady supply of stalks, it calls for better regulations and appropriate punishment for the illegal behaviors such as burning stalks. To solve the problems of disordered competition for stalks and reckless rise of prices, stalks should be included into the management scope of farm products. The government should introduce relevant policies to regulate the price and also, it could provide subsidies to those who positively collect and sell their stalks by the standard of 20–30 y/ha. Furthermore, some policies should be introduced to include the stalk collection and storage facilities into the range of state subsidies of agricultural machinery to benefit the organizations and individual persons who are involved into the collection and storage of stalks. At the same time, the government can cancel the restriction of height and width during the transportation of cellulosic ethanol and provide appropriative green channel and reduce the road tolls to decrease the costs of raw materials.

(4) Strengthening promotion and education

Affected by the traditional life styles, people have no clear knowledge on the importance and feasibility of the utilization of stalks. Thus, it is essential to take advantage of broadcasting, television, newspaper, and network to strengthen the promotion of stalks and deepen the understanding of stalks as an important resource. In this way, we can form the thought that stalks are resources and put the utilization of stalks into our development strategy of energy.

(5) Rationally distributing the large-scale enterprises

When building the pilot enterprises for power generation, gasification, solid molding, and cellulosic ethanol production from stalks, people should arrange it scientifically based on full consideration of resource distribution, collection radius, and materials cost, in order to avoid the situation of expanding collection radius, intensifying collection strength, and rising price of raw materials.

4.2.3 Properties of Lignocellulosic Materials

4.2.3.1 Heterogeneity in Structures of Raw Materials

Plants are made up by different tissues and organs which have various functions, leading to the difference of constitution and structure of different tissues and organs.

For example, from the perspective of plant anatomy, rice straw shows different constitution and properties on different layers of structure, resulting in the heterogeneity of structure [32].

① At organ level, rice straw can be divided into leaf, sheath, knob, internode, and ear of rice, which accounts for 16–22, 36–40, 6–8, 28–32, and 4–7 % of the total mass of whole rice straw, respectively. Additionally, the proportions differ according to the varieties and origins.

② At tissue level, rice straw can be divided into vascular tissue, parenchymatous tissue, epidermal tissue, and fiber band, and these tissues have different structures and constitutions.

③ At cellular level, rice straw can be divided into fibrocytes, parenchymal cell, epidermis cell, duct cell, and sclereid. Cells with different functions show different morphologies and various locations. Epidermis cells showing protection function are distributed on the epidermis of stems and leaves, which are presented to be zigzag, blunt sawtooth with almost the same distance between two teeth. Parenchymal cells have functions of storage and nutrition, owning thin cell walls and large cell cavity. Fibrocytes with supporting and mechanical functions are distributed around the vascular bundles and subcutaneous fiber bands, showing thick cell walls, small cell cavity, and short fibers. Non-fiber cells including epidermis cell, parenchymal cells, and duct cells are called mixed cells. Generally speaking, knobs and leaves contain less fibrocytes and more mixed cells [8]. Compared with other marram grass and grass, rice straw has shorter fibers with an average length of 1 mm and width of 8 μm. The properties of rice straw fibers are listed in Table 4.4 and the relative contents of cells proportion are listed in Table 4.5.

④ At molecular level, the cell wall of dry rice straw is composed of cellulose, hemicellulose, and lignin besides some mineral substances, cutin and cork, which form a compact protection system of plants. The main compositions of rice straw are crude protein, acids, vanillic acid, coumaric acid, and ferulic acid besides cellulose, hemicellulose, and lignin. In general, the cells account for 21 % of the total mass of rice straw, 79 % cell walls (including 33 % cellulose, 26 % hemicellulose, 7 % lignin, and 13 % silicide). Compared with other fibrous materials, rice straw contains more hemicellulose and less cellulose. The lignin content in rice straw is lower than that of wood, but higher than that of cotton.

Table 4.4 Length and width of fibers in different organs of rice straw

Part	Length/mm				Width/μm				Length–width ratio
	Average	Maximum	Minimum	General	Average	Maximum	Minimum	General	
Whole plant	0.92	3.07	0.26	0.47–1.43	8.1	17.2	4.3	6.0–9.5	114
Internode	1.00	2.13	0.47	0.75–1.17	8.9	20.6	4.3	6.5–12.9	112
Sheath	0.85	2.61	0.26	0.44–1.14	8.1	12.3	4.9	5.9–9.8	105
Leaf	0.64	1.21	0.18	0.39–0.88	6.7	9.3	4.9	5.9–8.3	96
Node	0.33	0.68	0.14	0.20–0.46	9.9	14.7	4.9	7.4–13.7	33
Spike	0.58	1.38	0.18	0.29–0.88	10.1	17.2	5.9	8.3–13.7	57

Table 4.5 Composition of different types of cells in rice straw

Types of cell	Fibrocytes	Parenchyma cell	Epidermal cell	Conduct
Content (area ratio %)	45.8	46.7	1.3	6.2

4.2.3.2 Diversity of Constitutions

Cellulose, hemicellulose, and lignin are the main three constitutions of lignocellulosic materials and they have difference in properties (such as degree of polymerization, crystallinity, and branching degree) and monomers besides their contents in cells. Additionally, there are a small quantity of minerals, pectin, fat, and wax.

As shown in Table 4.6, the huge difference of constitutions of various plants results in the difference of conversion path. Among softwood, pines and cypress contain high contents of organic extracts, especially in heartwood, but the main compounds are abietic acid, terpene, fatty acids, and unsaponifiable matter. Extracts of hardwood mainly exist in ray cells and parenchymal cells, including free esterified fatty acid and neutral substances with little abietic acid (less than 1 %). Gramineae has lower content of organic extracts than wood which includes a bulk of wax without little high-grade fatty acid and alcohols. Due to the small quantity of alcohols, fewer bubbles are generated during pulping, which has small impacts on production and the recycle of waste liquor. The waxy matters in sugarcane are about 1.5–2.0 kg/t, including 66 % lipid compounds, 27 % free fatty acids, 5 % high-grade alcohol, and 2 % high-grade hydrocarbon compounds.

Generally speaking, wood contains low content of ash (less than 1 % and 0.3–0.5 % in most cases). Gramineae and barks contain higher content of ash, mostly being 2–5 % (10–15 % in rice straw). Furthermore, more than 60 % of the ash in Gramineae is SiO_2, which is different from wood.

Pectin is mainly distributed in intercellular layers acting as the bonding materials between cells. Primary walls of dicotyledons and skins of plants such as hemp, cotton, mulberry, and wingceltis also contain a lot of pectin (that is the reason for high content of ash). Softwood and grass materials contain less pectin. In general, the pectin content in monocotyledon is only 10 % of that in dicotyledons [33].

4.2.3.3 Resistance to Degradation

Lignocellulosic materials, including wood, agricultural stalks and grass, are organics formed by cellulose, hemicellulose and lignin, and a small amount of minerals, pectin, fat, and wax. Cellulose, hemicellulose, and lignin are the main three compounds in lignocelluloses. Cellulose forms the cellular skeleton in the form of microbeams. Hemicellulose and lignin are distributed around the fiber microbeams as substrate to protect cellulose from microorganisms and enzymes.

Table 4.6 Compositions of different plants [34]

Categories	Ash/%	Liquid extract/%					Cellulose/%	Hemicellulose/%	Lignin/%	Protein/%	Pectin/%
		Cold water	Hot water	Ethyl ether	Phenethyl alcohol	1 % NaOH					
Sprunce	0.78	1.42	2.68	0.37		12.43	46.92	17.48	28.43	0.62	1.32
Yeddo spruce	0.31	0.96	2.35	0.89		10.68	48.45	17.05	29.12	0.57	1.28
Poplar	0.32	1.38	2.46	0.23		15.61	43.24	23.47	17.1	0.73	1.76
Moso bamboo	1.10	2.38	5.96	0.66		30.98	45.5	21.12	30.67		0.7
Sinocalamusaffinis	1.20	2.42	6.78	0.71		31.24	44.35	25.41	31.28		0.87
Reed	2.96	2.12	10.69		0.74	31.51	43.55	22.46	25.4	3.4	0.25
Triarrhena sacchariflora	20.6	4.58	12.3		0.68	27.15	40.2	26.82	23.9	4.5	0.21
Wheat straw	6.04	5.36	23.15		0.51	44.56	40.4	25.56	22.34	2.3	0.3
Rice straw	15.5	6.85	28.5		0.65	47.7	36.2	18.06	14.05	6.04	0.21
Cornstalk	4.66	10.65	20.4		0.56	45.62	37.68	24.58	18.38	3.83	0.45
Cotton stalk	9.47	8.12	25.65		0.72	40.23	41.26	20.76	23.16	3.14	3.51

Cellulose is a polymer chain formed by D-glucose via β-1, 4-glucosidic bonds, with one reducing end and one non-reducing end of the two ends of the chain. A bulk of cellulose chains could form microcrystalline bundles of cellulose through the interactions of hydrogen bonds and VDW (Van der Waals force). Some microcrystalline bundles of cellulose can further form microfiber structure through parallel combination. Microfibers are embedded in the substrate formed by hemicellulose, lignin, and pectin, which can strengthen the mechanical strength and plays a supporting role. Due to the compact microcrystalline bundles of fibers between cellulose molecules, cellulose is steady in property and insoluble in common organic solvents, water, dilute acid, and alkali. Moreover, cellulose can hardly be hydrolyzed at normal temperature and even at high temperature the hydrolysis is slow. Only with the presence of catalysts, the hydrolysis of cellulose could be proceeded dramatically.

Hemicellulose is the general name of a series of heterogeneous polysaccharides formed by xylose, mannose, glucose, and galactose, which usually has side chains and small molecular groups such as acetyl. Hemicellulose in Gramineae and hardwood is mainly xylan formed by xylose via β-1,4-glucosidic bonds. Hemicellulose has a porous structure and the glucosidic bonds are easy to break, thus leading to the degradation of hemicellulose, especially at acid conditions. For example, hemicellulose can be hydrolyzed at 100 °C in dilute acid or hydrolyzed with enzymes. However, hemicellulose within the biomass is usually interwoven with cellulose and could not be totally hydrolyzed.

Lignin is one of the main parts constituting biomass. Though there is still not a clear understanding of the structure of lignin, it can be summarized as a netlike polymer formed by several phenylpropane units (guaiacyl propane, syringyl, and P-hydroxy phenyl propane) via ether bonds or carbon bonds. In plants, lignin is connected with hemicellulose around cellulose molecules, which strengthens the strength of cell walls and protects cellulose from being degraded. Lignin is hard to degrade and insoluble in water, but it can be dissolved slightly in acid solution at high temperature and even more in alkaline environment.

Besides, biomass contains pectin, plant oil, and minerals and all these compounds interweave with each other to form a compact structure, resulting in high tensile strength and mechanical strength as well as good resistance to degradation. Hence, large resistance should be conquered in order to break such structure and degrade or separate cellulose, hemicellulose, and lignin within it. In general, various physical, chemical, and biological methods are applied to separate cellulose, hemicellulose, and lignin in order to break the crystal structure of biomass.

4.2.3.4 Difficulty in the Separation of Structure

Different tissues have different compositions of cells and play different roles during the growth of plants; thus, there should be various conversion methods according to various values. In the present utilization of lignocellulose, usually only one part is used, so different tissues should be separated before utilization. Cells in plants are connected with each other via bonding materials in intercellular layers. Intercellular layers consist of amorphous materials such as pectin and lignin (usually lignin content is higher than that of pectin) with 0.1–0.2 μm in width. Chemical pulping is the process to remove or partly remove the intercellular layers using chemical solvents to break the bonding force between cells and thus to separate cellulose into individual cells.

During the utilization of lignin different parts have different applications and conversion methods, so it is necessary to separate these parts. But due to the matrix structure such as concrete, it is hard to separate each part.

4.2.3.5 Shrinkage and Bulking

Water plays a more important role in biomass materials than in most synthetic polymers, because almost every biomass material has abundant hydrophilic hydroxyls as well as hydrophilic groups such as amino groups and carboxyl. These hydrophilic groups result in an obvious hygroscopicity of biomass via hydrogen bonds. Therefore, biomass presents to be swelled in humid environment and shrink at dry condition with some changes in properties.

4.2.4 Utilization Status and Existing Problems of Lignocellulose

4.2.4.1 Utilization Status of Lignocellulose

For a long time, straws have been the basic resources for farmers to guarantee their life and the development of agriculture. Straws can be the raw materials for fertilizers, feedstuff, fuels, edible fungus cultivation, and pulping industry. However, traditional utilization ways are changing with the rapid development of rural economy and the increase of farmers' income. Investigations showed that straws used as fertilizers were 102 million tons, accounting for 14.78 % of the collective resources; as feedstuff 129 million tons, accounting for 18.72 %; as substrates for edible fungus 15 million tons, accounting for 2.14 %; as raw materials for pulping industry 16 million tons, accounting for 2.37 %; as wastes or being burned 215 million tons, accounting for 31.31 % [30] (Fig. 4.16). Therefore, the utilization ratio of straws is low as the raw materials for industry.

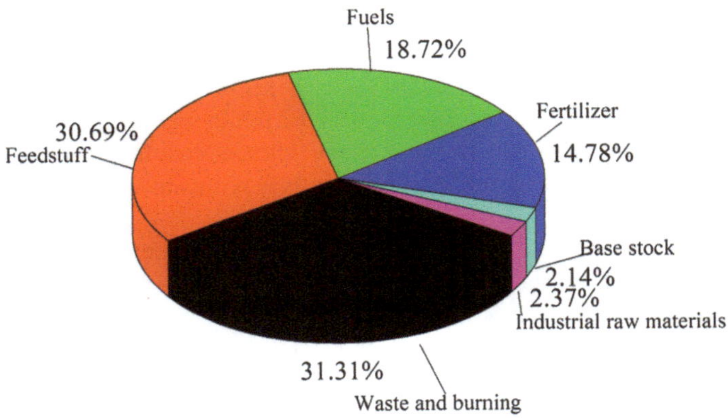

Fig. 4.16 Proportions of straws with different usages of the total collective resources

4.2.4.2 Existing Problems in the Development of Lignocellulosic Products

Faced with problems of resource shortage, energy exhaustion, environmental pollution, and grain deficiency, we have to seek for renewable resources to realize the materials' substitution and process replacement. Due to the abundance and renewability of lignocellulose, lignocellulose is a potential source to displace fossil fuels and produce biobased products for human beings. At present, utilization of lignocellulose is simply single application and the industrial utilization of lignocellulose is still at the primary level. The problems in conversion technologies of biobased products and chemicals to replace fossil fuels are as follows.

(1) Poor properties of products

Some biobased products cannot compete with oil-based products. For example, the difficulty in PHA fiber processing is that PHA has greater brittleness, poor mechanical properties, and narrow processing temperature range. If we could get breakthroughs the key technology of spinning and obtain greater improvements on cost controlling and dyeing, PHA could be the most competitive fiber with polyester fiber in the future.

(2) High manufacturing costs

In most cases, the costs of lignocellulose are higher and cannot compete with the processing technologies using hydrocarbon materials. Now the price of cellulosic ethanol is around \$0.7–1.0/L, which is 50 % higher than that of oil.

Environmentally friendly materials such as PLA and PHA belong to emerging material industries. In view of price, the price of polypropylene is lower than \$1/kg while that of the cheapest biodegradable material is \$3–6/kg and cannot compete with plastic materials obtained from oil.

High cost is caused by many factors. From the perspective of production, the large-scale industrial technologies are far from being mature and the manufacturing technology cannot meet the demands for products.

(3) Limitation of industrial products

Now there are few industrially successful products based on the biomass materials. One of the most frequently used materials is agricultural straws as pulping raw materials, mainly wheat straw. Besides, there are products such as xylose, xylitol, and man-made boards based on the cornstalks.

(4) Difficulty in development of staple products

Due to the abundance of agricultural straws, bottlenecks should be solved to develop staple products to replace oil resources and realize the industrial development and utilization of straws. At present, staple products such as energy (fuel ethanol and butanol), materials (cellulose acetate and 1, 3-propylene glycol), and chemicals (furfural, levulinic acid, xylitol, and lactic acid) cannot jump out of the trap of economy and be produced in a large quantity. For some products such as phenols, there are still no mature technologies.

(5) Immature key technologies

Biobased materials belong to emerging industries and the relevant technologies are far more from being mature. Moreover, the existing technologies do not fit for different raw materials due to the variety between materials. We suggest that key technologies such as pretreatment, biological conversion, chemical conversion, modification and esterification, and compound molding should be broken through during the process of the development of biobased materials.

(6) Backward key facilities

Development of new technologies relies much on new facilities instead of the existing ones. However, the present research of facilities is far behind the development of technologies.

(7) A lack of technologies integration

The main reason of the lack of economic feasibility in straw conversion is that only part of straw is used in practice, leading to new pollutes and a waste of resources. It should be noticed that the biomass refinery process integrates many technologies and may realize the goal of full utilization of biomass.

(8) Small scales of industrialization

Presently, researches of most biobased products are on laboratory level and there is still a long way to go for industrialization. Therefore, researchers should pay attention to the large-scale production and demonstration of important biobased materials in order to create a platform for the development of biobased materials.

4.2.5 Necessity of Lignocellulose Refinery

Biobased raw materials contain complicated components compared with oil resources; thus, the development process of biobased materials has similarities with that of oil-based materials. Generally speaking, biobased materials should be separated into several proper parts before pretreatment and then produce all the products, respectively.

Pretreatment of biomass aims to break the compositions and structure of biomass and increase the homogeneity of tissues through various physical, chemical, and biological methods and then provide better platform for the successive processing technologies, such as biological conversion, chemical conversion and separation and purification of products. Pretreatment influences the utilization of raw materials, products' properties, and production technologies directly. For saccharification and fermentation of biomass, the purpose of pretreatment is to break the structures and remove constitutes that hinder saccharification and fermentation and thus eliminating the protection of lignin. By breaking down the compact crystal structure of cellulose to improve the accessibility to enzymes, high sugar yield is got which provides enough carbon sources for fermentation. At the same time, the contents of inhibitors should be controlled in order to guarantee the efficiency of fermentation.

There are many kinds of lignocelluloses which have different constitutes and products, determining the difference of pretreatment. Moreover, due to the varieties of constitutes which has various values, pretreatment technologies should be integrated with other technologies to fully utilize each component. Therefore, during the utilization of lignocellulose, people should notice the heterogeneity of its structure and composition and choose proper methods to separate and use each part according to the structural properties and pretreatment technologies of different materials.

To conclude, it is necessary to break through the key problems of straws using as raw materials for biological and chemical industries in order to establish a new industrial mode using lignocellulosic materials as usual raw materials. People should take use of basic scientific researches, engineering practices, and the concept of circular economy to separate and utilize straws to produce biobased energy, chemicals, and materials. For raw materials, the homogeneity should be improved for structural separation and oriented conversion. For technologies and facilities, the key technologies should be broken through to improve the properties of products, decrease costs, and realize the goal of multi-production.

4.2.6 *Refinery of Lignocellulosic Materials*

4.2.6.1 Existing Problems During Refinery of Lignocellulosic Materials

(1) Heavy pollution

Traditional acid pretreatment and alkaline pretreatment will result in a large amount of waste water which will pollute the environment and cause equipment's corrosion in spite of higher enzymatic hydrolysis ratio.

(2) Single technology

In general, most pretreatment processes only use a single technology and the results are not satisfactory.

(3) Pretreatment technologies cannot meet the demand of industrial production

Some technologies developed are driven by novelty which may be applicable in laboratories but not applicable for industrial production.

(4) Poor connection with successive processing technologies

In some cases, pretreatment technologies are poorly connected with enzymatic hydrolysis and fermentation process, leading to disjunction between pretreatment and successive processing process.

Refinery of lignocellulose is the primary key technology of the production of biobased products. Refinery of lignocellulose determines the successive processing treatment of lignocellulose and even the whole development process. Therefore, researchers should strengthen the study of pretreatment technologies of lignocellulosic materials and develop relevant facilities, providing a guarantee for the industrial development of biobased products.

4.2.6.2 Pretreatment Technologies

(1) Steam explosion

Steam explosion technology is one of the most efficient technologies used in processing lignocelluloses with properties of low capital investment, low energy consumption, simple process, and high efficiency. Until now, steam explosion is widely used in industries of cellulosic ethanol, pulping, hemp degumming, ecological boards' production, and extraction of bioactive components.

Steam explosion works on materials through chemical degradation and physical tearing. During digesting, the pressure can reach 1.6 MPa with temperature of 170–200 °C. Steam can penetrate into cell spaces and cavities and generate protonic acid at high temperature to degrade hemicellulose. Meanwhile, acetyl fallen from hemicellulose would convert into acetic acid, together with other acids, acetic acid increases the acidity of the digesting environment which further promotes the degradation of hemicellulose. Besides, lignin becomes soft at high temperature and the ester bonds are easy to break, leading to the degradation of lignin. In the instantaneous discharge process, materials are exposed to the atmosphere environment and torn into slices by steam. Moreover, during cooling of materials, the cell components are rearranged, result in higher crystal degrees of cellulose. According to different purposes, parameters such as temperature, time, and moisture can be adjusted to reach different aims.

The purpose of pretreatment using lignocellulose to establish sugar platform is to increase the enzymatic hydrolysis ratio. Hence, the conditions of steam explosion can be properly more drastic to degrade cellulose and hemicellulose, increasing porosities and specific surface area of materials. At the same time, steam explosion conditions should be controlled to reduce generation of inhibitors. While in pulping industry where the complete fibrocytes are necessary, conditions of steam explosion should not be high to protect cells from being destroyed. To prevent cellulose from oxidation and degradation, Na_2SiO_3 and NaOH are added into the system to avoid oxidation and neutralize organic acids, respectively.

(2) Coupled pretreatment

① Steam explosion coupled with mechanical carding

Lignocellulosic materials, especially non-plant-fiber materials, such as straws, bamboo, and grass, have highly heterogeneous structures. For example, the stem–leaf ratio is around (5:5)–(4:6); the bark–pith ratio in stems is about 7:3; fibrocytes account for 30.8 % in cornstalks and mixed cells account for 69.2 %. Though fibrocytes and mixed cells are composed of cellulose, hemicellulose, and lignin, their morphology and structures are totally different. Fibrocytes are thin and long with small cell cavity, containing high content of cellulose and low contents of hemicellulose and lignin. Therefore, fibrocytes can be used for paper making, dissolving pulp, and laminated boards. Mixed cells especially parenchymal cells look like balls or rods with large cell cavity, containing low content of cellulose and high contents of hemicellulose and lignin. The crystallinity of cellulose and polymerization level in mixed cells is low, so cellulose in such materials is easy to expose to the environment, leading to high enzymatic hydrolysis ratio. Therefore, classification and separation are necessary during pretreatments of lignocellulosic materials as well as oriented conversion to reduce production costs and realize the aim of multi-production.

Mechanical carding is loading steam-exploded materials from one end of the machine at a certain feed rate, adjusting the rotary speed to separate fiber textures from others through the impact effect of spike teeth and the kneading effect of walls within the cylindrical shell. Fiber textures roll along the shell in the cork screw path and expel from the other end. Non-fiber textures fall onto the bottom of the shell under the action of gravity and centrifugal force and then expel from the meshes on the bottom of the shell. In this way, fiber textures and non-fiber textures are separated and collected separately.

② Steam explosion coupling with delignification

Through ethanol extraction of steam-exploded materials, lignin could be separated effectively. The delignification ratio of steam explosion coupling with ethanol extraction is higher than that of direct extraction from wheat straw. After ethanol extraction, the fibrocytes in steam-exploded wheat straw are separated, increasing the accessibility of cellulose and improving properties of enzymatic hydrolysis and fermentation.

③ Steam explosion coupling with ultrafine grinding

Separation of lignocellulose on cell level can be reached by coupling wet process of ultrafine grinding with steam explosion. With high moisture, on the basis of differences of water holding capacity and toughness between fiber textures and non-fiber textures, the fiber separation degree can reach 2.04 by grinding steam-exploded rice straw in a fluidized bed with ultrafine jet mill (the fiber separation degree of original rice straw is 1.00).

4.2.6.3 Separation of Structures and Constitutes

Establishing new ecological balance system and constructing new industrial chain at the core of "lignocellulose component separation, fractionation, and oriented conversion" is the basic solution to realizing the maximum utilization of lignocellulose and changing the deteriorating environmental situation. New techniques should be adopted in the lignocellulosic industry to solve problems such as low utilization ratio, low grade of products, high production cost, and heavy environmental pollution, which will provide a new stage for new techniques to improve traditional industries. Process industries based on natural solid organic materials are the basic industries of the nation, but they are also the root of present environmental pollution. Components separation for raw materials will guide the multi-utilization and recycling for natural materials.

Plant fiber is the basic raw material for pulping. During this process, fibrocytes are used while lignin and hemicellulose are removed according to different purposes. Therefore, during pretreatment of raw materials people should reduce damages to the fibrocytes of plants and avoid the degradation of cellulose to remove mixed cells to the limit.

For fermentation industry, sugars are the main kinds of carbon source and glucose is the most applicable one to be used by almost all microorganisms. During the process of sugar platform establishment using lignocellulosic materials, the purpose of pretreatment is to destroy the crystal structure between cellulose molecules to improve the enzymatic hydrolysis efficiency and get glucose as many as possible.

4.2.7 Process Integration of Steam Explosion Technologies

Biomass is abundant on Earth with wide varieties. The chemical compositions of different plants are not the same. For example, grains mainly contain starch; agricultural stalks mainly contain cellulose, hemicellulose, and lignin. To conclude, all biomass materials are composed of carbohydrates, lignin, lipid, and protein. Besides, there are hundreds of organic compounds with commercial values, such as medicines, nutrients, and industrial products. For instance, the active components of Chinese herbs include alkaloid, glycoside, flavonoids, terpene, organic acids, and polysaccharides; rosin and robber belong to kinds of important industrial products.

What should we do to deal with such complicated materials? The only way may be biomass refinery. With the guidance of full utilization and components separation to make use of lignocellulose by breaking the traditional concept of single utilization, we can realize the aim of refinery integration of biomass.

For example, during the process of biological conversion of straws, soluble hemicellulose can be used to produce xylooligosaccharide after steam explosion and the solid fractions can be used to obtain fiber textures and parenchymal textures through mechanical carding. Finer textures are used for papermaking, while the other components are used for fermentation. Figure 4.17 shows the path of full utilization of steam-exploded straws after mechanical carding.

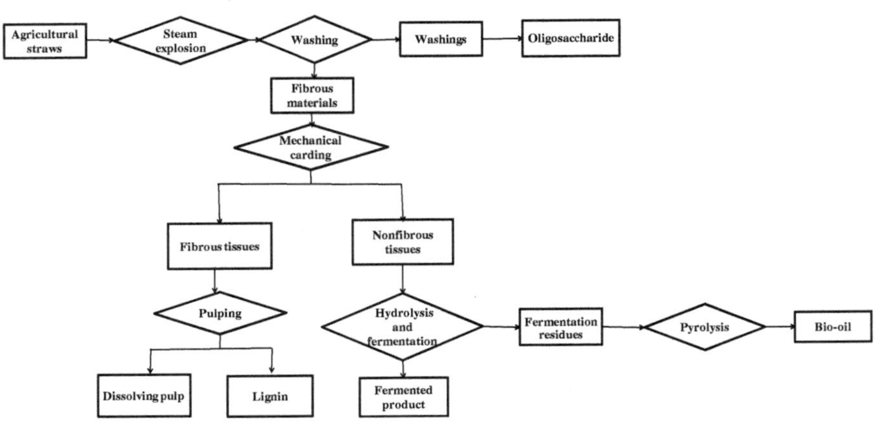

Fig. 4.17 Comprehensive utilization of straws using steam explosion

4.2.8 Examples of Ecological Development of Multi-component Solid Materials

4.2.8.1 Industrial Development of Short-Fiber Enzymatic Hydrolysis and Preparation of Renewable Cellulose from Straws

At present, renewable cellulose materials are obtained from linters and wood with dilute acid pretreatment before digesting using NaOH or sulfites to remove lignin. But the method has problems of high costs for raw materials and production, easy corrosion for facilities, and heavy pollution. China is short of forest with only 18.21 % coverage rate of forests, ranking 121 worldwide for the average forest area per person. Therefore, it is important to seek for replacements for cellulose materials and cleaner and more efficient technologies.

Steam explosion is a new pretreatment method of low cost without pollution, in which high-pressure steam enters the internal pores of materials to disperse raw materials through instantaneous discharge, resulting in materials with porous structure and high accessibility. Traditional pulping technology uses sulfites or alkali for high-temperature cooking, leading to heavy pollution and single utilization of materials. Organic solvents can dissolve lignin due to excellent solubility and volatility and then separate cellulose. Thus, such method has developed rapidly. In this method, solvents can be recycled through evaporation; meanwhile, a series of by-products are obtained, which realizes economic and environmentally friendly utilization.

The authors studied the process to wash steam-exploded wheat straw by DI water to recycle soluble hemicellulose and then extracted lignin using ethanol. Proper methods were adopted to obtain cellulose from residues. Then, the separated cellulose was dissolved into ion liquid [bmim]Cl and NaOH solution to get cellulose film through regeneration. Recycled lignin and hemicellulose could also be used after successive treatments, realizing clean separation and application of wheat straw.

(1) Technological process

Due to properties of long fibers, high-yield pulping, and excellent quality, *Pennisetum hybridum* was used to produce high-quality pulping. *Pennisetum hybridum* is adaptable to various environments and has a high productivity. As reported, the absolute dry yield of renewable *Pennisetum hybridum* can reach 7 t/mu[1] of land, 2–3 folds more than that of fast-growing woods. The technological process of overall utilization of *Pennisetum hybridum* is described in Fig. 4.18.

---

[1] 1 μ = 666.7 m^2.

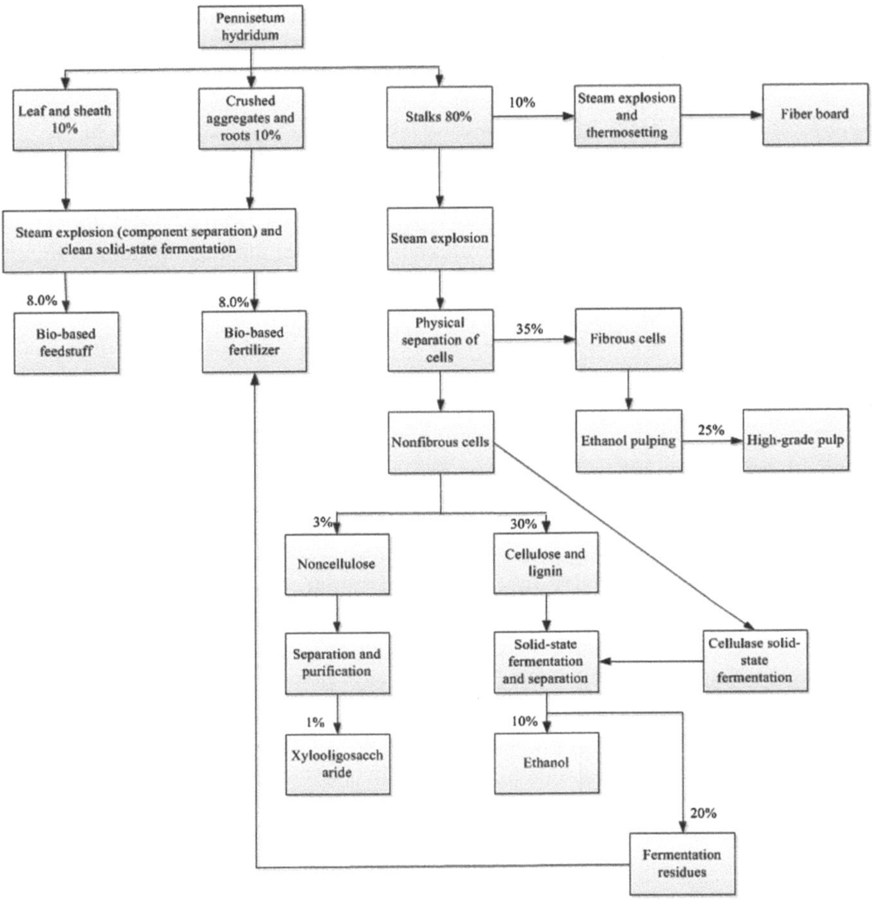

Fig. 4.18 Flowchart of the comprehensive utilization of *Pennisetum hybridum* using steam explosion

(2) Proof for the project feasibility

① Consistent with policy

First, the project has centralized the high-tech achievements of CAS and superior resources in Liu An City to produce ethanol to replace fossil fuels. Second, using *Pennisetum hybridum* to produce pulping will save amounts of forests, which is consistent with the sustainable development policy. Third, the utilization of plants resources meets the demand of circular development. Forth, developing in-depth processing industry based on *Pennisetum hybridum* can connect farmers with enterprises and increase the income of farmers. Fifth, relying on high technology to establish a company of renewable resource processing can drive the economic development in developing areas. Thus, the project will lead to huge economic profit as well as social benefits.

② Large market demand

Investigations show that the demand of products in this project such as high-quality pulping, fuel ethanol, and organic fertilizer exceeds supply with a big market gap. Besides, the production technology is advanced and the costs of raw materials and processing are low, so the products are competitive.

③ Scientific design and reliable technology

The technical route in this project is designed based on thousands of experiments, with consideration of advancement and maturity of technology. Thus, the technical route has good applicability. In the project, *Pennisetum hybridum* is steam exploded and extracted with DI water, while the steam-exploded materials after water extraction are cooked in ethanol and then the digestion residues are blanched using H_2O_2 to get pulping with whiteness higher than 60 %. During water extraction, xylooligosaccharide is purified and ethanol is produced through fermentation with organic fertilizer as the by-products. Due to full utilization of biomass, benefits of this project are improved and the costs are reduced.

④ Excellent economic benefits

The project can bring about obvious economic benefits besides social and ecological benefits, with 2.04 billion yuan output value including 490.64 million yuan of tax and 557.68 million yuan of net profit. The project also has properties of short investment scale (which will be 1 times more using traditional technology), short collecting cycles and high reward rate and the project owns high ability of repaying. Meanwhile, it has high antirisk capacity and thus resulting in excellent economic profits.

⑤ Obvious social benefits

The project can better help farmers get rid of poverty and become rich. In this project, 800,000 t *Pennisetum hybridum* are needed which will take up 250,000 hectares of arable land with 32 t *Pennisetum hybridum* produced from each hectare. Compared with planting maize and rice, the profits can increase 8000 yuan/h and the total input increase is 0.2 billion yuan. Generally speaking, the income increase of each farmer will be 400 yuan based on the population of 500,000. Therefore, the implement of this project will bring about huge social benefits.

Besides, 700,000 m^3 woods are saved every year using *Pennisetum hybridum* to produce high-grade pulping, which makes huge contribution to the ecological construction. At the same time, *Pennisetum hybridum* itself is a kind of superior plants that can greatly improve the ecological system. Hence, projects that produce fuel ethanol using cellulosic materials and produce high-grade pulping through a clean technical path can play the part of demonstration role for the peer industry.

4.2.8.2 Pulping Preparation with Lignin, Biogas, and Feedstuff Using Cornstalk

(1) Characteristics of cornstalks

The maize yield ranks third worldwide with annual yield of 0.79 billion tons, of which the annual yield of maize in China is 0.264 billion tons, only ranking second to the USA. In China, cornstalk yield takes up 32.3 % of the total agricultural stalks. Thus, it is obvious that cornstalk resource is abundant and the stems can be used for wine-making, artificial board production and papermaking. However, the vast majority of cornstalks are deserted except for only a tiny proportion that is used as feedstuff.

Cornstalks are relatively thick in the grass family, with obvious knobs internodes, length of 0.8–3 m and diameter of 2–4.5 cm. The dry weight of cornstalks can be 400–500 kg/μ. Cornstalk consists of leaf and stem including cortex and pith. One feature of cornstalk is that there are amounts of pith within the stems. Table 4.7 shows the contents of leaf, cortex, and pith of cornstalks.

Cornstalks have various nutritive values at different stages, and Table 4.8 demonstrates the nutritive analysis of each part of cornstalks at mature stage. Implied by Table 4.8, leaf contains the highest content of crude protein in cornstalk at mature stage, followed by tassel and stem, and bract has the lowest content of crude protein; leaf also contains the highest content of crude fat, while tassel has the lowest content. According to their nutritive values, parts of cornstalks can be sorted as leaf, tassel, stem, and bract. Besides, the proportion of cortex in stem is 64.8 % while pith 35.2 %.

Crude protein is the least part in stalk (2–4 %) and the amino composition is not balanced; thus, the nutritive value of stalk is low as feedstuff for ruminants. Fiber protein feedstuff obtained from fermentation of cornstalks via *Chaetomium cellulolyticum* can be used as the source of crude protein to feed rabbits and mice. Analysis of toxicology and nutritional values shows that cornstalks are safe as feedstuff after fermentation; moreover, the crude protein is easy to digest and the residual fibers are hard to digest; thus, it can displace part of crude proteins for ruminants.

Leaf (leaf and leaf sheath) takes up 40 % of the total mass of cornstalks containing 30 % fibers. Leaf has properties of small thickness and big specific surface area with smooth wax layer. Leaf can be smashed into powder due to low mechanical strength. Hence, it is not proper to produce artificial boards and pulping.

Table 4.7 Contents and properties of different parts of corn stover

Items	Leaf	Cortex	Pith	Others
Density/g/cm^3	0.23	0.39	0.045	
Cellulose/%	30	50	20	
Weight ratio/%	40	35	15	10
Volume ratio/%	47.5	29.7	22.9	

Table 4.8 Nutrition analysis of different parts of mature spring corn stover

Parts	Dry matter	Crude protein	Crude fat	Crude fiber	Ash	NFE[a]	Total energy (MJ/kg)	Ratio in whole plant
Tassel	90.43	4.24	0.62	30.60	9.23	45.74	13.79	1.80
Leaf	90.70	4.67	1.25	24.93	11.60	48.25	14.00	25.54
Stem stalk	90.89	4.20	0.81	34.32	4.28	47.28	14.04	52.77
Stem cortex	92.54	3.01	0.75	38.16	5.60	45.02	16.75	34.20
Stem pith	92.80	3.54	0.78	31.12	6.00	51.36	15.93	18.57
Bract	90.33	2.75	0.91	31.98	2.74	51.95	15.01	19.87

[a] Nitrogen-free extract

There are no obvious differences for leaf using as feedstuff compared with stalks and furthermore, some nutritive indicators are higher than stalks.

Pith takes up 15 % of the total mass of stalks containing 20 % fibers. Pith consists of parenchymal tissues and the vascular bundles inside of the tissues; thus, it is fluffy with low density, strong hygroscopicity, and low mechanical strength. Leaf and pith take up over 55 % of the total mass of stalks, which are not fit for production of artificial boards and paper. But they are fluffy and soft and are fit for preparation of package materials for the packaging of vegetables, eggs, ceramics, and glass.

The cortex of cornstalks is the part with the highest mechanical strength which is about 0.04 mm thick, accounting for 35 % of the total mass of stalks containing 50 % fibers. Moreover, the fibers within the cortex are as good as that in sugarcane and cotton stalks which are fit for producing artificial boards and paper. For example, the main indicators of flakeboards made by the cortex of cornstalks can meet the requirements for A-level by the national standard. The problem is that cortex is just a small part of cornstalks, so it will be a waste of resource to only use cortex and desert the other parts.

The fiber within the cornstalks is generally 520–1550 μm in length, owning two sharpened ends and obvious knob lines and not that many pits on cell walls. The determination of cornstalk fibers is shown in Tables 4.9, 4.10, and 4.11. Comparison of fiber morphology between cornstalks and other plants is listed in Table 4.12. From Table 4.12, we can see that fibers of cornstalks are superior to that of other grasses and can be used to produce high-grade pulping.

(2) Integrated refinery technology of cornstalks

The proportion of stem, leaf, pith, and bract in cornstalks is about 35:40:15:10 and the chemical compositions and physical properties of different parts differ from each other, which is caused by the differences of cell compositions of various parts. Therefore, integrated refinery of cornstalks is necessary to realize the aim of

Table 4.9 Length of the stem fiber of corn stover determined by Kajaani method

	Average length/mm			Length distribution ratio/% (mass ratio)									
	Average	Weight-average	Double weight-average	0.00–0.40	0.40–0.60	0.60–0.80	0.80–1.00	1.00–1.20	1.20–1.40	1.40–1.60	1.60–1.80	1.80–2.00	2.00 above
Stalk	0.61	1.08	1.54	13.6	13.0	14.4	13.8	12.3	9.3	7.0	4.9	3.5	8.2

Table 4.10 Length and width of the stem fiber of corn stover determined by a projector

	Length/mm				Width/μm				Length–width ratio
	Average	Maximum	Minimum	General	Average	Maximum	Minimum	General	
Stalk	1.36	2.80	0.40	0.70–2.00	15.1	29.6	7.20	10.0–20.0	90

Table 4.11 Wall thickness and lumen diameter of stem fiber of corn stover determined by optical microscope

		Average/ μm	Maximum/ μm	Minimum/ μm	General/ μm	Wall–lumen ratio
Stalk	Wall thickness	3.0	3.9	2.0	2.7–3.5	0.34
	Lumen diameter	17.5	20.5	12.3	13.8–18.8	

Table 4.12 Morphology comparison of the fiber of corn stover and other plants

Raw material	Fiber length/mm	Fiber width/μm	Length–width ratio
Cortex of cornstalk	1.6	10.67	156
Leaf of cornstalk	1.28	13	98
Wheat straw	1.32	12.9	102
Bagasse	1.7	22.5	75.5
Cotton stalk	1.01	22.2	46.4
Rice straw	0.92	8.1	114
White brich	1.21	18.7	65

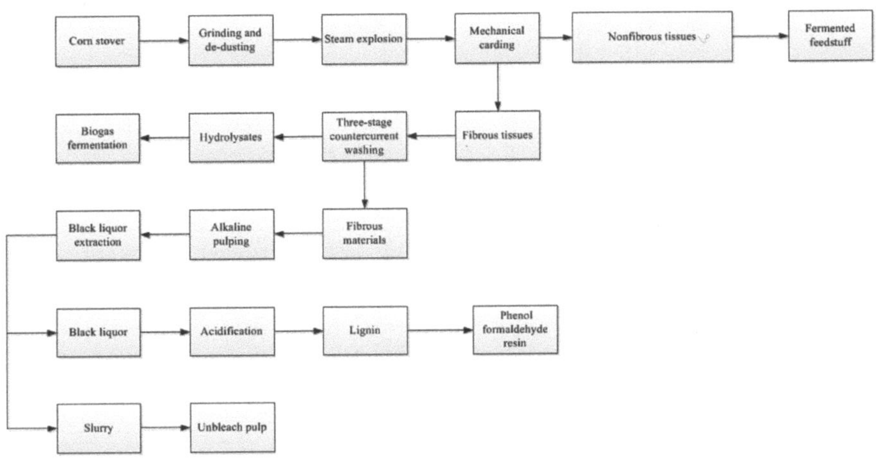

Fig. 4.19 Refinery of corn stover

high-value utilization which can overcome the structural heterogeneity of cornstalks for multiple usages. Figure 4.19 demonstrates the multiple usages of cornstalks.

Technical characteristics of integrated refinery technology:

① Steam explosion degrades almost 70 % of hemicellulose and makes the tissues fluffy, which is fit for successive tissue separation and alkaline pulping technology.

② Three-stage countercurrent washing technology can recycle sugars from hemicellulose degradation and reduce the consumption of chemicals during pulping.
③ Mechanical carding can separate parts that are rich in fibers and parts without fibers, improving the homogeneity of tissues.
④ Coproduction of pulping, lignin, biogas, and feedstuff realizes the integrated utilization of cornstalks, which is favorable to reducing pollution and increasing profits.

4.2.8.3 Coupled Technology of Steam Explosion and Degumming of Hemp Fibers

In recent years, the integrated utilization of hemp fibers has got breakthroughs due to the unique properties of hemp and its products. Hemp fibers become cottonized through steam explosion, which can displace cottons to produce yarn; during such process, the by-products can be used for circular economy. In Liu An City, hemp has great superiority. Professors from Institute of Processing Engineering (IPE) have applied for more than 10 national patents based on steam explosion technology to deeply develop hemp resources. It will undoubtedly bring about huge economic and social benefits combining high-tech advantages of IPE and abundant hemp resources in Liu An City. Moreover, the deep utilization and development of hemp resources accord to the national policies.

Cellulose and lignin can be partly degraded through instantaneous depressurization during steam explosion and the hydrogen bonds within the cellulose can be rearranged to form materials with new properties. The basic technical path is as follows: the collected raw hemps are steam exploded to separate hide fibers and stalk fibers; then, the hide fibers are ready for successive treatment after water extraction and the pectin and oligosaccharides in hydrolysates are extracted; stalk fibers and hemp cortex are under secondary steam explosion to produce fiber boards and organic compound fertilizers. In this way, 5 kinds of products are obtained using high-tech methods without any addition of chemicals and pollution release.

Figure 4.20 shows the technical path of hemp-integrated utilization technology.

(1) Preparation of ecological fiber board from hemp stems using steam explosion

China is a country with low forest coverage and short of wood materials. Thus, how to promote the comprehensive utilization of stalks has become a significant problem involving resource utilization and environmental protection. The overall utilization of stalks help farmers solve their problems of wastes disposal, leading to new kinds of products in building material industry and decoration industry. Also, the results can make contributions to the environmental protection and aviation safety.

At present, certain amount of thermosetting resins and formaldehyde is needed when using stalks to produce wall materials, green fiber boards, green inner package materials, disposable tableware, and green plant grower. Under such

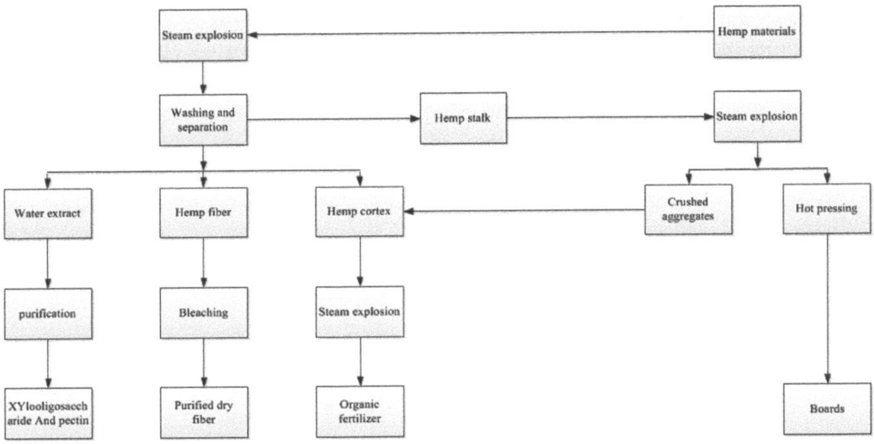

Fig. 4.20 Flowchart of the comprehensive development of hemp fibers

condition, the cost percentage of gum materials has risen to 60 %, making it harder to compete with plastics and other decoration materials from techno-economic perspective; furthermore, much pollution is caused due to such technology. Therefore, it is attractive to produce environmentally friendly materials using hemp on aspects of economy and environment. The absence of sizing materials in the technology of environmentally friendly materials simplifies the production process, avoids glue mixing process and the related equipment, and reduces production cost, and the products are degradable in nature.

Prof. Chen proposed the concept of modified stalks and developed a novel technology to produce environmentally friendly materials using modified stalks, based on the similarities and differences on chemical compositions and structures of stalks and wood. The structure and properties of stalks are changed through series of physical, biological, and chemical methods to produce modified stalks. Hemicellulose and lignin are degraded, while the hydrogen bonds within the cellulose are rearranged to prepare stalk materials with new properties, which can be used to produce various products. For example, during steam explosion the active groups in lignin dramatically increase, leading to similar properties of polyphenols, which can be used as natural adhesives; hemicellulose can be degraded into soluble sugars, dehydrated sugars, and furfural, which can replace formaldehyde to react with lignin. Cellulose itself is not degraded during steam explosion and conversely, its crystallinity increases. During thermosetting, certain amounts of water molecules have strong capacity to destroy and generate hydrogen bonds and destroy the compact and ordered structure of cellulose to make cellulose redistribute. Taking advantage of such phenomenon, wasted hemp fibers can be made into fiber boards through separation and carding after steam explosion, which can intensify the economic profits and reduce environmental pollution.

With development of technologies on modified stalks and the growth of awareness of environmental protection, application fields of modified stalks will be broader, showing great potential as a new industry. At the same time, using modified stalks to replace wood and plastics would save lots of forestry resources and remove the plastic pollution. Also, the air pollution caused by burning of stalks can be avoided, which provides new opportunity and growth points for the formation of high-efficient agriculture and the integrated development of city and countryside as well as industries and agriculture.

(2) Recycling of xylooligosaccharide and pectin from hemp fibers using steam explosion

Due to the unique physiological functions, active xylooligosaccharide has attracted wide attention from both scholars and entrepreneurs, especially on the aspect of development of bifidus growth factor. As a potential alternative for bifidus growth factor, active xylooligosaccharide has properties of oxygen and acid tolerance, low production cost, not easy to be deactivated and can be taken together with antibiotics. Xylan in stalks are degraded and separated through steam explosion pretreatment, resulting in plenty of monosaccharides and xylooligosaccharides with low molecules. Then, the xylooligosaccharides are separated from dissoluble cellulose and lignin by extraction. The obtained xylooligosaccharides are purified by chromatographic separation and condensed to get xylooligosaccharides with 70 % purity, which presents superior properties compared with fellow domestic products.

The method has advantages of simple processing technology, no pollution, cheap raw materials, low production cost, and high products yields compared with present production methods of xylooligosaccharides (enzymatic production). Furthermore, equipment involved in this method contains mainly steam explosion tank, chromatographic separation system and enrichment facility; thus, the production conditions are much easier to form large-scale industrial production.

In this method, pectin is separated from hemp fiber through steam explosion and extracted by following the same technology as used in xylooligosaccharides extraction.

(3) Organic fertilizer production from solid residues of steam explosion process

At present, the main raw materials to produce organic fertilizer are peat, crullers, and municipal wastes which are limited by producing areas and storage conditions, hindering the large-scale production. Some technologies to produce organic fertilizer from stalks are not so efficient to get high manorial effects, such as simple smashing. Another technology to get organic fertilizer from stalks is to adopt steam explosion pretreatment and the pretreated stalks are compounded with mineral fertilizer after natural retting, during which the sugars are wasted and lead to environmental pollution. Furthermore, the conversion efficiency of organic matter is low and the stalks play the sole role of carrier. In addition, the main manorial effects come from the mineral fertilizer; thus, the effects of stalks are not fully exploited, limiting the promotion of organic production from stalks.

Based on the shortage of the existing technology, Prof. Chen developed a novel technology to produce organic-mixed fertilizer using hemp wastes as the main raw materials. In this technology, hemps are pretreated with ammoniation processing after steam explosion. As a result, the natural structure of hemps is destroyed, hemicellulose is degraded, and humic acid substances are generated through reactions of lignin and ammonia. Finally, the natural fermentation products are dried and smashed to produce ecological organic fertilizer.

References

1. Chen HZ, Liu LY. Unpolluted fractionation of wheat straw by steam explosion and ethanol extraction. Bioresour Technol. 2007;98(3):666–76. doi:10.1016/j.biortech.2006.02.029.
2. Ballesteros I, Oliva J, Negro M. Enzymatic hydrolysis of steam exploded herbaceous agricultural waste (*Brassica carinata*) at different particle sizes. Process Chem. 2002;38 (2):187–92. doi:10.1016/S0032-9592(02)00070-5.
3. Fein J, Potts D, Good D. Development of an optimal wood-to-fuel ethanol process utilizing best available technology. Energ Biomass Waste. 1991;15:745–65.
4. Ropars M, Marchal R, Pourquie J, Vandecasteele J. Large-scale enzymatic hydrolysis of agricultural lignocelluloseic biomass. Part 1: Pretreatment procedures. Bioresour Technol. 1992;42(3):197–204.
5. Kessler R, Becker U, Kohler R, Goth B. Steam explosion of flax—a superior technique for upgrading fiber value. Biomass Bioenerg. 1998;14(3):237–49. doi:10.1016/S0961-9534(97) 10040-X.
6. Kokta BV, Ahmed A. Steam explosion pulping. In: Environmentally friendly technologies for the pulp and paper industry. New York: Wiley; 1998.
7. State of play in the biorefining industry. http://www.carbolea.ul.ie/persondetail.php?name=dhayes
8. Chen HZ, Qiu WH. Key technologies for bioethanol production from lignocellulose. Biotechnol Adv. 2010;28(5):556–62. doi:10.1016/j.biotechadv.2010.05.005.
9. Kling S, Neto CC, Ferrara M. Enhancement of enzymatic hydrolysis of sugar cane bagasse by steam explosion pretreatment. Biotechnol Bioeng. 1987;29(8):1035–9. doi:10.1002/bit.260290815.
10. Chen HZ, Yuan YT. A method to extract ephedrine using air-steam-coupling steam explosion. China Patent. 2006;200410090699:1.
11. Chen HZ, Fu XG. A wall-breaking method for pollens using air-steam-coupling steam explosion. China Patent. 2011;201110034102:1.
12. Bender R. Method of treating lignocellulose materials to produce ruminant feed. United States: 4136207. 1979.
13. Zheng Y, Lin HM, Tsao GT. Pretreatment for cellulose hydrolysis by carbon dioxide explosion. Biotechnol Progr. 2008;14(6):890–6. doi:10.1021/bp980087g.
14. Óconnor JJ. Exploding of ammonia impregnated wood chips. United States: 3707436. 1972.
15. Li HQ, Chen HZ. Detoxification of steam-exploded corn straw produced by an industrial-scale reactor. Process Biochem. 2008;43(12):1447–52. doi:10.1016/j.procbio.2008.05.003.
16. Foody P. Method for increasing the accessibility of cellulose in lignocelluloseic materials, particularly hardwood agricultural residues and the like. United States: 4461648. 1984.
17. Johnson T, Johnson B, Scott-Kerr C. Bioethanol-status report on bioethanol production from wood and other lignocellulosic feedstocks. 63rd Appita Annual Conference and Exhibition, Melbourne, pp. 3–11. 2009.

18. Yu E, Taylor J. Industrial scale testing of continuous high yield explosion pulping of aspen. New York: Tappi Press; 1992.
19. Kokta B. Process for preparing pulp for paper making. United States: 4798051. 1989.
20. Avella R, Scoditti E. The Italian steam explosion program at ENEA. Biomass Bioenerg. 1998;14(3):289–93. doi:10.1016/S0961-9534(97)10041-1.
21. Continuous Steam Explosion Pulping: Process Optimization For Non-Woody Fibers. http://www.tappi.org/Downloads/unsorted/UNTITLED-pulp97161pdf.aspx.
22. Plug Screw ADI. http://www.fischer-tropsch.org/DOE/DOE_reports/40904/40904-fr/6-%20%2087%20-%2091,%2040904-fr,%206.01.pdf.
23. Chen HZ, Liu J, Li ZH. A non-pollution method for pulping preparation from straw materials using steam explosion. China Patent. 99111449.3. 2001.
24. Chen HZ, Li ZH. Non-pollution steam explosion technology and application. Cellulose Sci Technol. 2002;10(3): 47–52. No. 1004-8405 (2002) 03-0047-06.
25. Chen HZ, Liu LY. Unpolluted fractionation of wheat straw by steam explosion and ethanol extraction. Bioresour Technol. 2007;98(3):666–76. doi:10.1016/j.biortech.2006.02.029.
26. Chen HZ, Zhang YZ. In-situ steam explosion and apparatus. China Patent. 201110068899.7. 2011.
27. Zhang YZ, Fu XG, Chen HZ. Pretreatment based on two-step steam explosion combined with an intermediate separation of fiber cells-Optimization of fermentation of corn straw hydrolysates. Bioresour Technol. 2012;121:100–4. doi:10.1016/j.biortech.2012.07.006.
28. Chen HZ, Li HQ, Liu LY. The inhomogeneity of corn stover and its effects on bioconversion. Biomass Bioenerg. 2011;35(5):1940–5. doi:10.1016/j.biombioe.2011.01.037.
29. Jin SY, Chen HZ. Fractionation of fibrous fraction from steam-exploded rice straw. Process Biochem. 2007;42(2):188–92. doi:10.1016/j.procbio.2006.07.030.
30. Investigation and Report of argo-straw resources. Science and Technology Department of Agriculture Ministry, Beijing. 2010.
31. Zhang YL, Wang F, Zhao LX. Operating mode, existing problems and development of straw collection and storage system in China. Renew Energ. 2009;27(1): 1–5. No. 1671-5292(2009) 01-0001-05.
32. Chen HZ. Eco-biochemical engineering. Beijing: Chemical Industry Press; 2008.
33. Yang SH. Chemistry of plants fiber. Beijing: China Light Industry Press; 2008.
34. Pulp and Paper Manual Part 1: Cellulosic materials and chemical materials. China Light Industry Press, Beijing; 1987.

Chapter 5
Characterization and Research Methods of Gas-Exploded Materials

5.1 Structural Morphology Characterization of Gas-Exploded Materials

5.1.1 *Length Measurement of Fibrocytes*

The cell length, cell wall thickness, and lumen diameter are the main characteristics of cellulose materials. Different products, such as paper, panel, and fuels, call for different length conditions of fibrocytes. Furthermore, during biomass refinery process, fibers are about to change through various physical or chemical treatments, which will affect the properties. Thus, it is necessary to analyze the cell length of fibrocytes in this part.

Due to the non-uniformity of cell length of the fibrocytes, the mathematic average values of cell length cannot fully reflect the detailed condition of fibrocytes. Therefore, besides the mathematic average values, other indicators are also needed, such as average fibrocyte cell length, minimum fibrocyte cell length, general fibrocyte cell length, and distribution frequency, to illustrate the information of fibrocytes.

The method GB/T 10336-1989 is usually adopted to determine the cell length of paper fibers, in which optical microscope and projector are used and the main procedure is as follow: emptying air → softening → slicing → dyeing → mounting → determination [1]. At present, fibrocytes can be separated using this method, and the cell length can be determined by a granulometer with photomicrography. One thing to notice, relatively low magnification should be adopted to observe the whole fibrocyte because the fibrocytes in many lignocellulosic materials are rather long in length. For example, not so many cornstalk fibrocytes are observed under magnification of 40× using OLYMPUS BX41. KajaaniFS300 made in Finland can be used to determine the cell length and width of fibers, which is widely used in paper industry to determine the length, roughness, bending deflection, torsion, and duct cells of fibers.

H. Chen, *Gas Explosion Technology and Biomass Refinery*,
DOI 10.1007/978-94-017-7414-7_5

5.1.2 Research of Fiber Roughness and Weight Factor

When materials are made from cellulosic biomass, the fiber roughness will affect the product properties, which is also influenced by the refinery technology.

Fiber roughness refers to the weight of 100-m fiber of absolute dry weight, indicated by decigrex (dg) [2]. Fiber roughness is related to the raw material density, cell wall thickness, cavity size, and cooking degree and can reflect all the factors synthetically.

All methods to determine the fiber roughness have something in common: A certain proportion of water is added into the fibers to make fiber suspension or fiber plate, and then, the fiber suspension is determined to calculate the total length of fibrocytes in the determined fiber suspension. At last, the weight of 100 m fiber of absolute dry weight is calculated.

The number of fibrocytes per milligram is related to cell length, cell width, cell wall thickness of fibrocytes, the fractions of cells, and fiber debris as well as the refinery technology. In practice, the number can be calculated with Kajaani to determine the number of fibrocytes.

The weight of fiber per unit length is defined as weight factor, also called mass factor [3]. Different materials have different weight factors. In paper industry, the weight factor of cotton pulp is defined as 1 and the weight factors of other materials are calculated by dividing the fiber roughness value of cotton pulp using their respective fiber roughness values.

Other determination methods are referred to the book *Handbook of pulp and paper* and *Experiment of pulp and paper.*

5.1.3 Microscope Characterization

Observation of the tissues and cell structures of lignocellulosic materials is the basis to determine the conditions of steam explosion pretreatment and analyze the performance of steam explosion. Thus, learning about the plant tissues is an important part of phytotomy. For example, to learn about the corn stem, we should observe the crosscutting producer through an optical microscope, analyze the stem epidermis, elementary tissues, and vascular bundles at low magnification, and further observe the vascular bundle sheath, phloem, and xylem within the vascular bundles.

According to the retention time, sectioning can be divided into two types [1].

① Temporary sectioning: Films made through this method are used for temporary observation and do not need long-term persistence (such as temporary slide, freehand section, frozen section, and timber section).

② Permanent sectioning: Films made through this method can be preserved permanently (such as paraffin section, semithin section, freehand section, timber section, and ultrathin section).

The main categories for plant sectioning technology are microtomy (freehand sectioning, paraffin sectioning, semithin sectioning, frozen sectioning, vibration sectioning, sliding sectioning, and ultrathin sectioning) and non-microtomy (segregation process, smear, squashing, and SEM preparation).

To know the anatomical structure of gas-exploded materials, freehand sectioning method is usually adopted, and through different methods such as crosscutting, rip cutting, and beveling, researchers can learn about the anatomical structures of different organs and different parts. For gas-exploded materials with high content of starch, especially with many starch granules, researchers can directly observe the starch granules by smashing the materials; but freehand sectioning should also be adopted to observe other structures such as epidermis. The general steps of sectioning are as follows: sampling → fixation → rinsing → dyeing → dehydration → clearing → mounting. Figure 5.1 shows the transverse sections of cornstalk pith. Figures 5.2 and 5.3 show the distribution of different components in cell wall by dyeing.

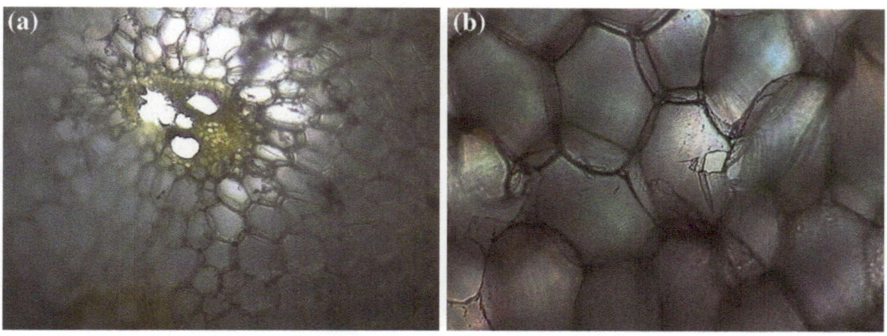

Fig. 5.1 Crosscutting views of the corn stover pith (**a** 40×; **b** 100×)

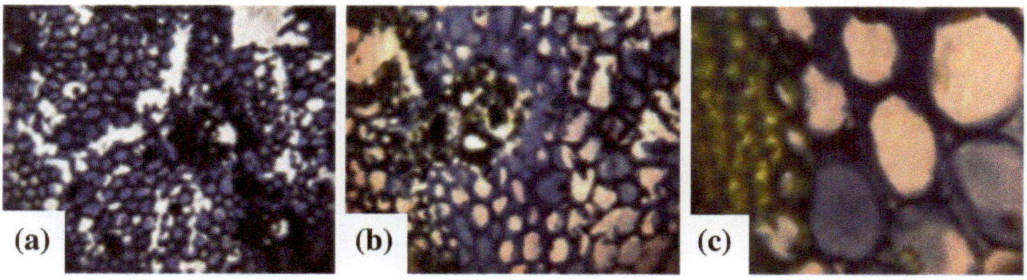

Fig. 5.2 Cellulose distribution of the cross section of corn stover (**a** 40×; **b** 100×) [4]

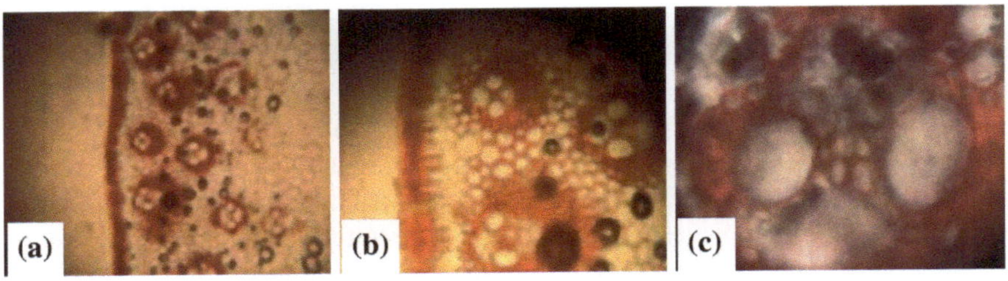

Fig. 5.3 Lignin distribution of the cross section of corn stover (**a** 40×; **b** 100×; **c** 400×) [5]

5.1.4 Scanning Electron Microscopy (SEM) Characterization

During steam explosion, destruction is caused by the tearing effects on different levels of the cell which can be observed via microscope. In general, optical microscope and electron microscope are used to observe the changes of cellulosic materials at cellular or sub-cellular levels. But the destruction at cell wall level should be observed using high-power SEM which can show a stereoscopic graph that will help recognize the changes of ducts and fibrocytes before and after steam explosion.

The thickness of cell wall is around 10 μm, while the resolution of electron microscope can reach 0.2 nm. Thus, SEM can clearly show the changes of materials at cell wall level before and after steam explosion. Figure 5.4 shows the SEM graphs of cornstalk after hydrothermal process.

5.1.5 Transmission Electron Microscope (TEM)

The trend of fibers on secondary wall of cell wall affects the biomechanical strength, which will further influence the selection of steam explosion intensity; hence, observation of the trend of fibers at cell wall level is necessary. In paper industry

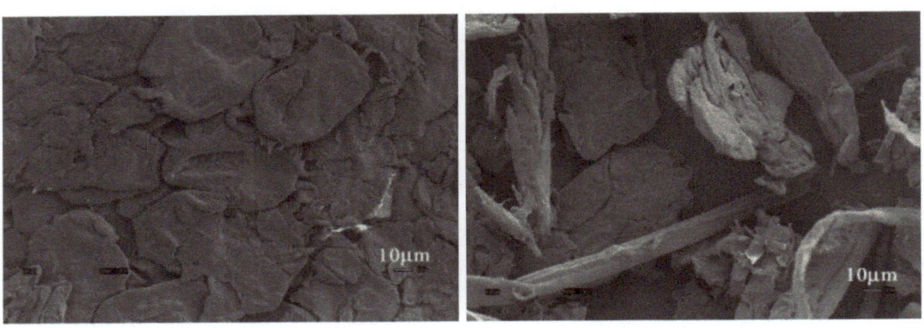

Fig. 5.4 SEM spectra of corn stover after hydrothermal treatment [5]

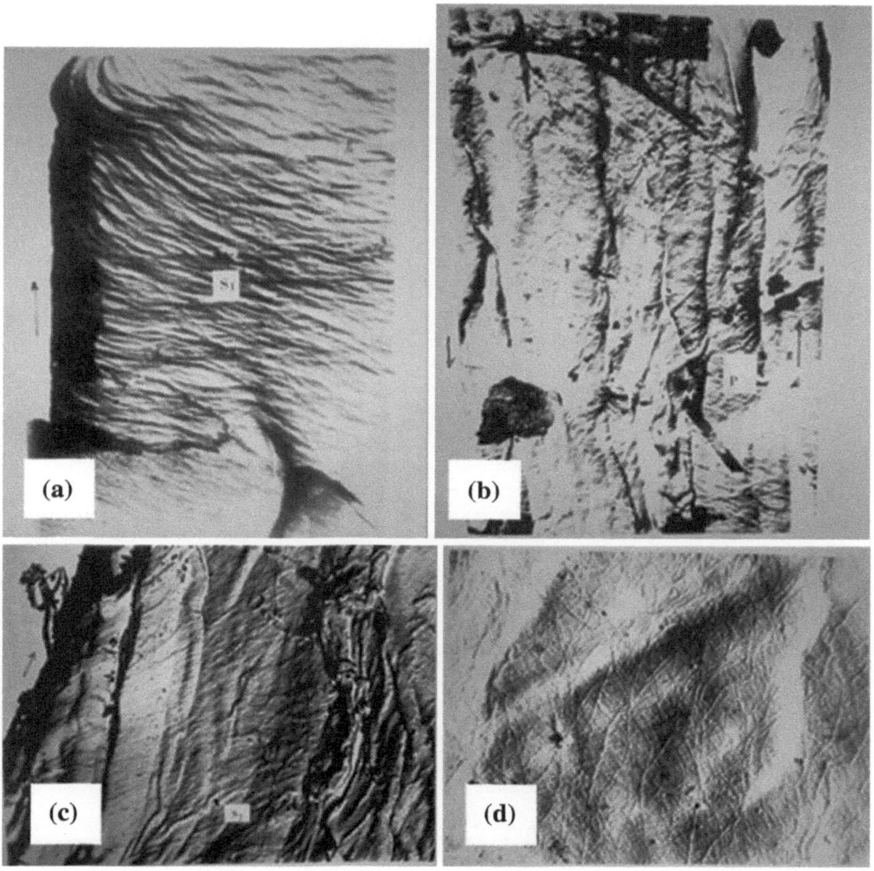

Fig. 5.5 TEM spectra of different raw materials [6]. **a**. Microfibrils in S1 layer of Yeddo spruce are horizontally arranged, 25,000×. **b** Arrangement of *P*-type microfibrils on the primary cell wall of reed fiber, 9000×. **c** Orientation of the microfibrils in S_2 layer of reed secondary cell wall, 6000×. **d** Neticular microfibrils on the primary cell wall of reed parenchyma cell, 15,000×

[6], the trend of fibers is usually observed using TEM that is also suitable for the observation of the distribution of microfibril in fibrocytes of materials. Figure 5.5 clearly demonstrates the TEM graphs of various raw materials.

5.1.6 Atomic Force Microscopy (AFM)

In order to observe the structural changes of gas-exploded materials more clearly, AFM with higher resolution can be adopted whose lateral resolution reaches 0.15 nm and longitudinal resolution reaches 0.05 nm [7]. Figures 5.6 and 5.7 show

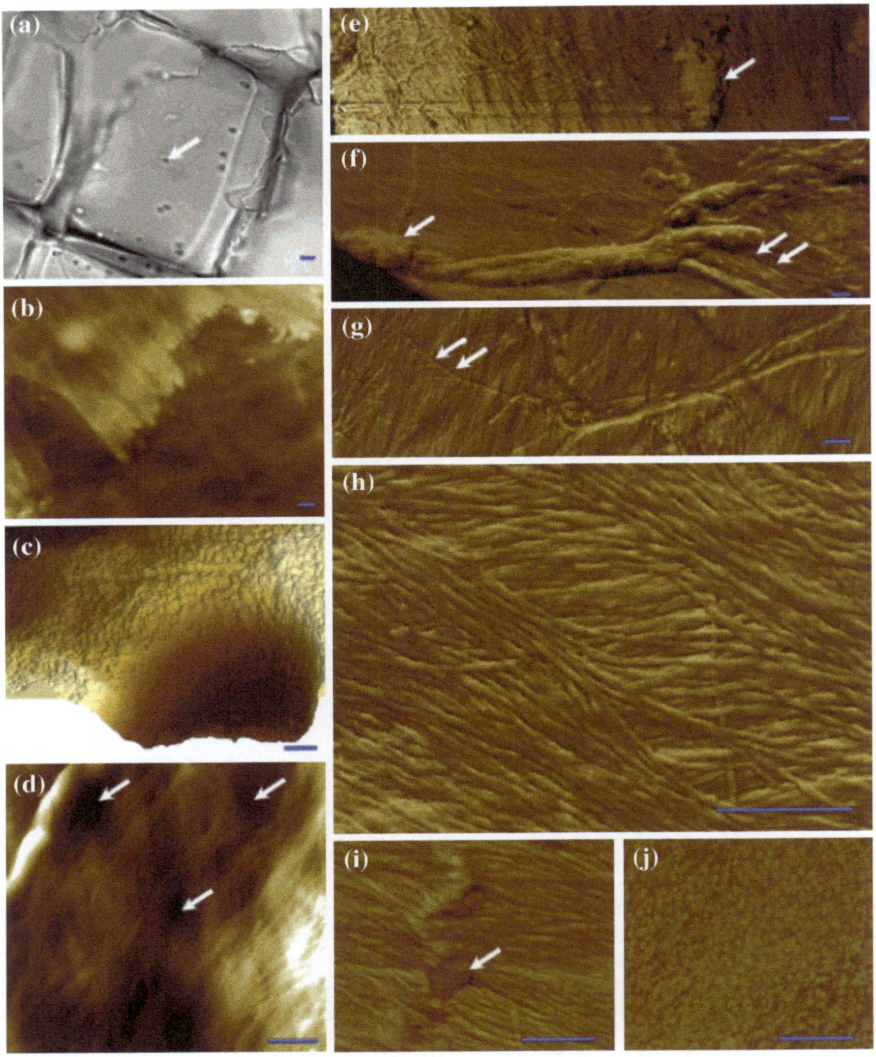

Fig. 5.6 Primary cell wall of the parenchyma cells of corn stover [8]. **a** Optical micrographs, which is transparent with primary pit, measuring scale 10 μm; **b–j** AFM micrographs of the cell surface, measuring scale 200 nm; (**b** height map of cell sheets; **c** 3D graph of the primary pit; **d** height map of the pit region; **e** phase diagram of the residual cytoplasm or cytomembrane; **f** the synthetic process of small fibril–macrofibril–microfibril, and the microfibril is synthesized from one point as the arrows indicate; **g** transformation of small fibrils into macrofibrils while the branches into microfibrils; **h** the sheet structure of the newly formed parallel microfibrils; **i** structure of microfibrils wrapping non-fiber protein macromolecule or particles, phase diagram; **j** other cell wall components settling in the cell wall structure, phase diagram

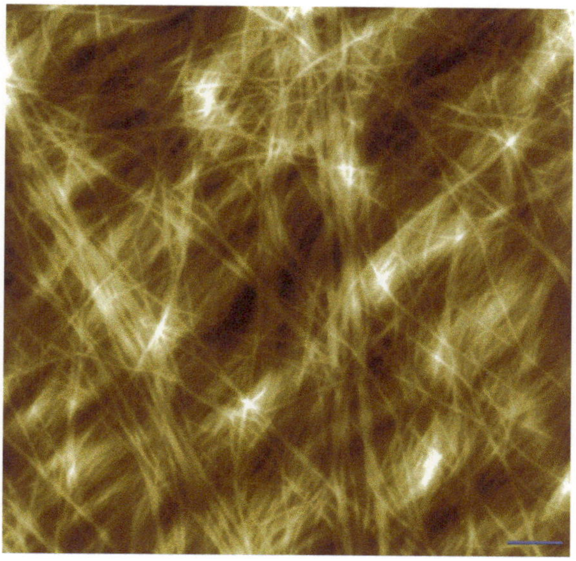

Fig. 5.7 High-resolution hypsography of the primary cell wall surface (microfibril in parallel arrangement and the macrofibril on the cell wall surface; measuring scale 200 nm) [8]

the AFM graphs of the elementary wall of cornstalk parenchymal cells [8, 9]. Figure 5.8 shows the AFM graph of the topological structure of plant cell after dilute acid treatment. Figure 5.9 gives the AFM graph of cotton fibers [9, 10], for which NanoScope III, a multimode AFM made by DI Co., is used with the tapping mode, 0.5–1 Hz of scanning rate, and a Needle Tip of tapping mode. The graph is a combination of height image and phase image without smoothing. Figure 5.10 shows the ultrastructure of microfibril after enzymatic hydrolysis.

Fig. 5.8 AFM spectra of the surface topological structure of plant cell using dilute acid treatment (microfibril keeps entire and seems to be the structure of primary fibers, which is actually spheroidal particles composed of lignin and cellulose after thermochemical treatment; the scanning range is 1 μm × 1 μm) [9]

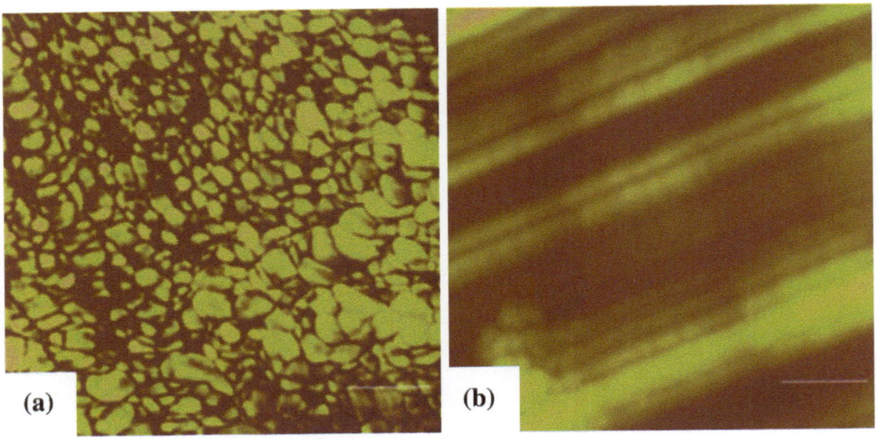

Fig. 5.9 AFM spectra of cotton fiber (**a** ultrastructure of the cotton fiber crosscuttings with measuring scale of 200 nm; **b** ultrastructure of paralleled microfibril with measuring scale of 150 nm) [10]

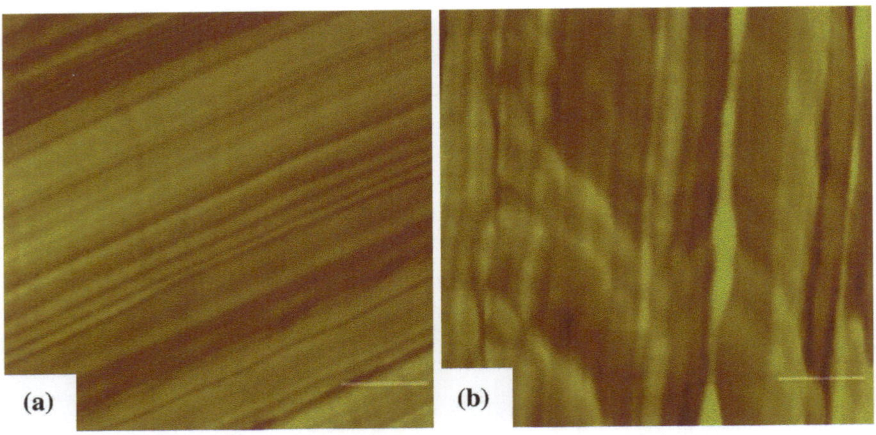

Fig. 5.10 Ultrastructure of microfibril after enzymatic hydrolysis with cellulase (measuring scale 200 nm) (**a** the structure of microfibril is homogeneous in the crystalline region; **b** microfibril is hydrolyzed by cellulase in the amorphous region) [10]

5.1.7 Environmental Scanning Electron Microscope (ESEM)

The sample chamber and lens cone of an ordinary scanning electron microscope are under vacuum, and thus, it is only applicable for the conductive solid samples or materials with conductive treatment. SEM with low vacuum value can be used to characterize non-conductive samples without pretreatment, but only the back-scattering electron micrograph is obtained under this condition. Besides the above properties, ESEM owns the following main advantages: ① The pressure of the sample chamber can be higher than the saturated vapor pressure of water under normal temperature; ② It is also applicable to secondary electron at normal environment; and ③ It can be used to observe the dissolution, solidification, and crystallization processes (in a range of −20 to 20 °C). ESEM can be used for the qualitative analysis and quantitative analysis of morphological observation and elements (C-U) of various solid and liquid samples and for the observation of phase change process of some solutions. For biological samples, wet samples and oil samples, ESEM can be used for secondary electron imaging and element analysis without dehydration or conductive treatment.

Figure 5.11 shows the ESEM graph of rice straw during compost. Samples are obtained at certain intervals during compost, cut into pieces of 2 mm × 2 mm, and observed using an XL-30 ESEM made by Philips [11].

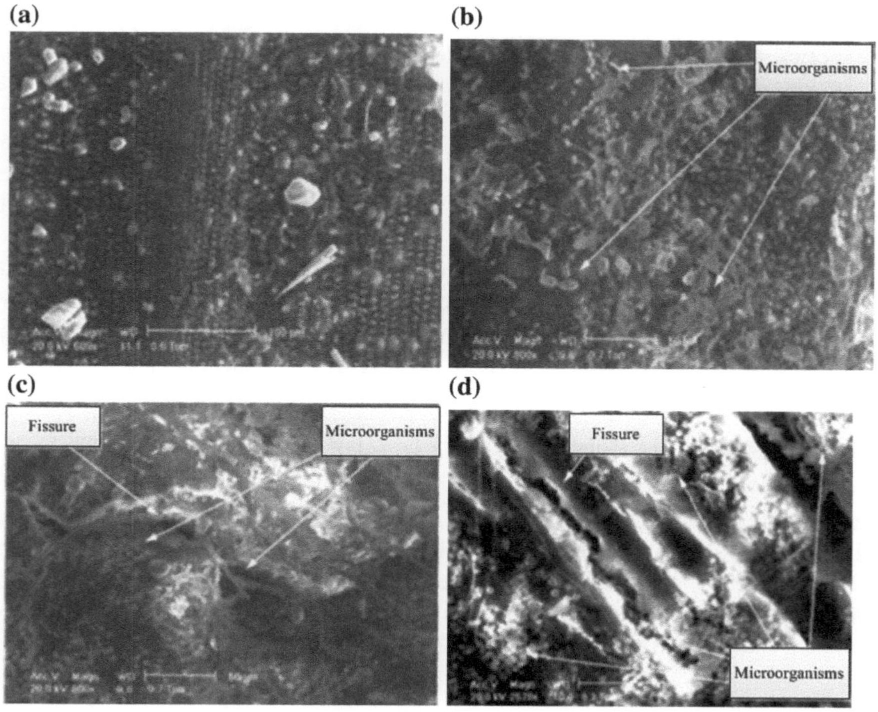

Fig. 5.11 ESEM spectra of rice straw compost at different stages (**a** fresh rice straw; **b** before composting; **c** initial stage of decomposition; **d** composting for 30 days) [11]

5.1.8 X-ray Diffraction (XRD) Characterization

Lignin and hemicellulose in gas-exploded materials are presented in amorphous form, while cellulose in crystalline form. For different products, the demand for existence form of cellulose is different.

XRD characterization is usually used for the crystalline structure. According to the distribution curves of XRD, ratios of crystalline regions can be calculated [12]. In addition to XRD characterization, adsorption method and method of specific gravity are also adopted. The ratios of crystalline regions are determined based on the phenomenon that the adsorption rate of amorphous regions is obviously faster than that of crystalline regions. Thus, adsorption method is more suitable for the determination of accessibility.

5.1.9 Molecular Weight Determination

Methods for molecular weight determination of cellulose can be divided into four categories according to the principles: chemical methods (end group analysis), thermodynamics method (vapor pressure, osmotic pressure, boiling point elevation, freezing point depression, etc.), kinetics method (ultracentrifugal sedimentation speed method, ultracentrifugal sedimentation balancing method, viscometric method, etc.), and optical method (light scattering method). All these methods have their specific advantages and application scope and can be used to obtain different types of molecular weight.

Determination of lignin molecular weight ranges from osmotic method, light scattering method, and ultracentrifugal method to gel permeation chromatography (GPC) [13]. When using GPC method, proper standard samples should be prepared.

5.1.10 Degree of Polymerization Determination

The molecular formula of cellulose is $(C_6H_{10}O_5)_n$ where n refers to the number of glucosyl groups, also called degree of polymerization (DP). DP directly reflects the average length of molecular chain of cellulose, which also has an effect on the viscosity of pulping. Generally speaking, determination of pulping viscosity is based on the method of GB/T 1548-2004, and then, DP of cellulose can be calculated according to certain formula.

5.2 Determination of Components of Gas-Exploded Materials

5.2.1 Determination of Cellulose Content

Holocellulose refers to the summation of cellulose and hemicellulose in lignocellulosic materials, which is also the total aggregation of carbohydrates [13]. Thus, to determine the holocellulose content, lignin in raw materials should be removed completely while protecting cellulose and hemicellulose from destruction. Methods for the determination of holocellulose content include sodium chlorite method, Cl ethanolamine method, ClO_2 method, peracetic acid method, and peracetic acid–sodium borohydride method. Sodium chlorite method is often used to determine the content of holocellulose, which owns advantages of simple separation, rapid removal of lignin, and broad application ranges. Details of sodium chlorite method can be referred to GB/T 2677.10-1995.

In nitric acid–ethanol method, samples are treated in the solution of nitric acid and ethanol during which lignin is nitrified and partly oxidized to generate nitrified lignin and oxidized lignin and dissolve into ethanol. Meanwhile, a large amount of hemicellulose is hydrolyzed, oxidized, and dissolved; hence, the residues are mainly composed of nitric acid–ethanol cellulose [3]. In this method, ethanol can protect cellulose from hydrolysis and oxidation by nitric acid. Specifically, 2–3 g smashed and dried samples are weighed, put into a 250-mL ground Erlenmeyer flask, added 25 mL nitric acid–ethanol solution, equipped with a condenser device, and heated in a boiling water bath for 1 h for three times. And then, the solution is filtered and washed to be neutral and dried until the mass keeps constant. Ash content is determined after that, and then, the holocellulose content is calculated according to certain formula.

The determination of holocellulose content in peanut shell contains hydrolysis by concentrated sulfuric acid and oxidation by potassium dichromate, and the principles are as follow: Cellulose is oxidized into CO_2 and H_2O by potassium dichromate in the sulfuric acid environment; excess potassium dichromate is reacted with sodium thiosulfate with starch-KI solution as indicator [14].

Van Soest method can determine the contents of cellulose, hemicellulose, and lignin all at once. Plant feedstuff such as pasture and roughage is degraded by neutral detergents (3 % SDS), while most of the cellular contents are dissolved into neutral detergents including fat, starch, and protein which is generally called NDS, and the insoluble residues are called NDF, including hemicellulose, cellulose, lignin, silicates, and tiny protein.

Acid detergents can further degrade NDF. The soluble part of plant feedstuff in acid detergents is called ADS which mainly contains NDS and hemicellulose, and the residues are called ADF including cellulose, lignin, and silicates. Moreover, the different value of NDF and ADF is regarded as the content of hemicellulose in raw materials.

Cellulose within ADF is dissolved after digestion by 72 % H_2SO_4, and the residues are lignin and silicates. Thus, cellulose content is obtained by taking away the residues after digestion by 72 % H_2SO_4 from ADF.

Then, the silicate content is obtained by ashing the residues after digestion by 72 % H_2SO_4. Meanwhile, the part of loss during ashing is the content of ADL.

Some improvements are made for this method. For example, Wang used 2.0 mol/L HCl instead of neutral detergents in a modified Van Soest method to determine the contents of cellulose, lignin, and hemicellulose [15].

Cellulose can be divided into α-cellulose, β-cellulose, and γ-cellulose based on the solubility [13]. α-cellulose refers to the part insoluble in 17.5 or 18 % NaOH solution at 20 °C; the sediment of lye extraction after neutralization is β-cellulose, while the part remains in the neutralized solution is called γ-cellulose. According to the viscometric method, DP of α-cellulose is higher than 200, β-cellulose between 100–200, and γ-cellulose less than 10.

For cellulosic materials to be used as feedstuff, traditional suction filtration, ANKOM filter bag, and CAU filter bag techniques can be adopted to determine the contents of NDF, ADF, and lignin (PL). Through comparison, we find that there is no difference among these three methods when determining the contents of NDF, ADF, and PL for most feedstuff materials. But technically, CAU method owns advantages of low costs, easy to order, and popularity [16].

5.2.2 *Lignin Content Determination*

Based on the properties of lignin, determination methods of lignin content include concentrated sulfuric acid hydrolysis and separation method [14, 17], spectrophotometry [18, 19], colorimetric method [18], nephelometry [19], infrared spectrometry [20], and REDOX titration method [14]. Of which, nephelometry is applicable to the determination of trace of lignin. GB/T 2677.8-94 is used for the determination of acid-insoluble lignin in paper-making materials in which 72 ± 0.1 % H_2SO_4 is used for hydrolysis of the extracted samples by benzyl alcohol mixture and then to quantificationally determine the content of hydrolysis residues.

5.2.3 *Hemicellulose Content Determination*

Methods to determine the content of hemicellulose include alkaline solution extraction method [21], 2 mol/L HCl hydrolysis [22], 12 % HCl hydrolysis, and combination of neutral detergents and acid detergents [15] etc.

5.2.4 Extract Content Determination

Extracts in gas-exploded materials refer to the tiny part that can be extracted by various solvents, including other kinds of lipid and protein except for cellulose, hemicellulose, and lignin. The existence of extracts will affect the medium transfer during steam explosion as well as the effective components in gas-exploded materials. Therefore, the determination of extract content in gas-exploded materials is necessary. Extraction methods of wood materials contain benzene/ethanol extraction, alkaline extraction, diethyl ether extraction [23], and water extraction which can be conducted at different temperatures. The book *Principle and application of permeation barrier of wood extracts* gives detailed reference of various extraction methods and extract components and the effects of extracts on permeability and structure [24].

5.2.5 Non-fiber Cell Content Determination

Non-fiber cells refer to the other cells except for fibrocytes [3]. The generally used method to determine the non-fiber cell content is an approximation method based on the area determination. Preparation of samples is similar to that of the determination of length and width. The prepared samples are put under the microscope with 70–100 magnification, and the area values are calculated and recorded, respectively. On an evenly distributed test piece, the areas of 100 fiber cells and the concomitant non-fiber cells are recorded and then the area ratio between different kinds of cells and the total cells is obtained.

5.2.6 Protein Content Determination

There are mainly four methods to determine the protein content, i.e., Kjeldahl, Biuret method, Lowry method, and UV absorption method. Another usual method is Bradford method. For comparison, Bradford and Lowry methods have the highest sensitivity; Kjeldahl is quite accurate but complex. Usually, the protein content determined by Kjeldahl is regarded as the standard value, and the detailed operation can refer to GB/T5009.5-2010.

5.2.7 Wax Content Determination

Generally, HPLC method is used for the determination of wax components and GC-MS for total wax content.

5.2.8 Lipid Content Determination

The determination of lipid content can refer to GB/T 14488.1-1993.

5.2.9 Ash Content Determination

Residues after high-temperature combustion and ashing are called ash. The content and components of ash differ from each other as regard to different kinds of materials and parts. Determination of ash content in cellulose can refer to GB/T 2677.3-1993.

5.2.10 Moisture Content Determination

Moisture content refers to the mass ratio of weight loss, while drying at certain temperature (105 ± 2 °C) and the initial mass, often expressed as percentage [3]. Exsiccation and distillation methods are used for moisture content determination, and the former has been classified as the standard method (GB/T 2677.2-1993).

5.2.11 Flavonoid Content Determination

Flavonoid substances react with Al^{3+} in alkaline environment with nitrites and generate stable red clathrate which has the highest absorption value at 510 nm. Thus, flavonoid content is usually determined using UV spectrophotometry.

5.2.12 Pectin Content Determination

GB/T 10742-2008 provides two methods to determine the pectin content, i.e., gravimetric method and colorimetry of carbazole. Besides volumetric method, titration and atomic absorption spectroscopy methods are also used [25]. Pectin content in ramie is determined using GB5889-86 method. Moreover, infrared spectroscopy method and microwave-assisted extraction method improve the determination by shortening the period [26, 27].

5.2.13 Tannin Content Determination

Determination of tannin content includes spectrophotometry and volumetric method [3]. Tannin is insoluble in benzene, but soluble in ethanol. Thus, in the spectrophotometry process, samples are extracted using benzene and then dissolved in ethanol. Then, the light density of soluble matter at 500 nm is determined, and the tannin content is obtained based on the standard curve.

5.3 Determination of the Active Groups in Gas-Exploded Materials

5.3.1 Determination of Methoxyl Group Content

Methoxy group mainly exists in lignin and less in cellulose and pectin. Chemical method (gravimetric and bulk density method) and instrumental method (Chromatography, nuclear magnetic resonance spectroscopy, and electrochemical methods) are common methods for the determination of methoxy groups. The basic principle of chemical method to determine methoxyl content is to make the sample react with concentrate iodine acid; thus, the methoxy group in lignin is cracked and the alkyl iodide produced by the reaction is distilled out. Then, absorb alkyl iodide by different absorbents and determine the content of compound generated in reaction; thus, we can determine the content of methoxyl group. According to different absorbents, the methods can be divided into silver nitrate method, bromination method, and pyridine method. Silver nitrate method belongs to gravimetric methods, while bromination method and pyridine method belong to volumetric methods. Bromination method is also called Verbeke method, in which bromine is used as the absorbent to measure the content of methoxy group. Bromination method is widely used at present for the determination of methoxy groups with advantages of high accuracy, simple operation, and speediness.

5.3.2 Determination of Hydroxyl Content

Cellulose, hemicellulose, and lignin contain large amounts of hydroxyl groups. There are two kinds of hydroxyl groups in lignin. One is phenolic hydroxyl on benzene ring, and the other is aliphatic hydroxyl (alcoholic extract hydroxyl) on the side chain of structural unit. There are two methods, i.e., chemical method and instrumental analysis method to determine the hydroxyl content [3]. Instrumental analysis methods include nuclear magnetic resonance, gas chromatography, ultraviolet spectroscopy, and electrochemical method. In the H-NMR spectroscopy, δ2.50–2.17 represents for phenolic hydroxyl, δ2.17–1.70 represents for alcoholic hydroxyl. When determining the content of phenolic hydroxyl by gas chromatography, phenolic hydroxyl is first etherized by dimethyl sulfate and then the ethane content is determined in order to convert to the content of phenolic hydroxyl. In addition, phenolic hydroxyl content can be determined by ultraviolet spectroscopy at the wavelength of 300 or 350 nm. The amounts of phenolic hydroxyl and alcoholic hydroxyl in lignin are regarded as the total hydroxyl content. When determining the hydroxyl content in lignin by chemical methods, the total hydroxyl content and the phenolic hydroxyl content are first determined and the alcoholic hydroxyl content is the difference between these two contents. The methods which are most widely used to determine the alcoholic hydroxyl content are periodate oxidation method and non-aqueous conductometric titration. Additionally, the non-aqueous conductometric titration can also determine the carboxyl content simultaneously.

5.3.3 Determination of Carboxyl Content

Carboxyl group mainly exists in hemicellulose within cellulosic materials. There are many ways to determine the carboxyl content [3]: direct titration with alkali, exchange reaction with phosphorus–nitrophenol silver, reaction with methylene blue, sodium bicarbonate–sodium chloride method, conductometric titration, and dynamic calcium acetate ion exchange method. Among these methods, dynamic calcium acetate ion exchange method (GB/T 10338-1989) and sodium bicarbonate–sodium chloride method are used more widely.

5.3.4 Simultaneous Determination of Carboxyl and Phenolic Hydroxyl

Non-aqueous titration, which can determine carboxyl and phenolic hydroxyl group content in cellulose materials simultaneously, includes non-aqueous conductometric titration and non-aqueous potentiometric titration. The principle of non-aqueous titration is to distinguish and titrate weak acids by non-aqueous solvents. Water is a strong polar solvent in which the representative strength of organic weak acids is low. Due to the homogenization effect of water, there is little difference of the representative strength between water and weak acids; thus, it is hard to analyze weak acids in water. But in organic solvents, the acidity of organic weak acid is greatly enhanced. So it is feasible to titrate weak acids by strong alkali. Carboxyl and phenolic hydroxyl groups in lignin are acidic groups with weak acidity. When determining its content, organic media with poor catalytic activity can be used as solvents and then the variation of conductivity or potentials before and after titration is recorded to calculate the content of acidic groups.

5.4 Particle Properties Characterization of Gas-Exploded Materials

5.4.1 Particle Size Analysis

Particle size measurement is essentially measured by comparing the particle with a ball made by the same material with target particle. Instruments of different principles choose different physical characteristics or physical behavior as the reference for comparison. For example, settlement meter uses the settlement speed; laser particle analyzer uses the distribution of scattering light, while sieving method uses the possibility of whether particles can pass the sieve pores. Methods that can be used for the particle size analysis of gas-exploded materials are introduced as follows.

Microscopic method includes microscopy, SEM, and transmission electron microscopy, and the measurement range is 1 nm–5 μm. The resolution of common scanning electron microscope is about 6 nm, and resolution of field emission scanning electron microscope is 0.5 nm. The measurement range of this method is small; thus, it is suitable for small materials, such as starch granule, or gas-exploded materials that are ground to a certain degree.

The advantage of electron microscopy to analyze particle size is that it can provide the data of particle size, distribution, and shape. Besides, general particle size ranging from 1 nm to a few microns can be analyzed by electron microscopy. And intuitive data of the particle image can be acquired by electron microscopy, which is easy to understand. But its drawback is that the sample preparation process may have a serious effect on the results. For example, the dispersion of sample preparation would directly affect the quality and analysis results of electron microscope observation. Also, the small size of sampling may lead to unrepresentative results.

SEM can make nano-sized powder samples by solution dispersion or by direct dry powder sampling, and the requirements for sample preparation are low. But certain conductivity is required for electron microscopy analysis; thus, evaporating a conductive layer, such as surface evaporated gold or carbon, on the surface of samples is needed. Generally, if the particle size is under 1 nm, carbon evaporation is used instead of gold evaporation because the particle size of gold is about 8 nm and may cause interference.

The principle of sedimentation method is that when particles are in a suspension system, its self-weight (or centrifugal force), buoyancy force, and viscosity resistance kept in balance. And the determination of viscous forces obeys Stokes's law. In this case, the particles in the suspension system settle at a constant velocity. And the settling velocity is proportional to the square of the particle size. Sedimentation method is suitable for the analysis of particles ranging from 10 nm to 20 μm in size.

In the laser methods, laser diffraction diameter analyzer gives accurate analysis for particles larger than 5 μm, while dynamic laser nanometer size analyzer gives accurate analysis for nanoparticles smaller than 5 μm. Laser light scattering method can measure the particle size distribution of particles ranging from 20 nm to 350 μm, and the result is the equivalent volume distribution with advantages of accuracy, speediness, good representation, and repeatability. Generally, laser light scattering method is available for all materials.

5.4.2 The Application of Fractal Dimension in the Particle Characterization

In fractal geometry, fractal D (also called fractal dimension) is a statistic that describes the degree of a fractal on space filling. There is no uniform definition for fractal dimension. The following two are mainly used [28]. M obtained from the measuring of an object whose dimension is D is related with the length unit ε, which can be expressed as $M(\varepsilon) \propto 1/\varepsilon$. For example, when calculating length ($D = 1$). Area ($D = 2$) and volume ($D = 3$), $M(\varepsilon)$ is directly proportional to $1/\varepsilon$, $1/\varepsilon^2$, and $1/\varepsilon^3$, respectively. That is, $M(\varepsilon) = V/\varepsilon^D$, where the constant is calculated by measuring the object with $\varepsilon = 1$. Taking logarithm of the formula, we can get the following:

$$D = (\ln M - \ln V)/\ln(1/\varepsilon)$$

When $\varepsilon \to 0, \ln M \to \infty$, then we get a definition of dimension D

$$D = \lim_{\varepsilon \to 0} \ln M(\varepsilon)/\ln(1/\varepsilon)$$

The dimension defined by the above formula is called the capacity dimension or Hausdorff dimension. In the actual calculation, divide the phase space or projection into small cells with side length ε, count the number M of cells passed through or covered by the object, and then calculate $\ln M(\varepsilon)/\ln(1/\varepsilon)$. The smaller the value of ε is, the more accurate the calculation value is. This method is called box-counting method.

From the definition of fractal dimension, we know that the concept is available to describe the particles of irregular morphology. The fractal dimension is more often used in the morphology characterization of soil particles [29]. In the analysis, basic morphology data are obtained by certain methods; then, the parameters are chosen and the values are calculated by the chosen definition. By the results, the morphology properties are described more accurately. Fractal dimension of gas-exploded materials will affect the percolation of the medium in the process of pressure increasing. The higher fractal dimension is, the lower the connectivity of materials will be, reducing the percolation probability in the pressure increasing process. Unevenness of media will lead to half-cooked gas-exploded materials. The fractal dimension characterization of materials after steam explosion also has effects on the further utilizations of material as substrates for hydrolysis, fermentation as well as physical and chemical treatment.

Prof. Chen Hongzhang's group has used fractal dimension in characterizing the morphology of gas-exploded material and in solid-state fermentation process [30]. Furthermore, corresponding models have been established to couple with digital image processing technology, in order to better understand the effects of mycelia growth on the morphology of substrate. Such method can be applied to the steam explosion process to better recognize the changing process of materials under different treatment conditions and then to reveal the principle of steam explosion and supervise the process as required.

5.5 Interface Characterization Performance of Gas-Exploded Materials

5.5.1 Determination of the Specific Surface Area

Specific surface area refers to the total area of per unit mass material. One of the main purposes of steam explosion is to break the ordered structure of the original material and expose the active ingredients within it, thereby enhancing the performance of subsequent processing. Thus, analysis of the gas-exploded materials, especially the specific surface area of gas-exploded materials, is a good way to evaluate the performance of steam explosion.

At present, the methods to determine the specific surface area values include gas adsorption method (BET method), the fluid permeation method, and the mercury method [31]. The accuracy and stability of various methods need to contrast in the trial and error. Different gas-exploded materials may require different methods due to various structures and specific surface area values. The authors' researches reveal that both the mercury method and BET method can determine the specific surface area of gas-exploded materials, but the comparison of these two methods needs deep investigation.

5.5.2 The Characterization of Interfacial Tension

Certain chemical changes occur in the steam explosion process, resulting in the changes of interfacial tension due to the changes of components and the surface active groups. The interfacial tension leads to different interface interactions on characteristics of gas-exploded material itself, as well as the microbe, enzymes, and chemical reagents used in the subsequent transformation processes, thus affecting the conversion process and the conversion efficiency. Therefore, analyzing the interfacial tension of the gas-exploded materials can efficiently adjust the media and conditions of steam explosion according to different purposes.

Through observing interfacial phenomena, especially the gas–liquid interface phenomena, it can be perceived that there always exists the tension at interface, which is known as the interfacial tension or surface tension [32–34]. Therefore, when immiscible objects contact with each other, the force generated at the interface is the interfacial tension. There are many ways to determine the interfacial tension, such as capillary rise method, drop weight technique, suspension loop method (De Nouy method), maximum bubble pressure method, hanging plate method(also called wilhelmy method), and hydrostatic method. The specific operations of these methods can be found in relevant experimental textbooks and monographs.

When the temperature, pressure, and composition are constant, the work that is done to reversibly increase the surface area by dA is called surface work (ω').

$$-\delta\omega' = \gamma \mathrm{d}A$$

where γ refers to the surface Gibbs free energy, J/m^2.

The unit of J is N m; thus, the unit of γ can be expressed as N/m. The surface free energy can be regarded as a vertical force on the phase interface per unit length, which is the surface tension.

5.5.3 Characterization of Contact Angle

The contact angle is the angle at which a liquid/vapor interface meets the solid surface. The contact angle is specific for any given system and is determined by the interactions across the three interfaces. The wetting degree can be measured by contact angle (Fig. 5.12).

If $\theta < 90°$, the solid is lyophilic and the liquid can wet solid. The smaller the angle is, the better the wettability is. If $\theta > 90°$, the solid is lyophobic, which means that the liquid cannot wet the solid. Under such condition, the liquid tends to move on the solid surface and cannot enter the capillary pores.

Wetting process is relevant to interfacial tension of the system. The relationship of contact angle is formed when the process of liquid particles moving on the solid surface reaches balance and the interfacial tension accords to the Young's equation.

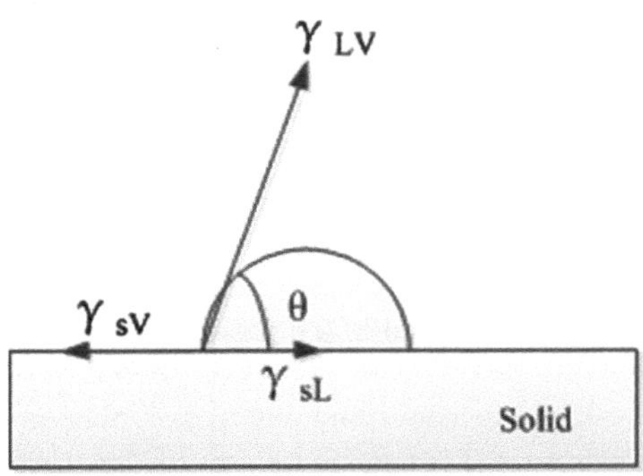

Fig. 5.12 Schematic of contact angle [34]

Young's Equation:

$$\gamma_{LV}\cos\theta = \gamma_{SV} - \gamma_{SL}$$

We can predict the following wetting condition by Young's Equation.

① $\theta = 0$, complete wetting.
② $\theta < 90°$, partially wetting or wetting.
③ $\theta = 90°$, boundary of wetting or not.
④ $\theta > 90°$, non-wetting.
⑤ $\theta = 180°$, completely non-wetting.

In the capillary phenomenon, liquid body rises or drops by the height of h, of which the positive and negative of h representing rising or dropping. The contact angle is an acute with wetting liquid while an obtuse with non-wetting liquid.

Rising height **h** = 2 × surface tension coefficient/(liquid density × gravitational acceleration **g** × liquid radius **r**).

Rising height **h** = 2 × surface tension coefficient × **cos** contact angle/(liquid density × gravitational acceleration **g** × capillary radius **r**).

Therefore, the contact angle can represent wetting properties of gas-exploded materials effectively. Lignocellulosic materials can be converted into bio-based energy and products through enzymatic hydrolysis and fermentation after steam explosion. Moreover, the contact angle would affect the fermentation process, especially for the solid-state fermentation process. Additionally, the wettability of fibers should have influence on the quality of paper and boards when using gas-exploded materials for pulping and preparing ecological boards [35, 36].

Some studies [37] have shown that with the prolonging of timber storage time, the force between water and not-extracted timber is reduced. The result implies that the extracts move outward to wood surface from inside during storage, resulting in a hydrophobic surface of the wood. Acid–base properties of the material surface after steam explosion have a certain impact on its subsequent transformation, whether it is converted into bio-based energy or bio-based products, because the acid–base properties of surface can characterize the accessibility of gas-exploded material for other materials. For example, the surface acid–base properties of gas-exploded material can significantly affect its sizing performance when they are used for the preparation of ecologic boards. The surface acidity can be analyzed by measuring the contact angle [38, 39].

There are two major methods to measure the contact angle. One is shape image analysis method, and the other is weighing method. The latter is usually called wetting balance or osmosis contact angle instrument. But the most widely used method is shape image analysis method which can get most direct and accurate values.

The principle of shape image analysis method is to drop the liquid particle on the surface of solid sample and obtain the shape image of droplets by the microscope lens and camera, and then calculate the contact angle of droplets in the image by digital image processing and certain algorithms.

The method of calculating the contact angle is usually based on a specific mathematical model. For example, the droplets can be regarded as part of the ball or cone, and then, the contact angle can be calculated by measuring specific parameters such as width or height, or by a direct fitting. Young–Laplace equation describes the relationship among internal and external pressure difference, the interface curvature, and interfacial tension in a closure interface. It can be used to describe contours of axisymmetric liquid droplet and thus to calculate the contact angle accurately.

5.6 Characterization of Porous Properties of Gas-Exploded Materials

5.6.1 Characterization of Pore Size Distribution

Pore size distribution of the material after steam explosion has an important reference value for subsequent processing with the addition of other media [39]. Different pore size distribution cases are suitable for different processing cases. In other words, only when the pore size distribution keeps in a certain range, the ideal transformation effect occurs.

Pore size distribution refers to the percentage of aperture at all levels in materials calculated by the number or volume.

Nitrogen adsorption method is a mature and widely used way to measure the pore size distribution. It is an extension of measuring the BET-specific surface area by nitrogen adsorption method, both of which make use of the nitrogen isothermal adsorption curve.

The mercury intrusion method, known as mercury porosimetry, can be also used to measure the pore size distribution. It is the method to measure pore size distribution of partial mesopores and macropores (above 2 mm). The basic principle is that mercury cannot wet the general solid; thus, to make mercury enter the hole, external pressure should be imposed. The greater the external pressure is, the smaller the pore radius that mercury can enter is. By measuring the amount of mercury entering into the hole under different external pressure, we can know the corresponding pore size and pore volume.

To analyze the mechanism of how gas-exploded materials influence the enzymatic hydrolysis, the author has analyzed the material pore size distribution under different steam explosion intensity and the structure–activity relationship between pore size distribution and enzymatic hydrolysis performance. The research results suggest that ① steam explosion damaged the integrity of the cell wall structure, forming nano- and micron-sized holes compared with before vapor blasting, and ② nano-and micron-sized holes have greater correlation with enzymatic hydrolysis performance, which enhances the enzymatic hydrolysis performance through increasing the specific surface area values and improving the transfer performance of cellulase and indirect products in substrate.

5.6.2 Characterization of Permeability Coefficient

Permeability coefficient can be used to characterize the transfer performance of materials in fluids before and after steam explosion [40, 41]. Both in steam explosion and in the subsequent transformation process of gas-exploded material processes, the transfer of fluid medium has certain influence on the conversion process and conversion rate.

The determination of permeability coefficient can refer to the method SL237-1999 for the determination of soil permeability. And there is one thing to note that only when the extracts are excluded, relatively stable value of permeability can be obtained.

In order to further analyze the mechanism of how pore size distribution influences the enzymatic hydrolysis performance, the author uses the method SL237-1999 to study the permeability coefficient of gas-exploded materials and crushed materials. The study shows that permeability coefficient of materials increases after steam explosion, but there is no positive correlation between permeability coefficient and enzymatic hydrolysis performance.

5.6.3 Characterization of Other Properties of Porous Media

The main properties of porous media are pore size distribution and permeability coefficient, but there are other parameters influencing the permeability performance, including the tortuosity, skeleton density, pore–throat ratio, and the percolation threshold pressure. There exists a relation between these parameters and permeability coefficients [41]. These parameters can be calculated by the software according to the existing model during the pore size distribution characterization by mercury porosimetry, which would be shown in the final analysis report.

5.7 Characterization of Biomechanical Property of Gas-Exploded Materials

5.7.1 Characterization of Hydrogen Content

As for gas-exploded materials, especially for lignocellulosic materials, the biomechanical properties are closely related to the content of hydrogen bonds. When hydrogen bond content reduces, the ordered structure of three components and even the crystalline cellulose is disrupted, thus contributing to the efficient follow-up utilization of individual components.

Hydrogen content can be determined by Fourier transform infrared spectroscopy, which is primarily used for qualitative measurement and quantitative analysis is difficult to achieve.

5.7.2 Tensile Strength

There will be tensile deformation on wood with the imposing of external force, and the maximum capacity to resist such tensile deformation is tensile strength [42]. Wood tensile strength includes longitudinal tensile strength and tensile strength perpendicular to grain. The determinations can refer to related works of timber experiment.

5.7.3 Compressive Strength

The compressive strength refers to the maximum capacity of wood bearing external pressure load. The compressive strength of wood includes first grain compression strength and cross-grain compression strength, and the determination methods can refer to related work of timber experiment.

5.7.4 Bending Property

The bending properties of wood can be described by bending strength and bending modulus of elasticity. The bending strength of wood refers to the maximum capacity of timber to bear the gradually applied load, which can be measured by the size of curve radius. The bending modulus of elasticity of wood refers to the ratio of stress and strain within the proportional limit when wood bends due to external force. The bending modulus of elasticity represents rigidity or elasticity of materials, and its determination can refer to related work of timber experiment.

5.7.5 Shear Strength

The maximum capacity of wood resisting the shearing pressure is called shear strength. It can be divided into rift grain and cross-grain shear strength. Its determination can refer to related work of timber experiment.

5.7.6 Hardness and Impact Toughness

Wood hardness refers to the ability of wood to resist other rigid body pushing in. The impact toughness of the timber refers to the energy sample absorbed per unit area when timber is bending to break by the impact force. The greater the energy is, the higher wood toughness is and the lower brittleness is.

5.8 Characterization of Wet and Dry Performance of Gas-Exploded Materials

5.8.1 The Moisture Content and Shrinkage

In wood science, the shrinkage and wet swelling refer to the following two phenomena: The phenomenon that wet material reduces its size and volume due to drying is known as shrinkage; the phenomenon that dry material increases its size and volume due to absorbing water is known as wet swelling. Shrinkage and swelling phenomena mainly occur in the case when wood moisture content is below the fiber saturation point. When the wood moisture content is above the fiber saturation point, the size and volume will not change. The main evaluation indices of wood shrinkage are air-dry shrinkage rate, total dry shrinkage rate, shrinkage coefficient, and different shrinkage. Its determination can refer to related work of timber experiment. The determination of shrinkage for herbaceous lignocellulosic materials can refer to the methods in wood science.

5.8.2 The Existing State of Water

For gas-exploded materials, the water content and the state of water have an important influence on the conversion performance. The water content is often measured by drying–weighing method. And the existing state of water mainly refers to water activity. Water activity can be determined using Conway dishes [43]. Place different salts, such as LiCl, in the outer chamber of each Conway dish separately and add small amount of water to make it a saturated solution. Then, put certain sample in the internal chamber of the Conway dish and cover the Conway dish with a glass plate and then put the Conway dish in an incubator chamber. Draw according to the sample moisture change and the corresponding salt water activity and get the water activity of sample through interpolation. Currently, water activity of food is measured according to GB/T 23490-2009. The standard is corresponding to International standard ISO 21807: 2004 *Microorganisms in food and livestock feeding material—Water activity determination*; the degree of consistency with GB/T 23490-2009 is not equivalent. GB/T 23490-2009 regulates the method to determine water activity in food is Conway dish diffusion method (application scope 0.00–0.98) and Water activity meter diffusion method (application scope 0.60–0.90), and Conway dish diffusion method belongs to arbitration law. Other methods to measure the water activity in food are as follows: double thermal equilibrium method, pressure measurement method, endo graphic, freezing point depression method, humidity measuring method, dew point measurement method, isobaric transfer method, chemical transfer method, GC, solvent moisture absorbent capacity measurement method, and batch effect measurement method. But the application of these methods in the determination of gas-exploded materials needs further study.

5.8.3 Fiber Saturation Point

Fiber saturation point [42–44], for timber, refers to the moisture content while only the wood cell walls adsorb water and reach saturation while there is no free water in cell lumen and cell gap. It is a turning point of whether the wood physical mechanical properties change with water content.

When the wood moisture content is above fiber saturation point, it indicates that besides the adsorbed water reaches saturation; there is still free water within it. Under such condition, just the free water content changes when wood is exposed to drying or wetting, avoiding the occurrence of swelling or shrinkage.

When the moisture content of wood is below the fiber saturation point, swelling or shrinkage would happen. The volume of timber will expand with water moisture content increasing, the volume of timber will decrease with water moisture content reducing.

Based on the relationship between the fiber saturation point and the performance of timber, the fiber saturation point can be measured by the link between timber strength, dry shrinkage, electrical conductivity, and moisture content.

5.9 Characterization of Physicochemical Properties of Gas-Exploded Materials

5.9.1 Chemical Bond Energy

Chemical bond energy is closely related to chemical stability of compound, the reaction rate, and product yield [45]. Therefore, understanding chemical bond energy of materials before or after steam explosion is the basis of designing equipment and process of steam explosion, as well as the high-value utilization of gas-exploded materials. The methods to determine chemical bond energy include reaction kinetics method, gas-phase ion thermochemical cycle method and mass spectrometry, photoionization method and zero electrical dynamic energy spectrum, photoionization with synchrotron radiation-molecular beam mass spectrometry, photoacoustic calorimetry, and electrochemical method [45].

5.9.2 Thermodynamic Energy

Thermodynamic energy refers to the sum of energy of translational energy, rotational energy, vibrational energy, electronics and nuclear energy of the system, and the molecular interaction potential energy [46]. Thermodynamic energy is the sum of the internal energy of the system. Although it is difficult to measure the absolute value of the thermodynamic energy, it is enough to know the variable in physical or chemical processes. Thermodynamic energy is one of the properties of the system itself; thus, it only depends on the status of the system. And it is a single-valued function of the system, owning definite value in a given state.

5.9.3 Enthalpy Value

In physical chemistry, (U + *p*V) is defined as the enthalpy. At present, we still cannot measure the absolute value of thermodynamic energy and the enthalpy. For a system, in the absence of other work conditions, the heat absorbed by the system in an isochoric process is used for increasing the thermodynamic energy. The heat absorbed by system in an isobaric process is all used for increasing the enthalpy. Therefore, thermodynamic energy and enthalpy can be determined by setting special system and using certain calorimeter [47].

5.9.4 Specific Heat Capacity

Specific heat capacity, the heat capacity of per unit mass material, is the internal energy absorbed or released when unit mass object changes a unit temperature. Specific heat capacity is a physical quantity that can represent the thermal properties of materials, usually described by symbol c. Specific heat capacity is an important factor that can influence energy consumption and effect of steam explosion, which is also an important parameter for the mechanism analysis of steam explosion.

Since the gas-exploded materials may contain a certain amount of water, its specific heat capacity is a wet basis specific heat capacity. It can be calculated by the following formula:

$$c_{ps} = \frac{c_{pd} + Wc_{pw}}{1 + W}$$

where W refers to moisture content; c_{pd} refers to the solid specific heat capacity; c_{pw} refers to the specific heat capacity of water.

5.9.5 Thermal Conductivity

Thermal conductivity refers to the proportional coefficient of heat quantity through unit area during unit time and temperature gradient. Thermal conductivity of solid-state materials has relationships with its moisture content, structure, porosity, and density. Usually, materials with large moisture content have large thermal conductivity. Thermal conductivity can be measured by probe method [48]. In the study of timber, the relation between thermal conductivity and the aperture gap degrees was proposed according to its structure, especially the cell structure [49]. The relation shows that the larger the porosity is, the smaller the thermal conductivity will be. The calculation error of formula is about 20 %.

5.10 Rheological Characterization of Gas-Exploded Materials

Rheological properties of gas-exploded materials can be determined by rheometers, such as rotary rheometer, capillary rheometer, torque rheometer, and interfacial rheometer. Of which, rotary rheometer is suitable for the rheological properties determination of gas-exploded materials, and the detailed operations can refer to the corresponding literature [50, 51].

The author studied rheological properties of gas-exploded materials based on the solid–liquid ratio in the enzymatic hydrolysis process and found that the enzymatic heterogeneous solution belonged to pseudo-plastic fluids.

References

1. Li HP. Plant microtechnology. Beijing: Science Press; 2009.
2. Pulp and Paper Manual, Part 1: Cellulosic materials and chemical materials. Beijing: China Light Industry Press; 1987.
3. Shi SL, He FW. Analysis and testing of pulping and paper. Beijing: China Light Industry Press; 2003.
4. Xing S. Establishment of semi-quantitative electrophoresis technology and the application in functional proteomics of Aspergillusniger. Ji'nan: Shandong University; 2009.
5. Zeng M, Mosier NS, Huang CP, Sherman DM. Microscopic examination of changes of plant cell structure in corn stover due to hot water pretreatment and enzymatic hydrolysis. Biotechnol Bioeng. 2007;97(2):265–78. doi:10.1002/bit.21298.
6. Wang JH. Characteristics and micrographia of pulping fibers. Beijing: China Light Industry Press; 1999.
7. Zhang XZ. Electronic micro-analysis. Beijing: Tsinghua University Press; 2006.
8. Ding SY, Himmel ME. The maize primary cell wall microfibril: a new model derived from direct visualization. J Agric Food Chem. 2006;54(3):597–606. doi:10.1021/jf051851z.
9. Himmel ME. Corn stover conversion to biofuels: DOE's preparation for readiness in 2012. Cellulose. 2009;16(4):531–4. doi:10.1007/s10570-009-9335-8.
10. Wang LS, Gao PJ, Shi DX. Quantitative analysis of natural cotton fiber surface ultrastructure and its changes—determination of surface roughness using atomic force microscopy. J Shandong Univ. 2007;41(6):132–139. No. 1671-9352(2006)06-0132-08.
11. Piao Z, Li YM, Ma S. Environmental scanning electron microscope observation of microorganisms invading straws during compost. J Ecol Rural Environ. 2011;5:98–100. No. 1673-4831(2011)05-0098-03.
12. Li ZG. Cellulose physicochemistry. Beijing: China financial economic publishing house; 1965.
13. Gao J, Tang HG. Cellulose Science. Beijing: Science Press; 1996.

14. Fan PC, Tian J, Huang JM. Determination methods of cellulose and lignin in peanut shell. J Chongqing Inst Technol. 2008;10(5):64–65. No. 1673-1980(2008)05-0064-02.
15. Van Soest P, Wine R. Use of detergents in the analysis of fibrous feeds. IV. Determination of plant cell-wall constituents. J Assoc Offic Anal Chem. 1967;50:50–5.
16. Xue HF, Meng QX. Comparison of determination methods of NDF, ADF and lignin contents in ruminant's forage. Chin J Anim Sci. 2006;42(19):41–45. No. 0258-7033(2006)19-0041-05.
17. Chen WJ, Cheng X. Determination of lignin content in peanut shell using sulfuric acid method. J Minjiang Coll. 2002;23(2):72–73. No. 1009-7821(2002)02-0072-02.
18. Ren Q, Hu YJ, Li ZY. Lignin content and peroxidase activity in injured Pinusmassoniana. Acta Ecol Sin. 2007;27(11):4895–4899. No. 1000-0933(2007)11-4895-05.
19. Zhang XY, Wang LX, Liu B. Determination of trace lignin in flax fiber using nephelometry. Chem Adhes. 2004;6:368–369. No. 1001-0017(2004)06-0368-02.
20. Li GY, Huang AM, Wang G. Determination of Klason lignin content in moso bamboo using near infrared spectroscopy. Spectrosc Spect Anal. 2007;27(10):1977–1980. No. 1000-0593 (2007)10-1977-04.
21. Wankheds DB, Tharanathan RN. Sasame (Sesamunindicum) carbohydrates. J Agric Food Chem. 1976;24(3):655–9. doi:10.1021/jf60205a065.
22. Jing JH, Ding ZR. Biochemical analytical methods of plants. Beijing: Science Press; 1981.
23. Ren SX, Jiang GQ, Qu HJ. The chemical experiment tutorial of plants. Harbin: Northeast Forestry University Press; 2008.
24. Peng WX. Theory and application of wood extracts osmotic barrier. Guangzhou: South China Agricultural University; 2006.
25. Cao DJ, Huang XM. Study of plants' pectin determination using AAS method. J Anhui Agric Univ. 2000;27(2):202–203. No. 1000-2197(2000)02-0202-02.
26. Xiao AP, Li W, Leng J. Study of the rapid determination of ramee pectin using near infrared spectroscopy. Plant Fiber Sci-China. 2009;31(4):238–241. No. 1673-7636(2009)04-0238-04.
27. Xiong CD, Li HY, Zeng QF. Determination of ramee pectin content using microwave-assisted method. Plant Fiber Sci-China. 2008;30(2):79–83. No. 1673-7636(2008)02-0079-06.
28. Cai SH, Zhou HP, Wang CX. Duty ratio and fractal dimension calculation of Particulate debris under different stacking conditions. GuizhouSci. 2007;25(1):9–12. No. 1003-6563(2007) 01-0009-04.
29. Jia XH, Li XR, Zhang JG. Spatial variability analysis of the soil particle fractal dimension in the ammopiptanthusmongolicus brush land. ActaEcol Sin. 2006;26(9):2827–2833. No. 1000-0933 (2006)09-2827-07.
30. Duan YY, Wang L, Chen HZ. Digital image analysis and fractal-based kinetic modelling for fungal biomass determination in solid-state fermentation. Biochem Eng J. 2012;67(15):60–7. doi:10.1016/j.bej.2012.04.020.
31. Liu PS. Determination of specific surface area and pore morphology of porous materials. Rare Met Mater Eng. 2006;35(A02):25–29. No. 1002-185X(2006)S2-025-05.
32. http://course.tju.edu.cn/wlhx/pages/exec/jiemian/gn12.1.htm.
33. Fu XC, Shen WX, Yao TY. Physical chemistry (volume 2). Beijing: Higher Education Press; 1990.
34. http://baike.baidu.com/view/637430.htm.
35. Tavana H, Simon F, Grundke K. Interpretation of contact angle measurements on two different fluoropolymers for the determination of solid surface tension. J Colloid Interf Sci. 2005;291 (2):497–506. doi:10.1016/j.jcis.2005.05.001.
36. Chen XM, Wang G, Cheng HT. Determining the contact angles of several plant fibers using mechanics method. J Cent S For Uni Sci Technol. 2011;31(4):192–519. No. 1673-923X(2011) 04-0192-04.
37. Saho XX. Research of the Lewis acids and bases of wood during contact angle analysis. Int Wood Ind. 2003;33(5):35.
38. Mao YA. Study of the carbon fiber surface acid-base property using contact angle determination method. Chin J Polym Mater Sci Eng. 1993;9(5):131–4.

39. Webb PA, Orr C. Analytical methods in fine particle technology. Norcross: Micromeritics; 1997.
40. Bei E, Li JS, Chen CX. Fluid dynamics of porous media. Beijing: China architecture and building Press; 1983.
41. Schroumldinger E, Scheideggcr A, Wang HX. Percolation physics in porous media. Beijing: Petroleum industry Press; 1982.
42. Xu YM. Wood science. Beijing: China forestry publishing; 2006.
43. Li JH, Yu SY. Water activity study of the shaft model solid state fermentation medium. Sci Technol Food Ind. 2007;27(2):77–9. doi:10.13386/j.issn1002-0306.2006.12.016.
44. Zheng YH, Hua ZL, Ma YZ. Determination of water activity in food. Mod Instrum. 2006;12 (2):11–4.
45. Luo YR. Chemical bond energy of modern science and its application. Hefei: Press of University of Science and Technology of China; 2008.
46. Fu XC, Shen WX, Yao TY. Physical chemistry, vol. 1. Beijing: Higher Education Press; 2006.
47. Yu QS, Fang WJ. Liquid enthalpy determination of oil fraction obtained from Xinjiang crude oil. Petrol Proc Petrochem. 1995;26(8):55–8.
48. Lu L, Lu F, Luo YH. Heat conductivity determination of rice straw using probe method. J Shanghai Jiaotong Univ. 2009;9:1461–1464. No. 1006-2467(2009)09-1461-04+1468.
49. Lin JG, Chen RY, Yang QX. Determination of wood radial thermal conductivity using analogy method. J Biomath. 2005;20(2):251–255. No. 1001-9626(2005)02-0251-05.
50. Samaniuk J, Wang J, Root T. Rheology of concentrated biomass. Korea-AustRheol. 2011;J23 (4):237–45. doi:10.1007/s13367-011-0029-z.
51. Ehrhardt MR. Rheology of biomass. 2008. University of Wisconsin, Master's thesis.

Chapter 6
Applications of Gas Explosion in Biomass Refining

6.1 Applications of Gas Explosion in Food Industry

Food industry mainly refers to the process using products from agriculture, fisheries, livestock, forestry, or the chemical industry as raw materials for food or semi-finished products production. The food industry is industrial system that presents a continuous and organized economic activity. Chinese food industry is currently in the stage of early processing of food ingredients and the degree of fine processing of relatively low. Gas explosion technique is originally used for wood processing. However, since the gas explosion technology systems are used to treat raw materials by heating and instant relief of pressure, it can also be used in food processing and treatments for the recycling of food processing residues. The specific technology favors to change low level of mechanization, single processing means, and low efficiency of component utilization in the current food processing industry.

6.1.1 *Processing of Fruit and Vegetable Residue*

With the improvement of people's living standards and changes of consumer attitudes, physical squeeze treatments of raw fruits and vegetables to obtain juice become more and more popular due to the convenience of drinking, easy preservation, and more retaining of nutrients in fruits and vegetables. However, with the mass production of fruit and vegetable juice, more residues of fresh fruit and vegetables are produced; for example, generally every processing of 1000 tons of apple produces about 300 tons of apple pomace. Since the fresh residues from fresh fruit and vegetables have higher water content, low pH value (3–4), relatively little nutritional content, poor palatability, and easy to rancidity, the direct usage of the fresh pomace as animal feed is very difficult. Therefore, the residues from fresh fruit

H. Chen, *Gas Explosion Technology and Biomass Refinery*,
DOI 10.1007/978-94-017-7414-7_6

and vegetables obtained while squeezing are dried and treated by fermentation as feed in most fruit and vegetable processing plants [1].

According to the analysis, dried apple residue contains 14.5 % pectin, 6.2 % crude protein, 6.8 % crude fat, 2.3 % ash, 0.06 % calcium, 0.06 % phosphate, and 16.9 % dietary fiber [2]. Dietary fiber has many important physiological functions to human body, and it is a kind of important functional food makings. Dietary fiber could increase the satiety, reduce food intake, stimulate the intestinal wall, and enhance peristalsis function. In addition, dietary fiber plays an important role in the prevention and treatment of obesity, diabetes, arteriosclerosis, coronary heart disease, hypertension, hyperlipidemia, constipation, and colon cancer. Europe, USA, Japan, and other developed countries have used dietary fiber as additives in all kinds of food, such as biscuits, bread, pastry, noodles, drinks, and dairy products. In the food industry, development of functional foods that are rich in dietary fiber has become a trend. With varieties of fiber and the final product, adding amount of dietary fiber usually ranges from 3 to 30 %. China's functional food market is about 20 billion yuan, which has a huge potential. Thus, the market prospect of dietary fiber consumption is very broad. To prepare dietary fiber and other valuable materials from the apple residue by using the existing technologies can not only solve the problem of apple processing enterprises by improving the added value of apple processing products, but also solve the problem of environmental pollution and provide more ways for the comprehensive utilization of apple residue. Currently, due to the poor taste of fruit and vegetable residue, the effective components of soluble dietary fiber cannot be absorbed adequately. The traditional process of dietary fiber preparation by apple residue, which includes acidic cooking to remove peculiar smell, alkali processing to remove proteins, dehydration by filtration, and squeezing and drying, presents high production costs due to the multiple processing steps. In addition, partially soluble dietary fiber, proteins, and other active ingredients still cannot be utilized fully. Although high-pressure homogenization or ultrasonic cell wall-breaking method can make full use of soluble dietary fiber in the residue from fruit and vegetable, the energy consumptions of pressure homogenizer (15–30 Mpa) and ultrasonic wall-breaking machines are high for the industrial production and there is no high-pressure homogenizer and ultrasonic wall-breaking machines especially for the treatment of fruit and vegetable residue.

Gas-phase explosion is to heat the material to a certain temperature by gas medium and maintain the pressure for a certain time followed by an instant relief of pressure. In this process, the material structure is destroyed by the mechanical force formed by the gas explosion. When gas-phase explosion technology is used to extract dietary fiber from fruit and vegetable residue, the acid/base treatment is not required, which essentially reduces operating process and processing cost. Due to its autocatalytic reaction in the high-temperature cooking and cell wall damage by the instantaneous pressure relief, the extraction yield of the dietary fiber is improved and sugars from hemicellulose degradation, which is rich in bifidus factors, could also be recycled. This technology makes full use of the fruit and vegetable residue resources, reduces the environmental pollution, and makes waste profitable.

The treatment of fruit and vegetable residue using steam explosion is as follows: The fruit and vegetable residue with 20–35 % water content is loaded into the steam explosion tank, the saturated steam is then aerated to allow the pressure of tank reaching 0.8–1.5 Mpa, and the pressure is maintained for 1–5 min. After that, the ball valve is opened immediately to discharge the fruit and vegetable residue into the atmospheric pressure cyclone separator. In this process, the cell wall of fruit and vegetable residue is destroyed and the soluble sugar (the main component of bifidus factors) from the degradation of hemicellulose in the fruit and vegetable residue is released. The cell wall of the fruit and vegetable residue could be processed into dietary fiber by directly applying drying and crushing process. In addition, the cell wall could also be used for the extraction of organic acid.

The fruit and vegetable residue mainly refers to residue from apple, pear, and vegetable processing, and its moisture content is usually controlled at 15–40 %. The moisture content of fresh fruit and vegetable residue before steam explosion is 66.0 %, and the taste is poor. After appropriate squeezing, the moisture content is then controlled at 35 % before steam explosion treatment. After steam explosion treatment, the fruit and vegetable residue shows homogeneous shape with moisture content about 70 %. About 15 % of the crude fiber is degraded into soluble dietary fiber. The advantages of steam explosion treatment of fruit and vegetable residue are as follows: (1) The swelling medium used is steam, and the cost is relatively low; (2) in the process of steam explosion treatment, no water or acid/base chemicals are added and no organic wastewater is produced and no ingredients are lost; (3) due to the effective destroying of cell wall, the intracellular substances could be released sufficiently, which favors the processing of cell wall from fruit and vegetable residue into dietary fiber; (4) in the steam explosion process, the hemicellulose in the cell walls of fruit and vegetable residue could be degraded into functional sugars which could be more fully utilized; and (5) finally, the fruit and vegetable residue is used in a high-value way.

6.1.2 Meat Residue Processing

With the rapid development of Chinese meat industry, a large meat processing enterprise has developed into a complete system consisting of livestock procurement, slaughtering and processing, meat product processing, and frozen transportation. During the slaughter process, a lot of meat by-products are produced, such as bone, skeleton, bone cake, fat, and oil residue. These by-products are often considered as low-value products, some of them are sold cheaply as animal feed, while some of them cannot be used and will create some environmental issues from their storage and disposition [3]. Compared with other conventional processing ways, gas-phase explosion technology can improve the utilization rate of meat processing residues, increase its utilization value, and solve the environmental pollution problem due to storage, which provides a new potential way for the reprocessing of the by-products from meat processing. In this section, the relevant applications of gas explosion technology in the processing of meat by-products (e.g., liver, bone, leather, and feather) are elaborated.

6.1.2.1 Animal Gut Processing

In the slaughtering and processing of livestock and poultry, a large amount of by-products are produced. At present, in addition to direct edible, these by-products have three utilization ways: food ingredients, biological chemical products, and feed. The most valuable way is the biological chemical products, which can be used as raw materials for biochemical drugs. The produced drugs have some advantages: fewer side effects, easy to be absorbed by body, and high added value. The economic value of some products has exceeded the value of the meat itself. Therefore, to vigorously organize and promote the comprehensive utilization of animal by-products will provide a convenient way for the improvement of enterprise efficiency.

Chicken intestine is the residue from chicken slaughter processing, which is numerous, low cost, and rich in nutritious substances. Using chicken intestine as a feed can reduce the pollution to the environment, save the grain, and improve the breeding benefit. However, the microbial species and quantity in the chicken intestine environment are quite abundant and some are pathogens, resulting in the difficulty to directly use as feed. Besides, if the chicken intestine is not handled in time, it will easily pollute the environment. Gas-phase explosion is to heat the material to a certain temperature by gas medium and maintain the pressure for a certain time followed by an instant relief of pressure. In this process, the material structure is destroyed by the mechanical force of gas explosion. Therefore, through the use of gas-phase explosion, the chicken intestine is disinfected during the high-temperature cooking with steam and then crushed by the instantaneous relief of pressure. The author uses gas explosion to process the mixture of the chicken intestine and bran to prepare feed, which not only reduces the waste pollution to the environment, but also reduces the use of protein feed and improves the economic efficiency. The procedures of steam explosion are as follows: Mix the chicken intestine with the bran in advance and control the water content. The temperature required for steam explosion treatment is about 150–180 °C, and the maintaining time is 8–10 min. After instantaneous decompression, the steam-exploded products with graininess and light brown or yellow color are obtained. The steam-exploded chicken intestine could be used as protein feed alone or in combination with other feeds after drying.

6.1.2.2 Feather Processing

The poultry feathers are rich in a variety of essential amino acids which can be used as ideal protein sources of animal feed, but have not been effectively utilized. Currently, the poultry feather processing technologies mainly include high-pressure boiling hydrolysis method, acid and alkali hydrolysis method, extrusion method, enzymatic hydrolysis, and microbial fermentation [4].

High-pressure boiling hydrolysis method is used to cook the feathers for certain time by high-temperature steam and crack the disulfide linkage of cystine of feather proteins. The vapor pressure must be more than 138 kPa which can achieve the goal of chemical bond breakage in feather proteins. The characteristics of this method are easy to control, but energy consuming. In addition, the longtime heating can destroy some of the heat sensitivity of amino acids, reducing some amino acid digestibility.

The acid and alkali hydrolysis is to immerse feather into a certain concentration of acid (hydrochloric acid and phosphoric acid) or alkali (sodium hydroxide) and heat to hydrolyze the feather. After then, the hydrolysate is then neutralized by clean water and dehydrated to the finished products. This process destroys disulfide bonds of keratin protein, so that the feather proteins are broken down into the digestible and absorbable state. Compared with high-pressure cooking hydrolysis method, acid and alkali hydrolysis results in the feather easier to digest. However, the equipment requirement is higher and the cost is larger. Moreover, the numerous salts generated by neutralization lead to the enhancement of product moisture absorption and inhibit the growth of animals due to the excessive salt in the feed.

Enzymatic hydrolysis and microbial fermentation are used to process the feather by special strain fermentation or to hydrolyze the feather into protein hydrolysate by protease actions. However, the equipment investment of this method is high, and scale-up production is not easy.

Feather meal protein made using the above methods as feed protein source has amino acid imbalance, such as low lysine content, which limits the application of feather powder as feed. The author used steam explosion to treat the mixture of feather and bran and crack the disulfide bond in the feather keratin to improve the crude protein content of feather meal and pepsin digestibility. After that, the steam-exploded feather is then treated by lactobacillus solid-state fermentation to enhance the ratio of lysine to tryptophan, balance the ratio of amino acids in the feather powder, and produce high-quality feather protein powder [5].

The procedures of high-value feather protein powder preparation by steam explosion include the following: (1) 50 kg cleaned feather is mixed with 25 kg wheat bran and then loaded in the reaction tank; (2) the reaction tank is then heated by steam to 130 °C for 5 min followed by the exhaust of steam to decrease the water content of feather to 30–50 %; (3) the reaction tank is heated to 150 °C for 15 min followed by the instantaneous decompression to release the raw materials; (4) the obtained product is further crushed to pass through 20-mm mesh; (5) the ground product is further dried at 80 °C for 12 h; and (6) 40 kg dried product is inoculated by lactobacillus for anaerobic fermentation at 37 °C for 2 h. After determination, the obtained feather protein powder contains 90 % crude protein and the pepsin digestibility is as high as 95 %. A high-value feather protein powder is shown in Fig. 6.1.

Fig. 6.1 Schematic diagram of high-value feather protein powder

6.1.2.3 Leather Waste Processing

In recent 10 years, China has developed into a center of leather production, processing, and trade. However, with the rapid development of leather industry, serious environmental pollution is accompanied. The chromium collagen (waste leather scraps) generated from the shaving and trimming of leather-making process is one of the main pollutions of leather production. It is reported that in the traditional leather industry, 1 t of wet skin can only produce about 200 kg of finished leather and produce more than 600 kg of solid wastes. About 1.4 million tons of solid leather wastes is produced per year in China [6]. In addition, leather goods also have durable years, and after they are abandoned, all the leather goods will become garbage. The main ingredients are proteins and will rot after stacking for a long time, which causes serious pollution to the ecological environment. The development and utilization of leather waste, converting pollutants into useful resources, thereby avoiding pollution and damage to the environment, already is an important issue to be solved before us.

The primary components of leather waste are collagen (about 90 % in a dry basis) which is a kind of widespread animal protein. The most promising processing way of leather waste is to take off the chromium and extract collagen protein and its degradation products.

The collagen extracted from leather wastes is purified and modified to prepare spinning solutions with certain concentration and viscosity and squeezed into the liquid solidification from the nozzle hole to form the silks. After the subsequent drying and drawing processing, the collagen fiber that can be used as textile is obtained.

Compared with general plant protein fiber, collagen fiber is more suitable for spinning production of protein fiber. This is because that collagen is a fibrous protein and has a unique bar–spiral structure and its physical and mechanical properties are very superior and the collagen fiber strength is higher than that of plant protein.

The moisturizing properties of collagen are especially excellent. When moisture content of furs and leather shoes prepared by collagen is 30 %, people do not feel wet, and it makes people feel very comfortable. The clothes prepared by spinning collagen fiber will partially have the properties of the natural leather, thus greatly improving the product grade. The raw materials of collagen are extracted from natural animal skin, its structure is quiet similar to human skin, and therefore, it has very good affinity to human skin.

Extracting collagen from leather wastes has a history of nearly a century. As early as in 1928, Italians had reported that. For decades, foreign scholars have carried out extensive research and the domestic research started relatively late in this respect. The key of leather waste recycling is to remove Cr^{3+} from the leather waste. The extraction method can be divided into alkali treatment, acid treatment, oxidation method, and enzyme method [7].

Alkali treatment method is based on the much higher complexing ability with chromium of free hydroxyl group than collagen carboxyl group. The treating agents used in the alkali treatment include lime, sodium hydroxide, sodium carbonate, and magnesium oxide. Extracting collagen from leather waste using lime is the first research method with the most practical applications. Compared with acid treatment method, alkali treatment method is simple and has higher elimination rate of chromium. However, due to the hydrolysis of protein by alkali, the collagen products obtained by this method show smaller molecular weight with relatively low application value. Acid treatment method is to treat leather waste with strong acid solutions. The high-concentration hydrogen ions can close the collagen carboxyl groups and then weaken the combination of collagen carboxyl and chromium. When organic acids, such as oxalic acid and citric acid, with strong complexing ability are used, the acid ion can directly form complexing structure with chrome and take off the chrome from the collagen carboxyl group to produce the effect of chrome elimination. The extraction efficiency of acid treatment method is much higher than that of alkali and enzymatic methods. However, the degradation degree of collagen molecule is much high, and the molecular weight of obtained collagen products is small. In addition, since Cr^{3+} is dissolved in acidic conditions, it is difficult to separate it thoroughly. Oxidation is to treat the leather waste with antioxidants, such as H_2O_2, and oxidize the Cr^{3+} into Cr^{6+}. After that, the oxidative leather waste is then rinsed and filtered to separate the collagen and chrome. The oxidation method shows higher speed and efficiency for chrome elimination, little damage to the structure of collagen, and higher molecular weight of collagen. However, the process produces toxic Cr^{6+}, and the recycling of hexavelant chromium for the environmental protection purpose should be strengthened for the industrial productions. Enzyme treatment method is also a kind of method studied earlier. The advantages of enzyme treatment method are quick speed, mild conditions, and less damage to the composition of protein, but the molecular weight of collagen hydrolysate is small, and the chrome elimination in advance is necessary.

These conventional methods used to remove chrome from leather are time-consuming and low chrome removal rate (generally below 90 %) and thus have limited applications. For this reason, our team uses steam explosion technology to extract collagen from leather waste. Firstly, the leather waste is pretreated with lime and then exploded at certain steam pressure. The obtained solution is further precipitated by salt to isolate collagen. Compared with the above methods, the technology shows two advantages: The collagen degradation is smaller in the extraction process, and the environmental pollution is decreased. The main experimental steps are as follows: The leather is cut into 3–4-cm scraps and soaked in the saturated solution of CaO for 1–3 days; the pretreated leather is then exploded at certain steam pressure, and the obtained solution is centrifuged and precipitated by $(NH_4)_2SO_4$ to obtain collagen. The effects of soaking time and steam explosion conditions are investigated.

As shown in Table 6.1, the increase of soaking time would enhance the efficiency of steam explosion due to the sufficient pretreatment.

As shown in Table 6.2, the increase of pressure also enhances the efficiency of steam explosion; however, the collagen is hydrolyzed more seriously.

As shown in Table 6.3, the decrease of particle size enhances the efficiency of steam explosion. In order to reduce the effects of steam explosion on the hydrolysis of collagen, the impact of heat pretreatment on steam explosion efficiency is also investigated.

As shown in Table 6.4, the increase of temperature would shorten the pretreatment time and the difference of steam explosion at 40 and 50 °C is little. So for the energy-saving consideration, pretreatment at 40 °C is suitable.

Concluded from the above steam explosion experiments, the leather sheared to 5–10 mm and soaked with saturated solution of calcium oxide for three days would completely explode with the pressure of 1.0 MPa and 15-min maintaining time. Steam-exploded leather could be precipitated with 60 % ammonium sulfate, and sticky collagen is obtained.

Steam explosion treatment could eliminate the chromium from leather with a removal rate of 95 % and significantly shorten the time to remove chromium by oxidation. The mechanism is that under the effect of high temperature and high pressure of saturated water vapor, the higher-order structure of leather collagen

Table 6.1 Effect of soaking time on steam explosion efficiency

	Soaking time (days)	1.5 MPa, 15 min
1	1	Not shattered
2	2	Not shattered
3	3	Most shattered

Table 6.2 Effect of pressure on steam explosion efficiency

	Pressure (Mpa)[a]	Results
1	1.0	Not shattered
2	1.2	Not shattered
3	1.5	Shattered

[a]Pressure maintaining time 15 min

Table 6.3 Effect of particle size on steam explosion efficiency (soaking 3 days)

Pressure Mpa (15 min)	5–10 mm	40–60 mm
1.5	Shattered	Shattered
1.2	Shattered	Not shattered
1.0	Shattered	Not shattered

Table 6.4 Effect of heating on steam explosion efficiency (1.5 MPa, 15 min)

Soaking time (days)	40 °C	50 °C
0.5	Not shattered	Not shattered
1	Not shattered	Not shattered
2	Shattered	Shattered

changes and the intermolecular force is reduced. In the steam cooking process, the arrangement regularity of macromolecular chain reduces, and in some cases, the macromolecular chain is degraded into small molecular chains. The subsequent sudden pressure relief accelerates the process, and Cr^{3+} falls off the peptide chain under the action of alkaline material such as CaO and NaOH. In addition, after the removal of chromium, leather can be used for the preparation of gelatin or animal protein feed.

6.1.3 Marine Products Processing

Ocean is the resource treasure for human survival and development. More than 200 thousand species live in the ocean and account for 80 % of all species on the earth. Among the vast species, some are applied as food, medicine, and other economic aspects and called marine products. These biological resources survive in the unique ocean environment with high pressure, high salt, low nutrition, and low temperature. In the long evolution process, the special structures and wonderful physiological functions are formed, which provide human beings with many novel structure and unique features of active substances, including polysaccharide, unsaturated fatty acids, alkaloids, active peptides, and proteins. For example, algin and agarose do not exist in the terrestrial organisms and they are natural treasure for human health care, medicine, and biological functional materials [8].

Currently, the processing technology of marine products has followed the traditional extraction methods which consume large energy and high dosage of chemicals. Steam explosion technology could be applied to the extraction of active substances, which could shorten extraction time and decrease production cost. In this section, the author will introduce the works related to steam explosion technology applied in the algae cell wall breakage and chitin extracted from shrimp shell.

6.1.3.1 Chitin Extraction from Shrimp Shell

Chitin is a natural polysaccharide consisting of N-acetyl-D-meglumine sugar connected by glycosidic bonds. It abounds in the carapace of invertebrate and arthropod and is also found in the cell wall of low-grade plants. The chitin is light beige to white, soluble in acid, and insoluble in alkali and other solvents, and also it does not dissolve in water. Chitosan is a product of chitin deacetylation and dissolves in water. The structure of chitin is similar with that of cellulose, and its molecular weight depends on its origin and subsequent processing, generally ranging between 10^5 and 10^7. Because of having similar structure as cellulose, the chitin with cation possesses special physical and chemical properties, which is widely used in medicine, food, chemicals, wastewater treatment, biological engineering, and agriculture.

The feedstock for chitin and chitosan is abundant, and at present, they are primarily prepared by using shrimp and crab shells as raw materials. In general, the components of shrimp shell are chitin, protein, and mineral ingredients, in which the mineral ingredients are the most. Thus, for the preparation of chitin, the main aim is to remove protein and calcium carbonate. There are mainly two ways to remove minerals. One is to use acid to react with carbonate ions and remove minerals by the formation of carbon dioxide. The most commonly used acid is hydrochloric acid; however, after treatment with hydrochloric acid, the chitin could be acetylated and the molecular chain of chitin could also be broken, which leads to the decrease in molecular weight. The other way is to use ethylenediaminetetraacetic acid instead of hydrochloric acid. By this process, the shrimp shell can be treated in a neutral environment and the produced chitin is not easy to deform. The degradation of molecular chains is reduced, and the molecular chains keep relatively intact. Thus, this method can produce higher molecular weight chitin. The disadvantages of this method are the long processing time and high processing cost. Some scholars also suggested that mild acids, such as acetic acid, sulfurous acid, or formic acid, could also be used to remove minerals in shell.

Proteins are another main component of shell raw materials. There are also two main ways to remove proteins: One way is to use alkali, usually sodium hydroxide, and the other way is to use biological treatment, such as protease. If alkali is used to remove protein, its action time is short and effect is good (removal rate 99.5–100 %). Compared with alkali, the advantages of using enzymes to remove proteins are operating at low temperature which has less effect on molecular chain degradation and reduces acetylation of chitin. However, the required time for processing is long, and the efficiency of removing protein is low (90–97 %). Therefore, the protein removal by enzyme is less adopted. In general, the quality of chitin is often evaluated with reference to ash and heavy metal content, and the superior chitin possesses low content of ash and heavy metal. In addition, the molecular weight and viscosity are also commonly used as reference index for the raw material processing or determination of the final product function.

From the above process (Fig. 6.2), it can be found that the chemical preparation of chitin has tedious steps, longer operating time, and large dosage of chemical

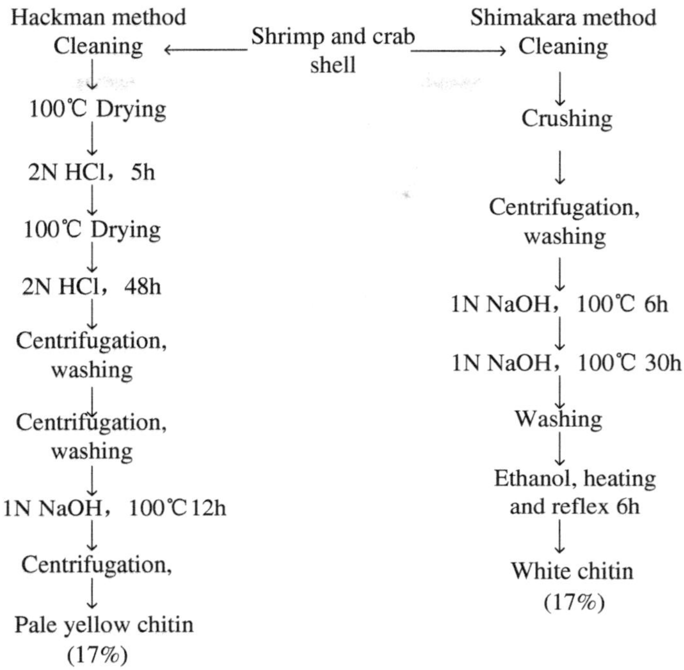

Fig. 6.2 Processes for the chemical preparation of chitin

reagents, especially acid and alkali. Steam explosion technology is used to heat the raw materials to a certain temperature, maintain a certain time, and instantly release the pressure to produce secondary steam and enhance the volume. The structure of raw materials is destroyed by the mechanical force. The process is as follows: The shrimp shells are loaded through the tank inlet, and steam is aerated to certain pressure. After maintaining for certain time, the ball valve is opened immediately to discharge the shrimp shells into the atmospheric pressure buffer tank. In this process, shrimp shell is broken, and substances such as chitin are exposed. The steam-exploded shrimp shell is then washed by water to obtain chitin.

Mikiji Shigematsu and his coworkers [9] from Giff University in Japan also used steam explosion to extract chitin from crab shell. The crab shell was ground first and then soaked in acetic acid solution. After that, the crab shell is treated at 230 °C for 16 min and then exploded instantaneously. The chitin obtained from the improved process of steam explosion undergoes simpler purification and post-processing technology. The obtained chitin is fiber-shaped and possesses higher N-acetyl groups, slightly higher crystallinity, and low molecular weight compared with the chitin prepared by Hackman method.

6.1.3.2 Algae Processing

Algae are grown in the sea, which includes several different classes of creatures to produce energy by photosynthesis. Algae are one of the most abundant sources of functional foods and seaweed chemical products. They are rich in nutrients such as high-quality protein, gamma-linolenic acid, and beta-carotene. *Spirulina* sp. is chosen as the most nutritious foods in the future by the United Nations. Algae are not only one of the most important sources of human food in the future, but also the important resources for the preparation of seaweed polysaccharide products such as agar and carrageenan.

China has very abundant seaweed resources. The algae cell has a thick layer composed of cellulose, hemicellulose, and other complex polysaccharides (algae rubber). The processing of algae in the today's world is mostly with acid, alkali, high temperature, and high pressure to destroy the cell wall. As in agar production process, sulfuric acid is added to destroy algae cell walls. The technologies used to extract chemical products from seaweed are of high costs, low processing utilization rate, and easy to cause environmental pollution.

Algae cell wall breakage by steam explosion does not add any chemicals and solves the currently existing issues of large economic seaweed processing, which include the high processing cost, low processing efficiency, and environmental pollutions. The process is as follows [10]: The equipment used is a large steam explosion tank with a quickly opening door and double inlet (high-pressure air and saturated steam). Through the quickly opening door, the algae are loaded into the tank. The saturated steam is inputted to allow the temperature of tank reaching 60–100 °C, and after 1–8 min, the steam valve is closed. The high-pressure air inlet valve is then opened to make the tank pressure 0.8–1.5 Mpa. Finally, the ball valve is immediately opened to discharge the algae into the atmospheric pressure tank. In the process, the algae cell wall is broken and the inclusions are released. The treated algae could be used as algae functional food directly after drying or as raw material to extract agar and other chemical products.

The algae obtained using steam explosion could be used as food directly without grinding, which are easy to digest and have unique puffed food flavor. The algae without steam explosion need special grinding for food processing, and other flavor materials should be added due to the insufficient utilization of intracellular nutrient. The agar extraction from steam-exploded algae can simplify the acidolysis pretreatment process and increase the yield by 5–10 % compared with untreated algae. The described algae mainly refer to the large-scale economic algae and microalgae with a moisture content of 25 %. The moisture content of algae after steam explosion is about 40 %.

The advantages of algae cell wall breakage by steam explosion include the following: (1) The expanding media is steam, and the cost is low; (2) not additional acid/base is added in the steam explosion process without the generation of vast organic wastewater and loss of active ingredients; (3) due to the effective breakage of cell wall, the utilization rate of raw material and extraction yield is greatly improved; and (4) less equipment investment and simple operation are needed.

6.1.4 Food Processing

Starch is the main raw material of food, medicine, chemical industry, and textile. The technology level of starch industry in China has been developing rapidly in recent years. Corn with an average of 71.3 % starch content has become a main cereal for human and livestock as well as the important industrial raw material.

At present, there are mainly two mature industrialization routes using corn starch as raw materials, one is represented by Dupont to prepare 1.3—propylene glycol by biological fermentation, and the other is represented by CDP Company from the joint of CARGILL and DOW CHEMICAL to prepare poly-lactic acid using biological fermentation. Our team develops a new process using steam explosion to complete the crushing of corn and separation of corn components, which includes steam explosion, coproducing alcohol-soluble protein and uranidin, and subsequent fermentation. Compared with conventional corn utilization, the process shows low energy consumption, low pollution, and economy feasibility, which leads to the high-value utilization of resources of corn (Fig. 6.3).

Prof. Hongzhang Chen from Institute of Processing Engineering, Chinese Academy of Sciences, established a new corn component separation process by steam explosion and created a new way for the high-value utilization of corn. Steam explosion is a feasible way for corn component separation. Compared with the existing corn component separation, this technique shows low energy consumption, little pollution, less process, short treatment time, and good separation effect. The conditions of steam explosion are relative to the moisture content of corn grain and the dense degree of corn structure. The optimized steam explosion process is to adjust the moisture content of corn to more than 30 %, the pressure is 1.0–1.5 MPa, and the maintaining time is 3–5 min. Steam explosion can not only realize the separation in the plant tissue level, which is the separation of embryo, endosperm, and corn husk, but also loosen the internal structure of corn to favor the extraction of intracellular substances. The hot and humid medium can also gelatinize the starch and omit the pregelatinization of maize endosperm, which is helpful to the high-value utilization of corn.

6.1.5 Roughage Processing

The 60 % of the crop straw contains carbohydrates which are raw materials for the fermentation industry. If the vast crop straw could be converted into feed grains, it would save a lot of food and solve the problem caused by the competition of human and animal for food and also can solve the problem of environmental pollution caused by straw burning. The effect of straw used directly as feed is poor. In order to improve the nutritional value of straw as feed, various means to change its natural structure and enhance nutritional value have been adopted.

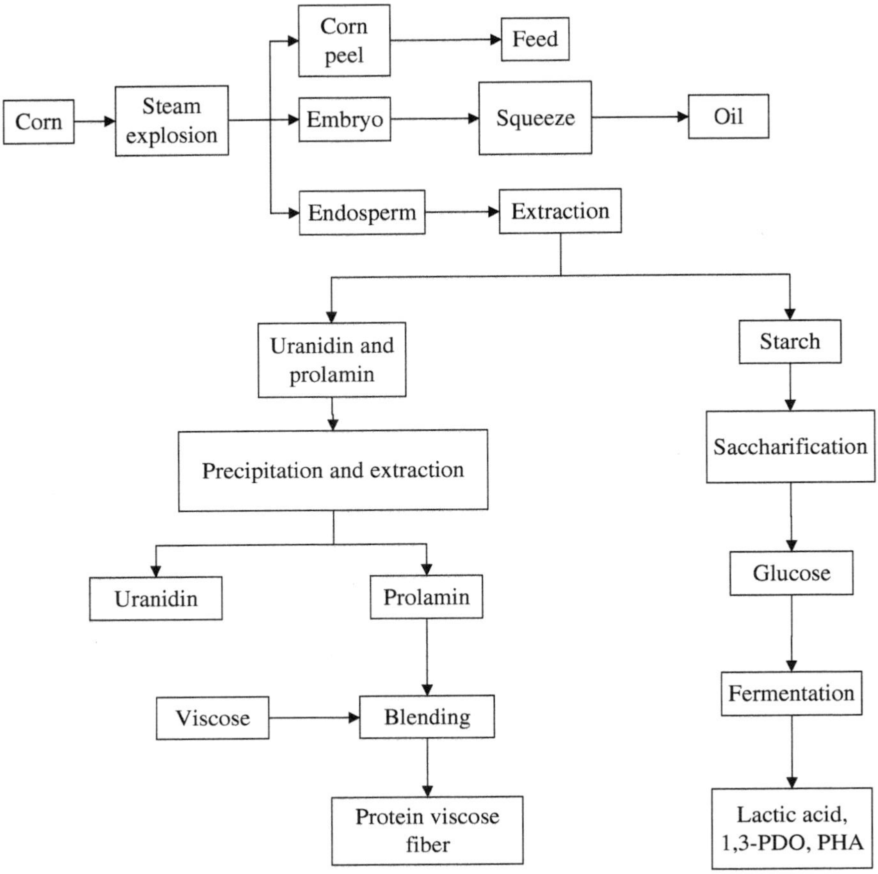

Fig. 6.3 Corn deep processing process diagram

Currently, widely used processing method is limited to silage and ammoniation. The processing quality is not high, the quality is not stable, and the effective ingredients of the products are not fixed. The processing ability of harmful bacteria and pesticide residues is poor, resulting in the high content of harmful substances in the products and high risk for pathogenic infection and metamorphism. The products should be stored for a long time and not convenient to transport.

Straw ammoniation technique can increase the nitrogen content of straw, partly change the natural structure, and increase the digestion rate, but the increase of straw nutritional value is limited. Steam explosion is a physical and chemical pretreatment method of straw. After steam explosion, the close union of lignin, cellulose, and hemicellulose in the straw cell wall is broken, the hydroxyl groups are fully exposed, the accessibility is increased, and the degradation rate and enzymolysis rate of carbohydrates are greatly improved. Through fermentation processing, the content of protein and sugar absorption rate of livestock are enhanced. Therefore, steam-exploded straw can partly replace corn starch as feed raw materials, reducing the pressure on the supply of feed grains, which is of great significance to ensure domestic food security. At the same time, the scale-up and commercialization of straw feed are also realized. Prof. Chen from Institute of Process Engineering, Chinese Academy of Sciences, used steam explosion to ammoniate straw, and the ammoniated straw is further processed by solid-state fermentation to improve the nutritional characteristics of straw. The influences of solid-state fermentation on protein feed are also investigated [11].

6.1.5.1 Ammoniated Steam Explosion of Straw

300 g corn stover after adding 5 and 15 % of ammonia and hydrogen peroxide solution according to the solid–liquid ratio of 1:1 was used for steam explosion. The conditions of steam explosion are 1.5 MPa pressure and 8-min maintaining time. The ammoniated straw is then extracted by water to determine total sugar and reducing sugar in the filtrate. The substrate and cellulose enzyme were weighed and added to the 0.2 mol/L acetate–sodium acetate buffer. The enzymatic hydrolysis experiments were carried out in a 50 °C shaker with the speed of 160 r/min. The enzymatic hydrolysis rate is calculated.

The strains for solid-state fermentation of straw after ammoniated steam explosion were *Penicillium decumbens* JU—A101 and *Phanerochate chrysporium* ME—4461. The medium formula is as follows: 4.5 g ammoniated straw, 0.5 g bran, 0.25 g $(NH_4)_2$ SO_4, 0.1 g K_2HPO_4, 0.08 g KH_2P0_4, and 0.01 g $MgSO_4$–$2H_2O$. The solid–liquid ratio was 1:2.5, and the fermentation time was 4 d.

The content changes of straw cellulose, hemicellulose, and lignin before and after treatment were determined, and the change of nitrogen content was also investigated. The nitrogen of treated straw after washing was insoluble nitrogen, and the soluble nitrogen was obtained by subtracting total nitrogen from insoluble nitrogen. The protein content was determined by Kjeldahl method.

As shown in Table 6.5, ammoniated steam explosion has greatly increased the degradation rate of hemicellulose compared with unprocessed raw materials, and the increase of ammonia concentration is beneficial to the degradation rate. When the ammonia concentration was 5 and 15 %, hemicellulose degradation rate was 46.5 and 52.2 %, respectively. The cellulose content was stable during the ammoniated steam explosion, while the lignin content increased, which was probably due to the pseudo-lignin generated during the treatment. The cleavage of lignin–ether bond during the explosion process enhanced its activity and caused the reaction with degraded hemicellulose to form humic acid.

The total sugar content of straw increased after ammoniated steam explosion, which was caused by the degradation of hemicellulose. When the ammonia concentrations were 5 and 15 %, the total sugar content was 22.6 and 32.3 % higher than the unprocessed raw material and the reducing sugar content was significantly reduced after ammoniated steam explosion. The reason still needs further research.

Table 6.5 The changes of chemical components of ammoniated steam-exploded straw (%, dry matter)

Ammonia	Hemicellulose	Cellulose	Lignin	Total sugar	Reducing sugar	Enzymatic hydrolysis	Total nitrogen	Soluble nitrogen	Insoluble nitrogen
0	35.38	26.03	6.83	4.07	5.32	12.89	1.06	0.02	1.04
5	18.93	26.80	11.30	4.99	4.05	38.68	1.62	0.62	1.01
15	16.93	27.15	12.43	5.41	2.41	41.98	2.41	1.23	1.18

The enzymatic hydrolysis rate increased greatly after ammoniated steam explosion. When the ammonia concentrations were 5 %, the digestion rate increased three times and 3.25 times, respectively. This indicates that significant changes have taken place in the structure and chemical composition of steam exploded materials, and these changes will help digestion. In the ammoniation process, ammonia addition is mainly to increase the straw nitrogen content. In the experiments, ammonia concentration was 5 and 15 %, and the total nitrogen content was 1.62 and 2.41 %, respectively, which were increased 0.52 and 1.27 times, respectively, compared with the unprocessed raw material.

6.1.5.2 Ammoniated Steam Explosion with Addition of Hydrogen Peroxide

In the ammoniation process, nitrogen fixation happens on the carbonyl and carboxyl groups of lignin, and the existence of oxidant can increase the number of these groups, thereby increasing the ammoniation effect. Therefore, this experiment also examined the effect of ammoniated steam explosion on the corn straw composition when adding hydrogen peroxide. The results are shown in Table 6.6.

As shown in Tables 6.5 and 6.6, when the ammonia concentration was the same, the hydrogen peroxide addition had impacts on the degradation of straw hemicellulose, the content of total sugar and reducing sugar, enzymatic hydrolysis rate, and total nitrogen content. When ammonia concentration was 5 %, after hydrogen peroxide addition, the hemicellulose degradation rate could reach 54.7 %, the total sugar content increased by 49.4 % compared with that of unprocessed straw, the reducing sugar content decreased by 16.9 %, the digestion rate increased by 3.13 times, and the total nitrogen content increased by 0.75 times. All these indexes had improved significantly than ammoniated steam explosion without hydrogen peroxide addition. When the ammonia concentration was 15 %, the trend was similar.

In a word, the straw could be ammoniated in the high temperature and short treatment time (8 min) by steam explosion. Compared with ammoniation at normal temperature (30 d), the time of ammoniation is shortened and the nitrogen content of straw after ammoniation increases obviously. Since the natural structure is changed during the steam explosion process, the treated straw is enriched with a large number of fermentable carbon source and nitrogen source.

6.1.5.3 Protein Feed Prepared from Solid-State Fermentation of Ammoniated Steam Explosion Cornstalk

The components of ammoniated steam-exploded straw after solid-state fermentation are shown in Table 6.7. After solid-state fermentation, hemicellulose and cellulose of straw were further degraded. When the ammonia concentration was 5 and 15 %, hemicellulose degradation after solid-state fermentation was 26.5 and 28.2 %, respectively. The cellulose was degraded by 43.6 and 55.5 %, respectively. For the

Table 6.6 The changes of chemical components of ammoniated steam-exploded straw with hydrogen peroxide blasting addition

Ammonia	H_2O_2	Hemicellulose	Cellulose	Lignin	Total sugar	Reducing sugar	Enzymatic hydrolysis	Total nitrogen	Soluble nitrogen
0	0	35.38	26.03	6.83	4.07	5.32	12.89	1.06	0.02
5	10	16.03	27.77	10.67	6.08	4.55	40.35	1.85	0.73
15	10	15.87	25.63	11.65	5.41	2.91	42.97	2.52	1.23
15[1]	10	15.02	29.52	10.93	5.41	2.47	40.94	2.46	1.18

1 The samples without impregnation

Table 6.7 Components' change after solid-state fermentation (%, dry matter)

Ammonia	H_2O_2	Hemicellulase	Cellulose	Lignin	Dry matter loss (%)	Protein content (%)
0	0	34.13	24.17	12.57	18.4	11.55
5	0	13.92	15.12	14.08	24.0	18.90
15	0	12.15	12.08	14.70	25.2	23.80

untreated straw after solid-state fermentation, the degradation rate of hemicellulose and cellulose was very low, which was 3.53 and 7.15 %, respectively. Thus, after ammoniation process, the natural structure of straw was changed and became more conducive to microbial decomposition of cellulose and hemicellulose.

Due to the microbial metabolism during solid-state fermentation, part of raw material is decomposed into water and carbon dioxide, which causes weightlessness of raw material. From the perspective of microbial metabolism, the weightlessness reflects the activity of microbial growth. As shown in Table 6.7, for the straw after ammoniated steam explosion, weightlessness rate of substrates increased significantly after fermentation and the value increased with the increase of ammonia concentration. When the ammonia concentration was 5 and 15 %, the weightlessness rate was 24 and 25.2 %, respectively. The microorganisms adopted in the experiments could not utilize lignin, and the lignin content in the raw material was constant. Due to the weightlessness of substrates during the fermentation, lignin content increased relatively after fermentation (Table 6.7).

6.1.5.4 Solid-State Fermentation of Cornstalk Treated by Ammoniated Steam Explosion with Addition of Hydrogen Peroxide

The results of solid-state fermentation of cornstalk treated by ammoniated steam explosion with addition of hydrogen peroxide are shown in Table 6.8.

After solid-state fermentation, cellulose and hemicellulose were further degraded. However, from the perspective of the loss of dry matter after fermentation, the effect of hydrogen peroxide addition was negative to microbial fermentation. When the ammonia content was 5 %, the weightlessness rate with hydrogen peroxide

Table 6.8 Components' change of ammoniated steam-exploded straw with hydrogen peroxide addition after solid-state fermentation (%, dry matter)

Ammonia	H_2O_2	Hemicellulase	Cellulose	Lignin	Dry matter loss (%)	Protein content (%)
5	0	34.13	24.17	12.57	21.6	11.55
5	10	11.75	12.4	12.3	24.0	20.65
15	10	10.37	12.23	14.03	16.8	23.45
15[1]	10	14.45	15.73	9.83	25.2	21.7

1 The samples without impregnation

addition was 21.6 %, while the weightlessness rate without hydrogen peroxide addition was 24.0 %. When the ammonia content was 15 %, the weightlessness rate with hydrogen peroxide addition was 16.8 %, while the weightlessness rate without hydrogen peroxide addition was 25.2 %. This suggests that adding hydrogen peroxide is not conducive to the growth of microbial metabolism; this may be due to the oxidative decomposition of lignin by hydrogen peroxide in the process of ammoniation, which produces small molecular substances to inhibit the microorganism growth.

Prof. Chen Hongzhang and his coworkers also proved that digestion rate increased significantly after the ammoniated steam explosion of straw (Figs. 6.4 and 6.5). After the addition of 15 % ammonia, 5 % $(NH_4)_2SO_3$, 5 % urea, and 10 % NH_4HCO_3, the steam explosion of corn straw was performed under the pressure of 1.5 MPa and the maintaining time of 1.5 min according to the solid–liquid ratio of 1:1. The digestibility determination of steam-exploded straw showed that the treatment group with addition of 5 % $(NH_4)_2SO_3$ had the highest digestibility (71.2 %, in vitro) and

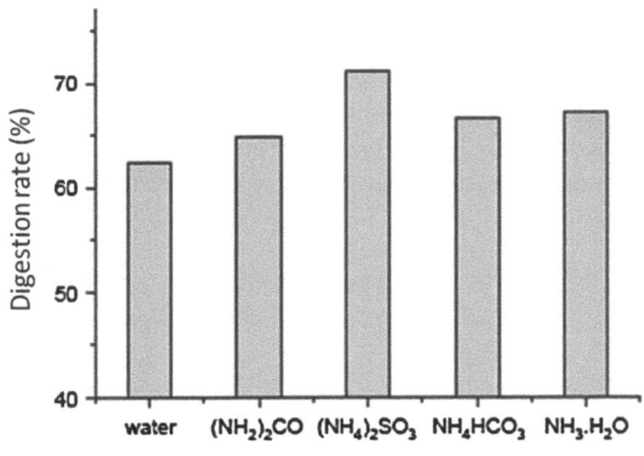

Fig. 6.4 Digestibility in vitro of ammoniated steam-exploded straw

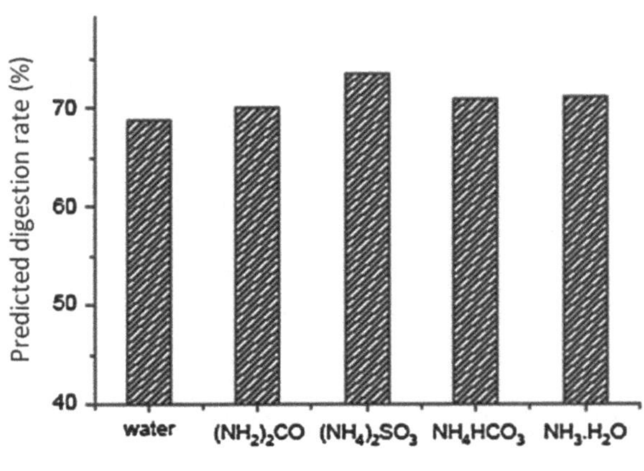

Fig. 6.5 Digestibility in vivo of ammoniated steam-exploded straw

the digestion rate in vivo was predicted to reach 73.4 %. The digestion rate of control group without addition of nitrogen source was only 62.4 % in vitro. The animal digestion rate of straw without any treatment is only about 20 %.

6.2 Application of Gas Explosion Technology in Pharmaceutical Industry

Currently, with the improvement of people's living standards and growing voice of the return to nature, people's demand for natural medicines is more and more urgent. Natural medicines have precise and stable efficacy and health functions and generally have less toxic side effects. While chemical drugs are easy to produce drug resistance and the pollution on the environment during production process, etc., which are difficult to meet the increasing demand for health. Traditional Chinese medicine (TCM) in the trend of "return to nature" again brings out strong vitality and demonstrates broad prospects for development. But the low extraction yield, low by-product utilization efficiency, non-standardized process operation, and low level of mechanization all led to a waste of medicinal resources, finally hindering a waste of medicinal resources. Gas explosion technology that combines chemical hydrolysis and physical tearing effect can effectively destroy the internally dense structure of herbal medicines in a short time (a few minutes). Its utilization in processing procedure of medicinal plants can increase the extraction rate of the active ingredient and act as a new means to improve the degree of mechanization of TCM herb processing, to achieve the comprehensive utilization of multi-components in plants and benefits to the modernization development of TCM.

6.2.1 Problems in Processing and Extraction Process of Medicinal Plants

TCM is the "treasure" prided by Chinese people. It has a wide range of kinds with long application history. The recorded TCM is of 12,694 kinds, including 11,020 kinds of medicinal plants. These plants belong to 2313 genera and 383 families, accounting for about 87 % of the total resources of TCM [12]. For thousands of years, medicinal plants have been used as the main weapon for preventing and treating disease, thus playing an essential role in protecting people's health and guaranteeing the multiplied descendants. However, the inherent structure of plant-based medicines from protection tissues to mechanical tissues such as epidermis and periderm to plant cell walls exhibits the antiextraction barrier, bringing hurdles for extraction process and hence resulting in serious waste of resources. Therefore, a pretreatment is crucial to destroy the structure of plant and promote the dissolution and transfer of active ingredients.

Traditional processing methods can be divided into preprocessing and post-processing. Preprocessing refers to medicine processing immediately after harvesting to form the raw material, and post-processing includes several procedures to the raw material such as cleansing, cutting, processing, drying, and other procedures, to make it into the intermediate pieces or semi-finished goods with a certain quality and specification.

Cleansing aims to sort herbs and remove impurities to reach medicinal cleanliness standards and specifications. It includes sorting and cleaning. Sorting uses picking, winnowing, screening, cutting, scraping, removing, brushing, grinding, and other methods to remove impurities or separate non-medicinal parts of herbs according to process requirement; cleaning uses washing, rinsing, spray washing, and other methods to wash herbs for reaching the clean class. But overcleansing of herbs easily leads to unnecessary loss of active components. Main cleansing machines are spray-type, circulation-type, environmental-friendly herbal washing machine, dry surface cleaning machine, magnetic belt separator, frequency conversion winnowing machine, and cleansing unit. Cutting is used to cut the medicine into slices, segments, wires, cubes, etc., and cut products should comply with the processing standards. Main machines correlated with cutting are cement pool, infiltrating machine (which is used to soften medicines by water penetration), reciprocating type and rotary herbal medicine slicing machine, which are widely applied in pharmaceutical companies. Processing refers to necessary procedures before the formulation of dosage form. Its main purpose is to eliminate or reduce the side effects of drugs to ensure the safety of drugs. It includes firing, grilling, calcining, steaming, making drugs into frostlike powder, sprouting, and fermentation. Herbal medicine roaster is the main processing machine, and its heat source mainly involves electricity, fuels, and gas instead of coals, which reduce the dust pollution to the environment. Drying is to dry the medicinal slices timely to avoid deterioration and rot, and additionally, dried medicines are easy to weigh. Main drying equipments are oven, belt drier, microwave drier, spray drier, etc. [13].

Even though traditional processing technologies have been used for nearly thousands of years with introduction of many new process and equipments, the overall situation still presents a low level of production with serious backwardness, which is not suited to the modernization of TCM. (1) Most active ingredients in TCM are intracellular products, which need to destroy cell structure to extract them; however, existing mechanical or chemical crushing methods is sometimes difficult to achieve the desired effect; (2) processing operations are not standardized, such as extensive washing for all kinds of herbs and too high processing temperature, which easily leads to especially some loss of heat-sensitive components; (3) there is a lack of modern processing equipments resulting in low productivity and non-adaptation to the market economy; and (4) owing to various kinds of Chinese herbal medicines and their different shapes, processing equipments have little universality. These factors all affect the processing quality and efficiency of TCM, making the processing process of TCM as a constraint to the development of industrial production.

Above problems in preprocessing procedures still bring several drawbacks in extraction process including large loss, long cycle, much operations, and low yield.

Traditional extraction methods of active components include decoction, impregnation, percolation, reflux, and steam distillation. These methods not only extract active components but also extract other invalid ingredients such as starch, gum, pectin, phlegm, and pigment, which bring adverse effect on subsequent refining process. In addition, long and continuous exposure to high temperature also leads to the loss of heat-sensitive components, and much consumption of solvent leads to the high cost of extraction process. What is more, traditional extraction only focuses on one single component without consideration of by-products, which greatly limits effective use of medicinal plants. In recent years, many novel extraction technologies appear as follows: Supercritical fluid extraction (SFE), which uses supercritical fluid as solvent to extract components from liquid or solid system, has advantages of quick extraction, high efficiency, easy operation, and high bioactivity and is especially suitable to heat-sensitive components; microwave-assisted extraction (MAE), which extracts and separates components by differences in the ability to absorb microwaves, has advantages of high selectivity, short operation, low solvent consumption, high extraction yield, and no noise production; supersonic extraction, which uses the cavitation effect of ultrasound to enhance the extraction of bioactive ingredients, has benefits of short extraction, high yield, and low temperature; enzymatic extraction, which takes the cellulase or other enzymes to destroy cell to extract components [14]. Compared to traditional extraction methods, these new technologies produce high extraction yield and purity, consume few solvents, and reduce the pollution. However, most new technologies are still limited to laboratory research, which needs further exploration of relevant principle and process and lacks industrial application and so may not be profitable in a short period.

Therefore, antiextraction barrier of plant structure and out-of-date processing and extraction technologies hinder the efficient utilization of effective components in TCM, which has become an important factor limiting the modernized development of TCM. The processing and extraction technologies play a vital role in improving the drug quality and accelerating the development of new drugs; the standardization of TCM and its large-scale production is the first step toward the world. Novel technology should be proposed based on natural plant structure and chemical composition to enrich the processing methods of TCM; meanwhile, corresponding novel equipments should be developed to promote the industrial production of TCM.

From the view of comprehensive utilization of components in TCM, gas explosion technology provides a good way for extraction, processing, and high-value utilization of TCM. Gas explosion technology has been recognized as one of the most widely used pretreatments for lignocellulose. During gas explosion pretreatment, materials are exposed to pressured steam with the high temperature of 180–235 °C for a certain period of time and suddenly exploded to the ambient environment with the disruption of solid structure [15]. This technology has a broad application prospect in TCM field, which is mainly due to the following advantages of gas explosion: (1) The combined effect of steam cooking and sudden decompression would lead to the disruption of plant structure from tissue level to cell wall level, which improves the dissolution of active components; (2) the plant tissue in high-temperature pressurized steam is swelled fully to significantly increase the cell permeability and shorten the extraction time; (3) the loss structure of gas-exploded materials after extraction of active components can be further utilized to produce fertilizer and feed; and (4) this technology can be applied to a variety of plant biomass for industrial production by the simple operation and support equipment.

6.2.2 Gas Explosion Enhancing Bioactive Ingredients Extraction from Traditional Chinese Medicines

Gas explosion is an effective pretreatment technology of TCMs to enhance the extraction of bioactive ingredients. Various kinds of gases such as air, saturated steam, CO_2, and N_2 are used as action media. During the pretreatment, there are an autohydrolysis stage and an explosion stage after the penetration of high-pressure steam into the plant cell wall. The thermal–chemical effect that is mainly due to the autohydrolysis of acetyl groups in hemicelluloses and the mechanical tearing force generated during explosive decompression is combined in this pretreatment to corporately provoke alterations in physicochemical structure of the feedstock. The disruption of tight biomass structure helps to overcome the plant extraction barrier and to enhance the extraction performance. Thus, gas explosion pretreatment facilitates the release of bioactive ingredients to improve the extraction yield and rate. It can be applied to a variety of herbal medicines, according to different locations and kinds of ingredients to change the pretreatment conditions. Particularly for heat-sensitive components, air-/steam-coupled explosion and other mixed gas explosion can be used to avoid degradation of heat-sensitive components. In addition, gas explosion is not only satisfied with single-component extraction, but also conducive to further utilization of by-products, to achieve multi-level fractionation and utilization of medicinal plants.

6.2.2.1 Application of Air–Steam Explosion on Ephedra to Extract Ephedrine

Ephedra is the dry herbaceous stems of *Ephedra sinica* Stapf, *Ephedra intermedia* et C.A. Mey, and *Ephedra equisetina* Bge. It is a commonly used clinical medicine, which is used to treat common cold, measles, cough, asthma, and other illnesses. The main active ingredient in it is ephedrine, which belongs to an amphetamine derivative and is adrenergic receptor agonists. Ephedrine has some effects as a relaxation function of bronchial smooth muscle, a contraction of blood vessels and an excitement of central role [16].

China has sufficient resources of ephedra, and ephedrine extraction has already been industrialized. Conventional extraction and purification methods include many steps such as boiling, alkalization, toluene extraction, oxalic acid extraction, bleaching, and refining. Extraction steps are complex, and extraction efficiency is low, resulting in a waste of resources and causing environmental pollution. Ephedrine alkaloids mainly present in the inner side of cortical fibers of ephedra in the form of salts. Its extraction should overcome the mass transfer resistance of epidermis, fibers, and especially the cell wall. Polysaccharides in plant cell wall are composed of cellulose, hemicellulose, and pectin, and a large number of lignin exist in the secondary cell wall, which is cooperatively a compact architecture obstacle to extraction of bioactive ingredients. As the cell wall of ephedra is effectively destroyed, gas explosion is expected to improve the extraction of ephedrine [17].

(1) Air–steam explosion condition of ephedra

The traditional gas explosion refers to steam explosion by which plant material is cooked at high pressure (0.8–3.4 MPa) and high temperature (180–240 °C), while ephedrine is easily volatile under this condition with the water evaporation. To avoid such drastic conditions, Chen Hongzhang proposed the strategy of inputting the air into reactor firstly to reach a certain pressure and then quickly inputting the steam to the settled pressure to offer a relatively low temperature environment for treating the ephedra. This method has been applied for a patent of air-/steam-coupled explosion of ephedra to enhance the extraction of ephedrine. Air-/steam-coupled explosion conditions are shown in Table 6.9. This method reduces the pretreatment temperature, while it maintains the gas-phase pressure before decompression. In addition, under the same explosion pressure, the steam contained in this method is less to avoid more condensate. The optimum gas explosion parameters were determined after subsequent ephedra extraction process.

Gas-exploded ephedra underwent extraction condition of solids: water = 1:8, extraction time of 70 min, and extraction temperature of 90 °C for one time, and then, ephedrine extraction yield was determined.

As shown in Fig. 6.6, ephedrine extraction yields after three gas explosion pretreatments were all higher than those of raw materials. The 3rd sample was the highest with 0.35 %, accounting for 33.65 % of total ephedrine content and indicating that gas explosion caused some damage in the structure of ephedra to achieve a higher extraction yield compared with the raw materials under the same extraction condition. For the treated samples, the 3rd sample demonstrates the higher extraction yield than the other two samples. These results indicated that only using steam as the gas media (2nd sample) may result in the loss of ephedrine, while taking air- and steam-coupled gas media can control the low pretreatment

Table 6.9 Gas explosion conditions of ephedra

Samples	Conditions	Temperature (°C)
No. 1	0.8 MPa air and steam to 1.3 MPa, 3 min	188
No. 2	1.2 MPa of steam, 3 min	
N o. 3	0.8 MPa air and steam to 1.5 MPa, 3 min	

Fig. 6.6 Ephedrine extraction yield of gas-exploded ephedra

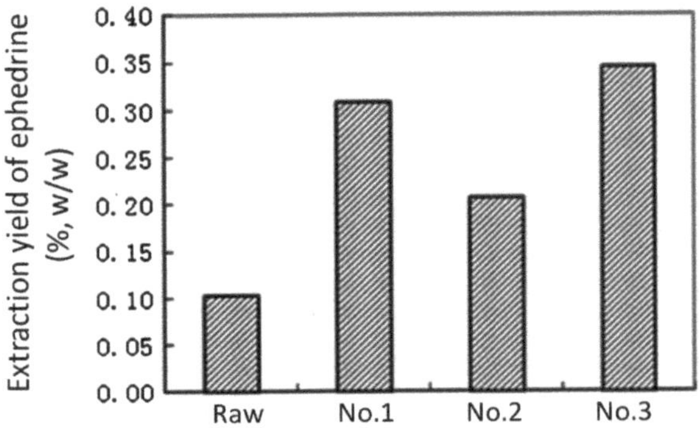

temperature. Meanwhile, the pressure also affects the gas explosion effect. First inputting the air of 8 kg/cm^2 and then quickly inputting steam of 15 kg/cm^2 is the optimum explosion condition. The addition of steam should enhance the penetration force of gas phase and make the autohydrolysis of hemicelluloses and breakage of part cellulose linking bonds, that is to say the water involved in the chemical reaction, thus effectively reaching gas explosion effect. Explosion time is also an important parameter. Too short time makes high-pressure media not fully penetrate the internal ephedra cells. Long time would waste energy and produce much condensed water, which is disadvantageous to pretreatment efficiency. The optimal retention time drawn from the experience and pre-test of ephedra is 3 min.

The first sample has the similar appearance with the third sample. Compared with untreated sample, they all appear dark color and have rough surface and partly fluffy, curly, and ruptured fiber. The second sample is darker than others and slightly black, and some part is fluffy and linked together (Fig. 6.7).

Scanning electron microscopy of ephedra to observe tissue changes before and after gas explosion is observed as shown in Fig. 6.8. After gas explosion, large changes in the structure of ephedra occurred. Comparison of Fig. 6.8a, b indicates

Fig. 6.7 Photographs of ephedra before and after gas explosion pretreatment. **a** Untreated ephedra. **b** Gas-exploded ephedra (No. 3)

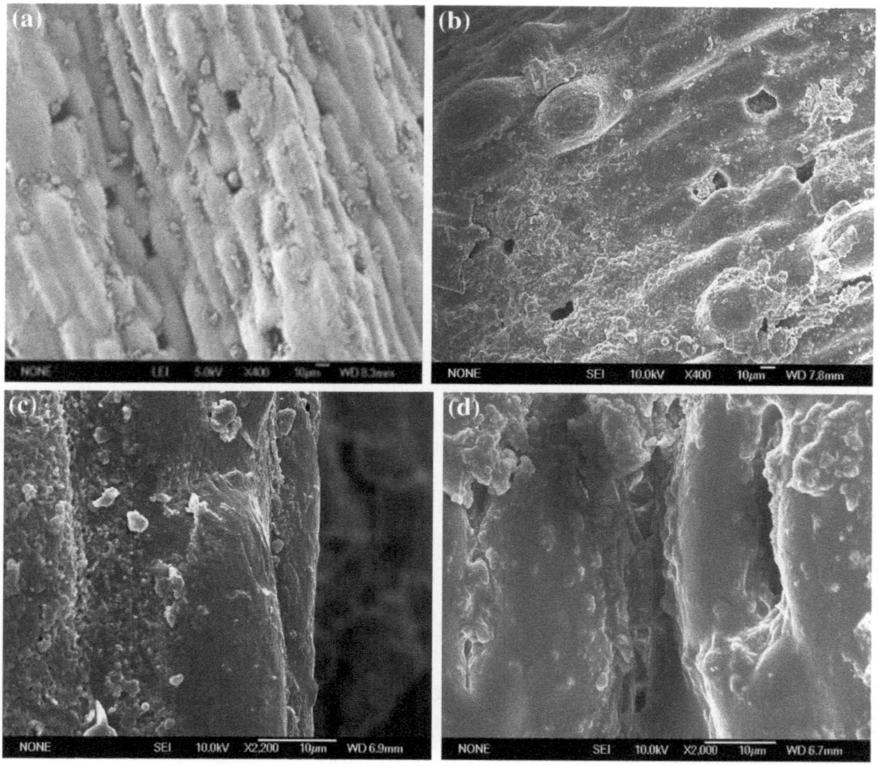

Fig. 6.8 SEM of ephedra before and after gas explosion pretreatment. **a** is untreated ephedra (400×), **b** is gas-exploded ephedra (400×), **c** is untreated ephedra (2200×), **d** is gas-exploded ephedra (2000×)

that pores in the surface of raw samples are small and thin, while they become large and dense after gas explosion. Comparison of Fig. 6.8c, d infers that fibers on surface and fiber bundles of pretreated ephedra are obviously curl and soft with some fiber breakage.

(2) Optimum extraction condition of ephedrine after air-/steam-coupled explosion of ephedra

After air–steam explosion of ephedra, the cell wall was destroyed, which may affect subsequent extraction conditions. Main parameters in the extraction process of ephedrine are extraction temperature, extraction time, and extraction times. Experiments have proved that the increase of extraction temperature and times as well as the prolonging of extraction time leads to the increase of extraction yield of ephedrine. Orthogonal experiments also indicated that the number of extraction times is the principle impact factor, followed by extraction time and temperature. The optimum condition is 3 times of extraction at 100 °C for 90 min for each time.

Under this condition, the extraction yield of ephedrine was 0.98 %, accounting for 94.23 % of total ephedrine in ephedra.

(3) Extraction-enhancing mechanism of air–steam explosion of ephedra

Air–steam explosion disrupted the pore structure at each level. Pores appeared in the multi-levels of tissue, cell and cell wall, in which cells has disappeared and inner parts of the cell were exposed. The changes at cell wall dimension have been readily seen under SEM and those in cell and tissue levels can be proved by the present study. The increased exposure of pores would liberate intracellular solutes and allow for a more effective penetration of extraction solvent through the porous structure. Therefore, the solute–solvent accessibility was improved to maximize the solubilization of active components. The changes of porous structure from rigid and ordered status to rough and messy status improved the mass transport pathway of solutes with the decreased tortuosity and the increased interconnection of pores. Under this condition, mass transfer occurred in more different ways instead of originally fixed pathway, which weakened the dominant internal diffusion resistance. Therefore, the changes of porous properties improved the solute–solvent accessibility and the internal mass transfer pathway in the extraction process. This is supposed to be the extraction-enhancing mechanism of steam-exploded plant porous medium.

(4) Extraction kinetics of air–steam-exploded ephedra

Certain amount of treated ephedra was extracted with distilled water at 100 °C for 20, 30, 40, 50, 60, 70, and 80 min. After filtration, the filtrate was measured for the content of ephedrine. Taking extraction time in *x*-axis and extraction yield of ephedrine in *y*-axis, the extraction kinetics of ephedrine (Fig. 6.9) are given as follows:

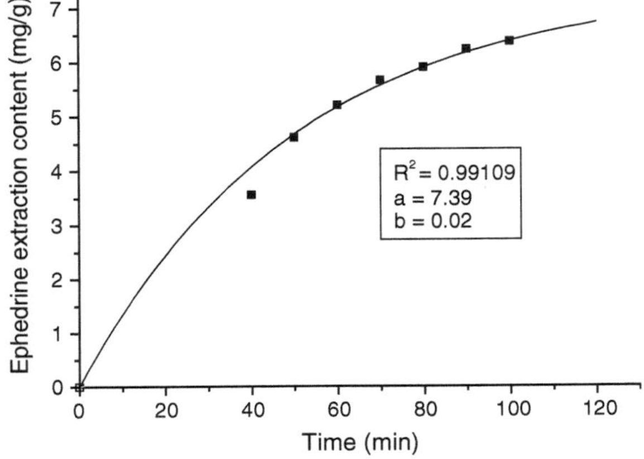

Fig. 6.9 Ephedrine extraction kinetics curve after gas-phase explosion

Extraction yield of ephedrine from per gram of gas-exploded ephedra at t time is as follows:

$$y = \frac{\text{Amount of extracted ephedrine at } t \text{ time}}{\text{Amount of gas exploded Ephedra}} = \frac{(30 - \text{Titration value}) \times 3.305}{5}$$

It can be concluded from the fitting model $V_t = V_t^{\infty}(1 - e^{-kt})$ that $V_t^{\infty} = 7.39$ and $k = 0.02$. Thus, the extraction kinetic equation is $y = 7.39(1 - e^{-0.02t})$, $R^2 = 0.99109$. This indicates that with the increase of extraction time, extraction yield of ephedrine is increased. The theoretical extraction yield of ephedrine at 100 °C for one time is 7.39 mg, accounting for 71.06 % of total amount of ephedrine in ephedra.

(5) Extraction of pigment from gas-exploded ephedra

5 g of treated ephedra was extracted with 50 ml of distilled water at 100 °C for 1 h. After filtration, the filtrate was diluted for 10 times and then measured at 535 nm by spectrophotometry. $E_{535\text{ nm}}^{1\,\%} = A \cdot R$ is used to calculate the color value (A: the ABS value of sample solution; R: dilution ratio). $E_{535\text{ nm}}^{1\,\%}$ is the color value representing the relative content of pigment.

Color value of extraction liquid of raw ephedra is as follows: $E_{535\text{ nm}}^{1\,\%} = A \cdot R = 0.101 \times 10 = 1.01$

Color value of extraction liquid of gas-exploded ephedra is as follows: $E_{535\text{ nm}}^{1\,\%} = A \cdot R = 0.130 \times 10 = 1.30$

Results show that the pigment content in extraction liquid of gas-exploded ephedra is higher than that of raw ephedra. This indicates that air-/steam-coupled explosion not only facilitates the extraction of ephedrine, but improves the extraction of other non-target components [15].

Since ephedrine is volatile, air-/steam-coupled explosion was applied to reach the settled holding pressure at lower holding temperature, by inputting air to a certain pressure before inputting steam. In addition, at the same holding pressure, this method consumed less steam compared with steam explosion, which avoided to produce a large amount of condensed water and reduced the loss of ephedrine. The processing condition of air-/steam-coupled explosion of ephedra is inputting air to 8 kg/cm^2, steam is subsequently inputted to 15 kg/cm^2, and then this condition is maintained for 3 min. Gas explosion pretreatment leads to the obvious curling and folding of fibers on the surface of ephedra and some fracture, which indicates that gas explosion destroys the cell wall. Gas explosion pretreatment significantly increased the extraction yield of ephedrine. Among various factors affecting the extraction yield of ephedrine, extraction times play a major role, followed by extraction time and temperature. The optimum extraction conditions are extraction of three times at 100 °C for 90 min for each time. Under this context, the extraction yield is 0.98 %, accounting for 94.23 % of total ephedrine in Ephedra.

6.2.2.2 Air–Steam Explosion Enhancing the Extraction Efficiency of Chlorogenic Acids from Leaves of Eucommia Ulmoides Oliver

Chlorogenic acid (CGA), a highly valuable natural polyphenol compound, is used as antioxidant. It is one of the effective components of many medicinal herbs and quality indicator of some medicine. It is also a promising precursor compound for the development of medicine. CGA is widely used in cosmetics, materia medica, and food industries.

The current commercial sources of CGA are mainly extracted from plant materials, such as the leaves of *Eucommia ulmoides* Oliver (*E. ulmoides*), which has been used in TCMs. Thus, the efficient extraction from plant materials is one of the key steps for economical utilization of CGA. The increasing interests in CGA are accompanied by a need to expand and modify efficient plant extraction methods. Conventional methods for enhancing extraction of bioactive ingredients from plant materials were characterized by high temperature, lengthy extraction procedures, and decreasing the material size. However, it is difficult to extract CGA from *E. ulmoides* leaves using those conventional methods due to the following two reasons. On the one hand, CGA is an ester compound of caffeic acid and quinic acid with unsaturated double bond and polyhydric phenol structure, which indicates that CGA is thermosensitive and labile. Moreover, oxidation, hydrolysis, and isomerization can be usually accelerated when CGA is subjected to higher temperatures. Therefore, increasing time and temperature is unsuitable for the extraction of CGA. On the other hand, the positive effects of decreasing particle sizes in CGA extraction process have been widely reported. However, *E. ulmoides* abounded with rigid biopolymers and fibrous long-chain trans-1,4-polyisoprene (*Eucommia*—rubber). These biopolymers are also accumulated in the leaves of *E. ulmoides*, forming a filament network. These networks result in the difficulty of size reduction. As CGA mainly exists in the cell walls of *E. ulmoides*, these networks and cell walls were therefore considered as barriers for effective extraction. Thus, a rapid and novel method should be developed to decrease the extraction barriers, in order to achieve the desirable extraction yield of thermosensitive CGA.

In order to radically remove the effect of cell wall compact structure on the dissolution of CGA and improve the extraction rate of CGA from the *E. ulmoides* leaves, Prof. Hongzhang Chen proposed a gas-phase explosion to assist the extraction of CGA from *E. ulmoides* leaves based on the thermal degradation of catechol structure of CGA [18].

Specific technical schemes are as follows:

① The dried *E. ulmoides* leaves are added into the adding acidic solution (acetic acid, phosphoric acid, sulfuric acid, hydrochloric acid, nitric acid, carbonate, and other inorganic acid or organic acid) according to the mass ratio of 1:0–1:4 and then soaked for 5–180 min at room temperature. ② The soaked raw material is then placed in the explosion tank and after inlet of gas media (air, liquid nitrogen, nitrogen, water vapor, carbon dioxide, ozone, supercritical CO_2 and ethanol), the temperature of explosion tank reaches 30–100 °C and is maintained for 1–30 min followed by the gas-phase explosion treatment. ③ Distilled water with the weight about 3–20 times of treated raw material is added into raw material to extract at 40–80 °C for 2–3 times. Each time of extraction is 1.0 h, and the respective extracted liquid is collected. ④ The extracted liquid is concentrated, and ethyl acetate is then added to obtain an ethyl acetate layer. After the neutralization of the ethyl acetate layer by 1–5 % NaOH, the CGA in the ethyl acetate layer is then leached into the water phase. CGA in the water phase is precipitated by the addition of HCl and recrystallized with a small amount of ethyl acetate. The crude CGA could be obtained after drying. ⑤ The crude CGA is dissolved in distilled water according to the mass ratio of 1:3–1:5 in continuous ventilation with 99.99 % of high-purity nitrogen. After the addition of 5–10 % activated carbon, the mixture is then heated to 50–60 °C for 0.5–1.0 h. The mixture is filtered and crystallized after cooling. The crystallized CGA is finally cleaned by pure acetone and dried with vacuum to obtain high pure CGA.

The method that uses gas explosion to assist the extraction of CGA from *E. ulmoides* leaves has the following advantages: ① The gas explosion effectively destroys the cell wall of *E. ulmoides* leaves, increases the specific surface area of the raw material to greatly enhance cell proliferation rate, and improves the extraction yield of raw material. The extraction yield of CGA by gas explosion was 2.81 %, which was increased by more than 30 % compared with 2.16 % by conventional crushing treatment. ② Compared with the conventional crushing, the operating equipment investment of gas explosion extraction is less. Other advantages are easy operation, shorter processing time, and lower energy consumption. ③ The raw material is soaked in acidic water during the treatment, which improves the stability of CGA. The *E. ulmoides* leaves are treated at lower temperature about 40–100 °C by using gas media, which does not damage the active structure of CGA. Thus, it is a suitable method for the pretreatment of *E. ulmoides* leaves.

Figure 6.10 shows the HPLC diagram of CGA extracted before and after gas explosion treatment, respectively. And Fig. 6.11 shows extraction yield and specific surface area of feedstock treated by gas explosion under different conditions.

6.2.2.3 Gas Explosion of Ginkgo Leaves for Flavonoid Extraction

Gingko biloba L is the most ancient gymnosperms remaining from quaternary glacial movement and is one of the most precious species. It is considered as "living fossil" in the plant kingdom. *Gingko biloba* L is broadly distributed in China. Since the 1960s, scholars have done lots of researches about its chemical constituents, pharmacological effects, and clinical applications. Pharmacological studies have shown that Ginkgo leaf extract may dilate coronary artery, increase cerebral blood flow, and improve brain nutrition with a clear antiplatelet activating factor and antibacterial effects. In particular, the role of Ginkgo leaf extract on nervous system

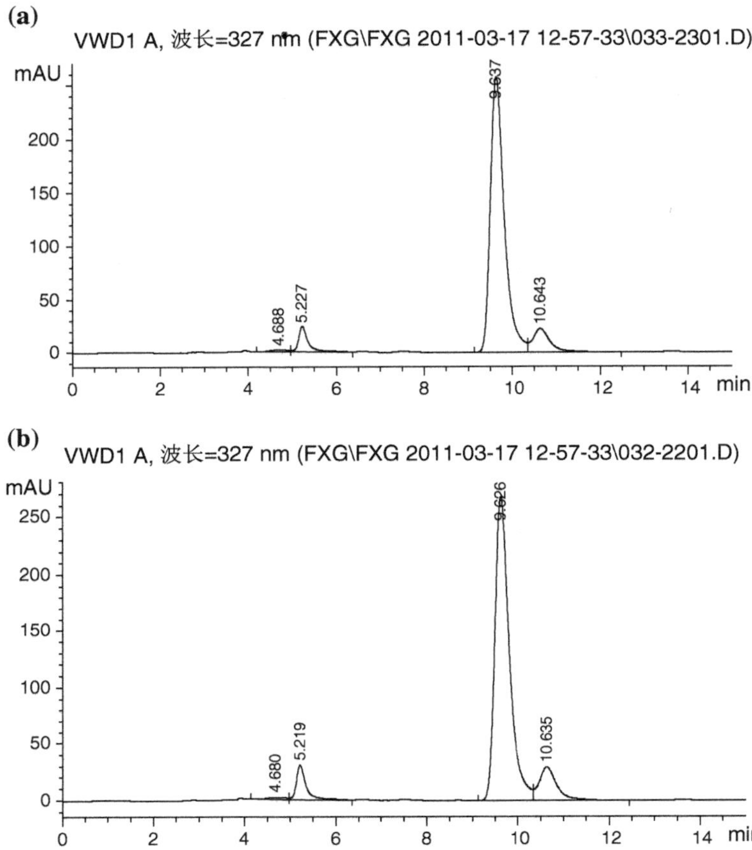

Fig. 6.10 **a** HPLC diagram of CGA extracted before explosion treatment. **b** HPLC diagram of CGA extracted after explosion treatment

is unique. The resurrection effect of Ginkgo leaf extract on the central nervous system can be used as agent for dementia (Alzheimer's disease) prevention.

Ginkgo leaf extract such as Ginkgo flavonoids belongs to coloring substances and primarily exists in vacuoles of plant cells. With the drying of plants, flavonoids will get attached to the plant cell wall. Plant cell wall is a dense structure composing of cellulose, hemicellulose, lignin, and pectin, which is a major barrier for flavonoid extraction. In the extraction process, substance exchange through the cell wall is a rate-limiting step. Therefore, regardless of the extraction methods used, the extent of damage to the plant cells will directly affect the efficiency of extraction and subsequent processing.

Traditional methods commonly used mechanical crushing method for material treatment. However, since the plant cell has a great resistance to the external force, the damage to plant cells during treatment is limited. If the plant-based medicine is

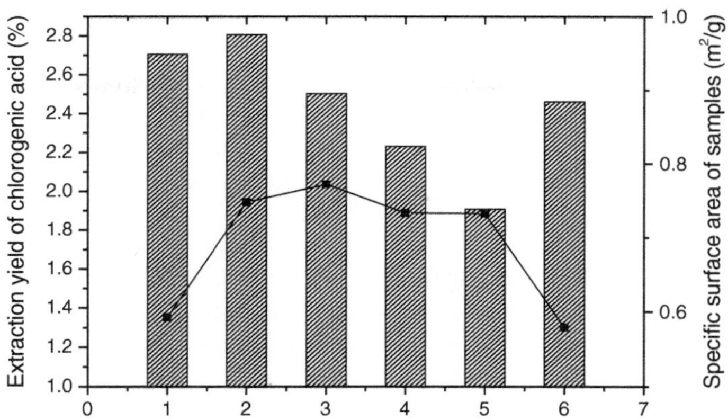

Fig. 6.11 Extraction yield and specific surface area of feedstock treated by gas explosion under different conditions

crushed to the micron level, the energy increases and the cost as well. In order to radically relieve the impact of dense structure of Ginkgo leaf cell wall on the dissolution of active ingredients and improve the dissolution efficiency of Ginkgo extract, Prof. Chen Hongzhang from Institute of Process Engineering, Chinese Academy of Sciences, presents a gas explosion process for *G. biloba* leaf [19].

Specific technical solutions are as follows: (1) A solution (an acidic aqueous solution of pH 2.0–6.5 including acetic acid, phosphoric acid, sulfuric acid, hydrochloric acid, nitric acid, carbonic acid and other inorganic or organic acids, neutral or alkaline aqueous solution of pH 8.0–11.0 including sodium hydroxide, potassium hydroxide, calcium hydroxide, calcium carbonate, sodium carbonate, and sodium bicarbonate) was added in the mass ratio of 1:0–1:4 of absolute dry *G. biloba* leaves, and then, the mixture was soaked at room temperature for 5–180 min; (2) the material was placed in the gas explosion reactor after soaking, once inputting the gas media (air, carbon dioxide, ozone, nitrogen, nitrogen, water vapor, supercritical CO_2, ethanol vapor or the combination of any two coupled gas above), the reactor temperature reached 30–250 °C and maintained 1–30 min. The tank was then suddenly decompressed, and material was exploded into the receiving tank; (3) the gas-exploded Ginkgo was crushed to pass through 60-mm mesh and was added 70 % ethanol solution at 85 °C water bath according to the liquid–solid ratio of 20: 1 (mL/g) and then was reflux-extracted by 2 h and filtered. The filtrate was recycled, the residues undergone the above process three times for the purpose of extraction, and the filtrate was then combined to determine the extraction rate of total Gingko flavonoids.

The process of flavonoid extraction from gas-exploded Ginkgo leaves has the following advantages. ① Under high pressure, gas medium penetrates into the pores between tissues and cells and then is instantly released to completely destroy the cell walls of Ginkgo leaves, thereby relieving the barrier of dense structure of cell wall on the dissolution of active ingredients from Ginkgo leaves and enhancing the dissolution efficiency of Ginkgo extract. ② Presoaking under acidic conditions of feedstock before gas explosion causes some swelling effect, which is conducive to the hemicellulose degradation and the ester bond cleavage of lignin of Ginkgo leaf cell walls, which thereby improves the damage degree of Ginkgo leaf cell walls by gas explosion. ③ Presoaking of feedstock under alkaline conditions could achieve great swelling of fiber bundles since the alkali solutions have stronger penetration ability to cellulose. Meanwhile, in the alkali soaking process, deacetylation of hemicellulose occurs under the action of base. The dissolution of hemicellulose gradually forms small pores on the intercellular layer and cell wall surface, which are in favor of water hydration and improve gas explosion treatment efficiency. ④ Pretreatment method using gas medium to avoid the damage of the flavonoids is applicable to feedstock properties of *G. biloba*. ⑤ The structure of Ginkgo leaf after gas explosion appears to be loosen, and the clear porous structure improves the dissolution efficiency of active ingredients but does not damage active ingredients. The extraction process from gas-exploded Ginkgo leaves reaches the balance in 15 min, and the extraction process of untreated Ginkgo leaves could not reach balance after 2 h. Moreover, the flavonoid extraction rate from gas-exploded Ginkgo leaves is much higher than that of untreated Ginkgo leaves. ⑥ The Ginkgo leaves after gas explosion could be directly used for active ingredient extraction or preparation of various Ginkgo products after ultrafine grinding.

Gas explosion technology as a pretreatment of plant materials could effectively extract the active ingredients from medicinal plants, such as flavonoids, alkaloids, oils, polysaccharides, and other substances. Gas explosion using steam as gas medium can utilize the cooking and penetration effect of steam, which plays a role in feedstock swelling to reduce the condensation and relies on the shearing force produced by the sudden release to damage the cell wall. This process could thereby enhance the diffusion and dissolution of active ingredients and improve the extraction of active ingredients from TCM. Overall, the investment of this pre-treatment technology is small and the equipments are simple, which can effectively reduce costs and save valuable resources of medicinal plants. With the deepening of researches about active ingredients of medicinal plants, gas explosion technique can be applied to extract a variety of active ingredients and has broad prospects for development.

6.2.3 Gas Explosion Processing of Traditional Chinese Medicines

Processing of TCM is a pharmaceutical technology based on Chinese medicine theory in accordance with the syndrome differentiation, the nature of the drug itself, and different treatment requirements. It has played an important role in disease prevention for Chinese to ensure the safe and effective clinical use of TCM by thousands of years. After the processing of herbs, a series of changes of chemical compositions occurs, which have a great impact on the role of drugs. The major roles of processing are as follows: ① to reduce or eliminate the toxicity or adverse drug reaction; ② change or mitigate drug performance to meet the needs of different personal conditions; ③ enhance drug efficacy; ④ change the action site of drug or enhance the action trend of drug; ⑤ facilitate agent formulation and relieve the unpleasant odor and taste; and ⑥ enhance drug clarity and ensure drug quality in favor of drug storage and preservation [13].

Gas explosion technique is widely used as lignocellulosic pretreatment technology. The team from Institute of Process Engineering, Chinese Academy of Sciences, has done lots of researches in this field, which includes the establishment of a low-pressure unpolluted gas explosion platform and application research in biomass energy, material, textile fibers, and other areas. As mentioned above, gas explosion technique for extracting the active ingredients of Chinese herbal medicines has been applied. Taking into account that the gas explosion is actually a short-term, high-temperature pretreatment technology, it could become a new method of TCM processing, which plays a unique role in the efficiency, attenuated, and so on. The applications of gas explosion in the processing of single herb medicine, compound drugs, and special herbs are illustrated by the following examples.

6.2.3.1 Gas Explosion Processing of Fuzi

As a typical toxic herb, the daughter root of *Aconitum carmichaeli* Debx. (Fuzi) has received considerable research attention over the years in China, India, Japan, and some other countries because of its outstanding medicinal efficacy and severe toxic property. Biologically functional components in Fuzi mainly consist of diester-diterpenoid alkaloids (DDAs), especially aconitine, mesaconitine, and hypaconitine, which exert cardiotonic, analgesic, anti-inflammatory, and diuretic effects in the treatment. However, many researches demonstrate that aconitine, mesaconitine, and hypaconitine are also responsible for highly toxic cardiotoxins and neurotoxins of Fuzi. Hence, a processing treatment on Fuzi is of vital importance for lowering DDA contents to the non-toxic range and reservation of the certain residual amount to afford the therapeutic effect. With features of short-time high-temperature cooking and instantaneous decompression, steam explosion enhances the mass transfer of intracellular components and prompts the reaction accessibility of substrate. It presents the great potential to develop into a novel processing method for increasing efficacy and eliminating toxicity of traditional herbal medicines [20].

(1) Preparation of gas-exploded Fuzi

① Materials

a. Medicinal material: the daughter roots of *A. carmichaeli* Debx. (Fuzi) from Sichuan Jiangyou Zhongba Aconiti Technology Development Co., Ltd., China.
b. Equipment: laboratory-scale (4 L) steam explosion reactor

c. Animals: ICR mice for acute toxicity test with both sexes weighing 18–20 g were purchased from Beijing Weitong Lihua Experimental Animal Technology Co., Ltd., China.

② Processing of Fuzi

Raw Fuzi was soaked overnight with one volume of distilled water before steam explosion treatment. Approximately 400 g of humid raw Fuzi was placed inside the steam explosion vessel, treated with saturated steam at 0.6 and 1.0 MPa for 2 min, which optimized previously and then terminated by sudden explosive decompression. The samples after steam explosion were dried at 50 °C and smashed to pass through 40-mm meshes. The Fuzi steam-exploded at 0.6 and 1.0 MPa for 2 min was named LSEFuzi and HSEFuzi, respectively. Appearance of Fuzi before and after steam explosion is shown in Fig. 6.12.

③ HPLC quantitative analysis of diester-diterpenoid alkaloids

Processed Fuzi (2 g) was extracted with ethyl ether (50 mL) plus 10 % aqueous ammonia solution (2 mL) by ultrasonic treatment for 30 min. After filtration, the filtrate was collected, and the filter residue was washed for 3 times with ethyl ether (10 mL) for each. The filtrate and washed ethyl ether portion were collected and dried at 50 °C in a forced-draft oven. The residue obtained was dissolved in 0.01 % hydrochloric acid–methanol (20 mL) and filtered through a 0.45-μm filter before the chromatographic analysis.

The high-performance liquid chromatography (HPLC) analysis was performed on a HPLC equipped with a UV detector (Agilent, USA). The chromatographic separation was performed on an Eclipse XDB-C18 column (Agilent, USA) at 35 °C with the mobile phase consisting of 40 mmol ammonium acetate buffer solution (A) and acetonitrile (B) in a gradient elution method (33 % of B at 0–15 min, 33–50 % of B at 15–45 min, 50 % of B after 45 min). The flow rate was 1.0 ml min^{-1}, and the detection wavelength was 230 nm.

Fig. 6.12 Appearance of Fuzi before and after steam explosion. **a** Raw Fuzi. **b** 0.6 MPa. **c** 1.0 MPa

④ Acute toxicity test

Fuzi sample (200 g) was soaked in distilled water (500 mL) until softened and boiled for another 30 min. After filtration, the leaching liquor of raw Fuzi was collected and concentrated at 80 °C to a final concentration of 2 g/mL. The extracts of LSEFuzi and HSEFuzi were concentrated to the maximum concentration of 1.16 and 1.46 g/mL, respectively.

Pre-experiment confirmed that all the mice given raw Fuzi in doses of 0.3–2 g/mL at the volume of 0.4 mL/10 g by oral gavage died. The median lethal dose (LD_{50}) of steam-exploded Fuzi could not be measured, and the maximum tolerable dose (MTD) was calculated.

According to the pre-experiment results, equal amount of male and female ICR mice were randomly divided into 9 groups with 10 animals each. Before intragastric administration, all mice were fasted for 12 h with water ad libitum. Six groups were randomly administered with raw Fuzi in doses of 0.25, 0.2, 0.15, 0.125, 0.1, and 0.08 g/mL at the volume of 0.4 mL/10 g. The control group received an equal volume of water. The other two groups were administered with LSEFuzi and HSEFuzi with the maximal concentration and maximal volume (0.4 mL/10 g) of water extracts. After a single administration, the animals were observed closely during first 24 h and kept under observation up to 14 days. The survival rates were calculated, and the acute toxicity of each kind of Fuzi was evaluated by LD_{50} and MTD.

(2) Actual efficacy of gas-exploded Fuzi

① Changes of major alkaloids in Fuzi after gas explosion

Modern pharmacological studies have shown that DDAs (mainly including aconitine, mesaconitine, and hypaconitine) are major active components in Fuzi, which are also responsible for the severe toxicity. To explore impacts of steam explosion on above aconitine-type compounds, the chromatographic comparison of Fuzi extracts at different treatment conditions was investigated with results shown in Figs. 6.13, 6.14, and 6.15. The retention time of mesaconitine, aconitine, and hypaconitine in all samples was 6.711–6.890, 9.907–10.301, and 63.817–63.932 min, respectively. A remarkable reduction of chromatographic peak height for each compound after steam explosion treatment is demonstrated and detailed content values are represented in Table 6.10. For LSEFuzi, the relative content of aconitine, mesaconitine, and hypaconitine lowered by 61.3, 75.6, and 96.0 %, and the total aconitine-type alkaloid content (calculated as the sum of three alkaloids) is substantially reduced by 77.6 %. With the increasing vapor pressure, a stepwise decrease of compound contents was observed in steam-exploded Fuzi. As for HSEFuzi, the content of aconitine, mesaconitine, and hypaconitine is decreased by 81.6, 84.7, and 99.8 %, and the sum content is represented the loss of 88.7 % compared with raw Fuzi. Thus, the results indicate that the contents of DDAs in Fuzi substantially decline after steam explosion treatment. The diester aconitine-type compounds share a common C19-norditerpenoid skeleton. When Fuzi was exposed in hot environment due to the lost of one acetic acid molecule on

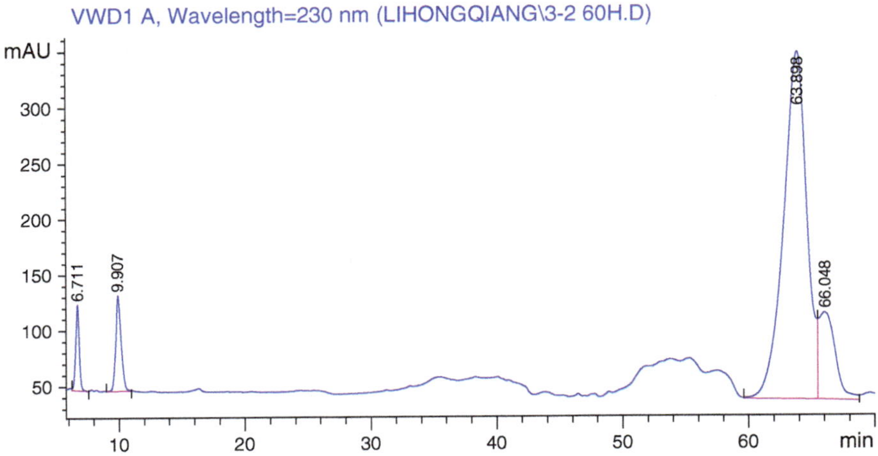

Fig. 6.13 HPLC of water extract of raw Fuzi. A(6.711) = 1495.9, A(9.907) = 2537.1, A (63.898) = 39793.2

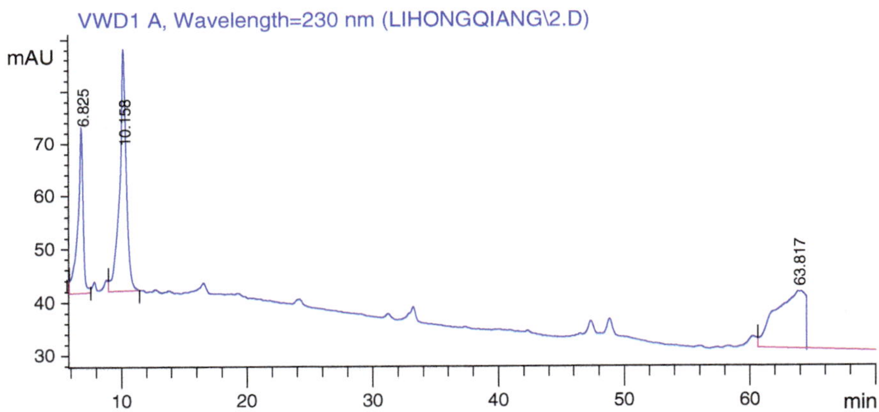

Fig. 6.14 HPLC of water extract of gas-exploded Fuzi at 0.6 MPa, 2 min. A(6.825) = 739.3, A (10.158) = 1660.3, A(63.817) = 3260

C8 position, the DDAs were majorly hydrolyzed to monoester diterpene alkaloids, whose toxicity was 1/200–1/500 of that in DDAs. After that, monoester diterpene alkaloids dropped one benzoic acid molecule at C14 position and subsequently broke down to form the hydrophilic amino alcohol aconines, whose toxicity was merely 1/2000–1/4000 of DDAs. In addition, under moderate conditions, the acetyl group on C8 position could be partially substituted by fatty acyl group, leading to the conversion of DDAs into lipoalkaloids with little toxicity. This provided the other path to alter the highly toxicity. Thereby, the hydrothermal processing is

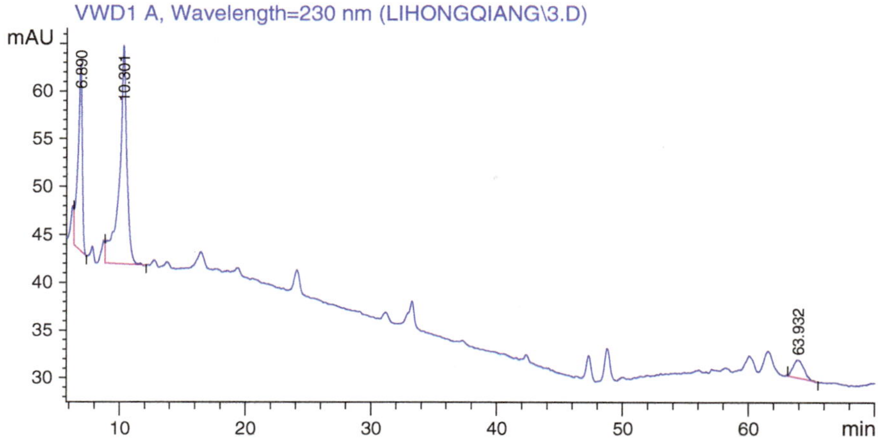

Fig. 6.15 HPLC of water extract of gas-exploded Fuzi at 1.0 MPa, 2 min. A(6.890) = 452.5, A (10.301) = 924.9, A(63.931) = 128.8

Table 6.10 Effect of steam explosion on the content of major aconite alkaloids (relative contents)

Sample	Mesaconitine	Aconitine	Hypaconitine
Raw Fuzi	1	1	1
Gas-exploded Fuzi (0.6 MPa, 2 min)	0.244	0.387	0.040
Gas-exploded Fuzi (1.0 MPa, 2 min)	0.153	0.184	0.002

contributed to the detoxification of Fuzi. And according to some studies, the extent of toxicity reduction was corresponding to the hydrolysis degree of the diester alkaloids. Research reported a long-time sterile approach to process aconite to reduce aconite toxicity. Although this method is very effective, it takes a long time and is not conducive to high-volume processing.

② Acute toxicity analysis of steam-exploded Fuzi

The acute toxicity test in mice in vivo shows that no mice died in the experimental process of steam-exploded Fuzi groups with no LD_{50} while calculating MTD. The calculated MTD of LSEFuzi and HSEFuzi is 46.4 and 58.4 g/kg, respectively (Table 6.11). Through the dosage conversion between human and mouse, steam-exploded Fuzi enables its safe dose to reach considerably high level (about 400 g) for human (calculated by 60 kg per person). It exceeds the human lethal dose of the routinely processed Fuzi (3–15 g) as well as the wild plant (1 g). According to the international classification of hazardous substances for acute oral toxicity testing, 2–5 g/kg has been designated as the limited dose (upper limitation on testing) beyond which a single oral dose of the tested substance can be considered non-toxic. In addition, most acute toxicity studies have defined that the non-toxicity of plant product as its LD_{50} is higher than 3–5 g/kg. Therefore, steam-exploded

Table 6.11 Acute LD_{50} and MTD values in mice of processed Fuzi by different methods by gavage

Sample	LD_{50} (g/kg)	Provenance	Comment
Raw Fuzi	4.40	this study	
Gas-exploded Fuzi (1.0 MPa, 2 min)	MTD: 46.6	this study	Water extraction and oral medication with 1.45-fold condensate
Gas-exploded Fuzi (1.0 MPa, 2 min)	MTD: 58.4	this study	Water extraction and oral medication with 1.82-fold condensate
Raw Fuzi	3.03	Zhang et al. [21]	
Steamed Fuzi (105 °C, 10–60 min)	>10	Zhang et al. [18]	
Hot processed Fuzi (120 °C, 40 min)	100	Li et al. [19]	
Microwave-processed Fuzi	52.84	Zou et al. [20]	
Processed Fuzi (0.245 MPa, 1.5 h)	MTD: 160	Zhang et al. [16]	Water extraction and oral medication with 4-fold condensate
Salted Fuzi	23.04	Zhang et al. [21]	Ethanol extraction and intraperitoneal injection
Processed Fuzi	MTD: 200	Zhang et al. [21]	Ethanol extraction and intraperitoneal injection

Fuzi can be regarded as the completely detoxified Fuzi due to its no lethality (no morbidity) and the high MTD.

6.2.3.2 Gas Explosion of Ganoderma Lucidum and Its Application

Ganoderma lucidum is the general term of *G. lucidium* (Leyss. Ex Fr.) Karst and *Ganoderma japonicum* (Fr.) Lloyd. of the genus *Ganoderma* (family Polyproraceae). It has the effects of increasing organism immunity and supporting healthy energy. *G. lucidium* spore is the extremely tiny spores ejected from Ganoderma cap in the growing maturity period and is the germ cell which has all the genetic active substances. *G. lucidium* spore powder is the collection of spores. *G. lucidum* spore is the essence of Ganoderma fruiting bodies. The content, medicinal value, and nutritional value of bioactive substances in it are several times than those of Ganoderma fruiting bodies. *G. lucidium* spore as the adjuvant drug for anticancer therapy has a high value in clinic. However, these bioactive components wrapped in two layers of hard cell walls of *G. lucidium* spore, hindering their complete absorption by the human body. Only the cell wall-broken spore can be easily absorbed by human body and realized their special medicinal value. Therefore, wall-breaking is the key step to improve the dissolution rate of bioactive components in spores. Currently, there are five common wall-breaking methods, which have some disadvantages. (1) Fermentation: After fermentation of *G. ludicium* spores at 70 °C for a certain time, their cell wall began to burst. This method is easy to operate, but the wall-breaking rate is low with some pollution and the most of the active ingredients in spores are hydrolyzed. (2) Enzymatic method: This method is to use a variety of lywallzyme to dissolve the cell wall of Ganoderma spores. Because the activity of lywallzyme is greatly influenced by external factors such as temperature and humidity, in actual operation, enzymatic hydrolysis time of lywallzyme is difficult to handle. If hydrolysis time is too short, the cell wall is hard to destroy; on the contrary, the active ingredients would be dissolved. (3) High-frequency ultrasonic method: This is a wet wall-breaking method with high energy consumption. It cannot achieve the good wall-breaking efficacy and full extraction of active ingredients limited by the ultrasonic frequency. (4) High-power and high-speed jet milling method: This has high investment and noise. *G. lucidum* spores after wall-breaking need to be stored in low temperature. (5) Microwave vacuum method: This is also a wet wall-breaking method with low productivity, high investment, and production cost.

To overcome the disadvantages of above wall-breaking method of *G. lucidum* spores, Chen Hongzhang et al. invented the carbon dioxide explosion technology to produce the slow release and long effect type of wall-breaking *G. lucidum* spores. The wall-breaking rate was improved to above 98 %, and the dissolving rate of crude polysaccharides from *G. lucidum* spores was 6.2 mg/g. The cost of this method is below the half of the cost of high-power and high-speed jet milling method. In addition, this is a pollution-free processing method of agricultural products [22].

The concrete steps of this method are as follows. The *G. lucidum* spores are top-loaded into the high-pressure vessel, which accounts for 10–25 % of the vessel by volume. After sealing in the vessel, the same amount of carbon dioxide gas and high-pressure steam are inputted into the vessel until the vessel pressure reaches 0.5–1.5 Mpa. After keeping this pressure for 1–15 min, the vessel is suddenly decompressed and the *G. lucidum* spores are exploded into the atmospheric buffer tank to get the gas-exploded *G. lucidum* spores. The treated spores are dried in 50–80 °C for 5–12 h until they are dried out and loose. After that, the dried spores are sterilized by cobalt 60 radiation sterilization method for 1–3 h to obtain the final products. Electron microscopic examination showed that the cell wall of treated *G. lucidum* spores was broken by the gas explosion, but the cell membrane of treated spores was intact (Fig. 6.16), which guaranteed the integrity and nature of effective ingredients in spores. The wall-breaking rate of products is more than 98 % with the wall-breaking cost decreased by over 50 %. The products can be stored in room temperature.

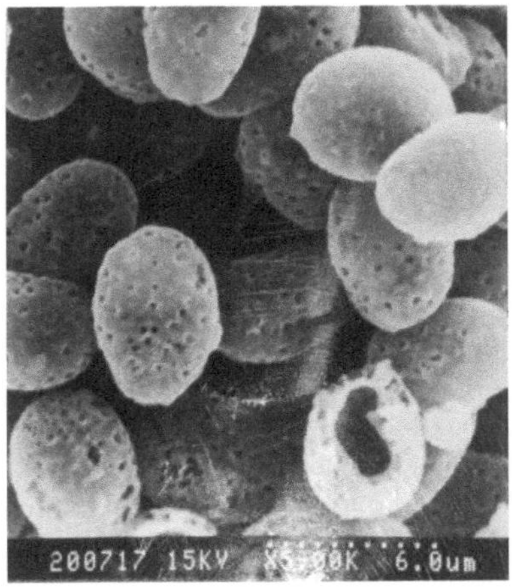

Fig. 6.16 Scanning electron microscope picture of *Ganoderma lucidum* spores (5000×) [15]

6.2.3.3 Gas Explosion Processing of Traditional Chinese Medicine Compounds (TCMs)

Taking TCM could be generally divided into two ways. One is to use technology to process TCM into Chinese patent medicines, which is convenient for taking. However, this way only has good effect for some typical cases, the patient's condition differs widely, and fixed compatibility cannot effectively suit the remedy according to the patient's specific situation. The other way is to take the medicinal broth from directly soaking in water and heating TCM. This way can be conducted on the basis of the condition of the patient compatibility. The advantages of TCM processing by water frying process are as follows: The medicinal properties and ingredients are neutralized, the toxicity of medicine is relieved, and the taste is better. Moreover, the clinical use of this way is flexible. However, TCM is natural and made up of natural organic ingredients, which are not easy to dissolve in water. Through general water frying technology, the dissolved drug quantity in water is about 2–3 % of total quantity and the highest is less than 5 %. The rest (more than 95 % of the total drug quantity) is discharged, which is a huge waste and also causes unnecessary economic waste for patients.

TCM processing is based on "fire." "Materia Medica Companion" had recorded that moderation is important during the medicine processing. This description has been regarded as the highest criterion in TCM processing. But it is a pity that how to "moderate" is vague. Even in the pharmacopoeia, the statements, such as mild fire, medium fire, and strong fire, are still used today. Since the TCM is the most important material base to control safety of TCM, the professionals of TCM processing are always wary about the changes of processing technologies. Thus, even for a slight change of processing technology, it is very difficult. This not only shows the modern people's awe for TCM, but also reflects the difficulty of TCM modernization. In fact, the processing control of TCM is mainly the temperature control in the TCM processing, which is a core issue in the TCM processing. If the problems of TCM processing are treated in this point of view, many uncertain and vague concepts in the TCM processing will have a good explanation and operation [23].

Although the TCM processing technology has been relatively stable, it also has been improved and developed. For example, the equipment for TCM processing is developed from the frying pan to stir-frying machine, electric thermostatic drying oven, etc. However, some new processing technologies are also necessary to solve the problems, such as long time for water frying operation, use difficulty of effective components, and lack of effective control of operating parameters. Using gas explosion technology, the treatment time and temperature could be chosen according to the type and nature of the herbs used. Cooperating with the appropriate additive, the cell wall of medicinal materials could be broken, through which the maximum use of effective components in TCM is achieved. Gas explosion environment can also promote the Maillard reactions of effective components to improve the therapeutic efficacy of drugs.

Specific operation methods are as follows:

(1) According to the main composition of prescription medicines, plant species, and parts of the source, the medicinal materials are classified appropriately to make the different medicines obtain proper gas explosion conditions. (2) The classified medicinal materials are adjusted to 30–60 % moisture content by addition of water or aqueous solutions. Aqueous solutions include vinegar, wine, rice wine, honey, and a certain concentration of sodium carbonate and sodium bicarbonate solution. These solutions can adjust the pH of the medicinal materials, increase the solubility of effective components from the medicine, and improve the effect of gas explosion pretreatment. After adjusting the water content, the medicinal material is presoaked at a certain temperature for a certain time. (3) According to the different groups, the different gas explosion temperatures and times are chosen. For starchy medicinal materials, they are 160–180 °C and 0–3 min, respectively; for lignocellulosic medicinal materials, they are 170–195 °C and 1–4 min, respectively; for oil and protein medicinal materials, they are 165–190 °C and 1–5 min, respectively; for medicinal herbs, they are 160–175 °C and 0–4 min, respectively; and for woody medicinal materials, they are 170–195 °C and 2–5 min, respectively. (4) The presoaked medicinal material is then placed in the explosion tank. After feeding of gas media (air, liquid nitrogen, nitrogen, water vapor, carbon dioxide, ozone, supercritical CO_2, and ethanol, etc.), the tank is heated to a certain temperature, and maintaining for a required time, the medicinal material is exploded. (5) The effective components in the obtained medicinal material could be extracted by solvent or vapor distillation. Extract residues can be used by direct combustion, mixing combustion, solid-state fermentation for organic fertilizer preparation, and enzymatic hydrolysis into fermentable sugars. (6) The obtained medicinal material could also be directly used for water decoction.

The gas explosion technology has the following advantages: (1) For TCM compounds, compared with other TCM processing methods, it has the functions of medicinal property neutralization and toxicity reduction. (2) For saving medicinal materials, since the effective destruction of plant cell walls by gas explosion could improve the dissolution of effective components in Chinese medicinal materials during the decoction process, the use of medicinal material is reduced and the medical expense is also decreased. (3) The gas explosion process is helpful to the Maillard reactions of medicinal material, of which an important aspect is to enhance the curative effect of medicinal material. (4) Gas explosion technology has the following advantages: simple operations, controllable conditions, and feasible industrial amplification, which is conducive to the controllability of processing parameters and the industrialization development of TCM processing technology. (5) For a single TCM, the gas explosion treatment could increase the extraction of effective components and combine the processing technology to the subsequent comprehensive utilization, which forms the ecological industry chain of TCM extraction [23].

6.2.4 Gas Explosion Technology Focused Ecological Industry of Medicinal Plants

Medicinal plant resource is a natural thing left for us, and we must do the rational development and effective protection to achieve the ecological, social, and economic harmony and unity, and lay a solid and sustainable development for the modernization of Chinese medicine industry. Currently, the main use of herbal medicinal plants as traditional processing model is difficult to adapt to the trend of the world. Particularly, the processing of medicinal plant causes great waste of resources and pollutions during conversion processes. For the use of a particular medicine, a common process is as follows: The first is to crush herbs and then to extract the active ingredient, and the dregs are discarded or used for mushroom cultivation or as fermented feed. Each operating unit in the described process is relatively independent with regard to the mutual impact of processes on each other, which results in the formation of isolation in various technical aspects and is not conducive to the work efficiency and potentially increases the cost of production.

In order to achieve the product diversification and comprehensive utilization of medicine plant resources, the establishment of ecological chain is necessary [24]. This requires the integration of multiple technologies. The core is key technologies about the raw material pretreatment, the conversion process, residue treatment, and optimal combination. The researches about unit operations are usually thorough and detailed, but the integration of the whole process is lacking. Thus, the product diversification and ecological industrial chain of technology integration could not be formed.

The key to reverse this situation is technology integration. The medicinal plant ecological industry chain with gas explosion as the core has the following characteristics: ① Couple several key technologies, such as gas explosion pretreatment and solid-state fermentation of TCM. ② Flexible process can be changed depending on the specific characteristics of the operational aspects of the feedstock, and the parameters can also be changed to add new technologies to further enrich and develop the system. For example, the gas explosion can couple not only with enzymatic methods but also with microwave extraction, ultrasonic extraction and SFE, and other extraction methods. Ultrafiltration membrane separation technologies can also be used for the separation and purification of the products. ③ Broad scope of application: The system is suitable for the majority of Chinese medicine and other natural products. ④ Product diversification [25] can achieve the transition from a single product to diversified products. This ecological industry chain will not only extract the medicinal ingredients, but also develop a variety of high-value by-products, thus improving the overall economic efficiency.

To use the above theory and technology system in the current utilization of medicinal plants makes the study of medicinal plants convert from the pharmaceutical industry to the integration of food, materials, energy, and other industries. Learning from a variety of technological processes forms a unique eco-industrial chain of medicinal plants, which improves the utilization of medicinal plant materials, reduces emissions, achieves the diversification and high value of products, improves the production efficiency and economic benefits, and promotes the development of modern medicine.

The eco-industrial chain establishment of medicinal plants through technology integration combines the resource utilization and environmental protection in the process of matter transformation and energy use. It thereby makes economic, environmental, and social benefits of system and turns the Chinese medicine plants industry from extraction of active ingredients towards medicine plant manufacturing composed of pharmaceuticals, materials, energy and other integrated productions [20].

The medicinal plant ecological industrial technologies are described in the following parts by the examples of Kudzu and Rhus fruits.

6.2.4.1 Ecological Industry Chain Model of Kudzu

Kudzu is the dry roots of *Pueraria lobata* (Willd.) Ohwi or *P. lobata* (Willd.) Ohwi var.*thomsonii* (Benth.) Vaniot der Maesen of Leguminosae plants. Kudzu adapts to humid and drought earth and is widely distributed all over the China. It can also be cultivated in the barren hills and slopes with high yield, thus becoming the development focus of economic crops in many areas. According to preliminary statistics, total Kudzu cultivation area including wild and cultivated Kudzu is about 400,000 ha, and the total annual resource is 150 million tons, of which a small portion is used to make medicines (essentially dry roots of *P. lobata* Ohwi) and starch processing. There are quite a lot of resources which have not been developed and utilized.

With the rapid development of human society, energy and resource crisis has become more apparent, and the use of biomass feedstock into fuel ethanol is the hot spots of world's high-tech research and industrialization. Countries use different raw materials for production of bioethanol, respectively, according to the actual situation. Considering comprehensive China's national conditions and biological resources, in compliance with "the development of fuel ethanol is not competing with human for food, not with food for land" principle, the feasible solution for development of biomass fuel ethanol is acting according to circumstances which are not suitable to plant high-yield crops. According to local conditions, we can cultivate crops which are high yielding and select wildlife resources which are tolerant to drought and barren as feedstock for producing fuels. For instance, Kudzu with high starch content is abundant in China. The dry starch content *in P. lobata Ohwi* can reach 50–60 %. It is a promising non-food feedstock for producing fuel ethanol, satisfying the principle of "not competing for land with food."

(1) Kudzu resource features and proposal of its eco-industrialized chain idea

Kudzu is majorly composed of starch, cellulose, protein, and isoflavones, and also contains a small amount of fat, pectin, tannins, and alkaloids [26]. The moisture content of fresh Kudzu is 50–60 %, and the starch content is 18.5–27.5 %, which can be equivalent to 50–60 % in dry Kudzu [27]. In addition, dry Kudzu also contains cellulose of 9–15 %, crude protein of 5–8 % and isoflavones of 3–5 %. So it can be used as starchy feedstock to produce ethanol.

Kudzu has become an important commercial crop in many places in China, resulting in a large area of artificial cultivation. Because it is rich in starch, it can be used as raw materials for fuel ethanol so as to solve the problems of cereal fermentation, which is restricted by the limited food sources and expensive cost. In fact, food fermentation is of high cost and low competitiveness, and excessive food consumption causes the reduction of per capita availability of food, thus threatening national food security. Except for above advantages, planting Kudzu is conducive to agricultural production and exploring a wealthy road to farmers.

In recent years, research on kudzu is concentrated in starch, kudzu flavonoid extraction, and refining. In application areas, kudzu is only utilized as starch resource to extract starch, or as raw material for extracting kudzu flavonoids. It is difficult to take into account the combining utilization of flavonoids and starch in kudzu, not even to say the utilization of 9–15 % of fibers and 5–8 % of protein contained in kudzu. In addition, in the existing extraction process of starch and flavonoids in kudzu, there must exist crushing equipment with the purpose of destroying the cell structure of kudzu, thereby releasing the starch granules or flavonoids. In the crushing process of raw material, the existing of fibers is thought to increase energy consumption for breaking material. Similarly, using the solvent extraction method to effectively extract total flavonoids from kudzu should overcome the mass transfer resistance composed of dense structures formed by the cellulose, hemicellulose, and other substances in the cell wall. In addition, it should overcome the mass obstruction of partially gelatinized effect produced by starch solvent at high temperatures (80–90 °C) for a long time (2–3 h).

Existing ethanol production process from starchy feedstock is "cooking → gelatinization → liquidation → saccharification → liquid fermentation → primary distillation." In the process, the energy consumed by the cooking of raw materials accounts for 30–40 % of the total energy consumption for ethanol production. Large amounts of highly concentrated organic wastewater are produced, which causes environmental pollution. By this way, kudzu flavonoids are difficult to extract and kudzu fibers are also not utilized.

As can be seen, for the use of Kudzu resources, the following problems exist. Firstly, the existing process only considers the single-component utilization (starch or flavonoids) without the utilization of other components (kudzu fibers), not only resulting in a waste of resources but also impeding further utilization. Adopting given pretreatment (crushing, grinding) can only separate and use starch or flavonoids, which is an incomplete separation means. Secondly, the existing utilization technology is relatively single showing as the separation of extraction process of starch and flavonoids, which lacks the concept of fractionation utilization of effective components in kudzu.

Finally, the kudzu resource utilization lacks the relevant technology integration system. The existing technology drives from starchy fermentation process of grain, resulting in a waste of raw materials. Meanwhile, the high cost of pretreatment of raw material and serious environmental pollution make the production costs too high, which led to the difficulty of industrialization of kudzu and other non-food starch resources.

Aiming at above problems in the utilization of kudzu resource and achieving the total biomass utilization, we should recognize that in the utilization process of kudzu starch and flavonoids, starch or kudzu fibers are not wastes but the valued and exploitable resource. Thus, it is necessary to search for a feedstock pretreatment technology [28] for separating multi-components at low cost and benefiting further industrial utilization.

Chen Hongzhang et al. [29] proposed Kudzu eco-industrial chain taking fuel ethanol from fermentation as major product. According to the results of the development of Kudzu eco-industrial chain, the process of simultaneous saccharification and fermentation of steam-exploded Kudzu to coproduce starch and flavonoids was put forward. Steam explosion technology can be used to decrease the dissolution barrier of celluloses and other constitutive components to starch and flavonoids. Then, after the simultaneous saccharification and fermentation, ethanol is produced and residues are used to extract flavonoids.

(2) Research on Kudzu eco-industrialized chain

According to the characteristics of Kudzu resources, the eco-industrial chain of Kudzu resource is established to pretreat Kudzu by steam explosion technology combined with the utilization technology platform of lignocellulosic resources. Additionally, they form a continuous coupling solid-state fermentation to produce ethanol and to extract Kudzu flavonoids and fiber [30], so as to achieve the fractionation of Kudzu components and integrated utilization. Process route is shown in Fig. 6.17.

In response to this process route, the effects of steam explosion pretreatment on kudzu flavonoid yield, soluble sugar of fermentation product, components, and ethanol yield after fermentation are investigated. The optimum condition of stream explosion pretreatment was holding pressure of 0.8 MPa and holding time of

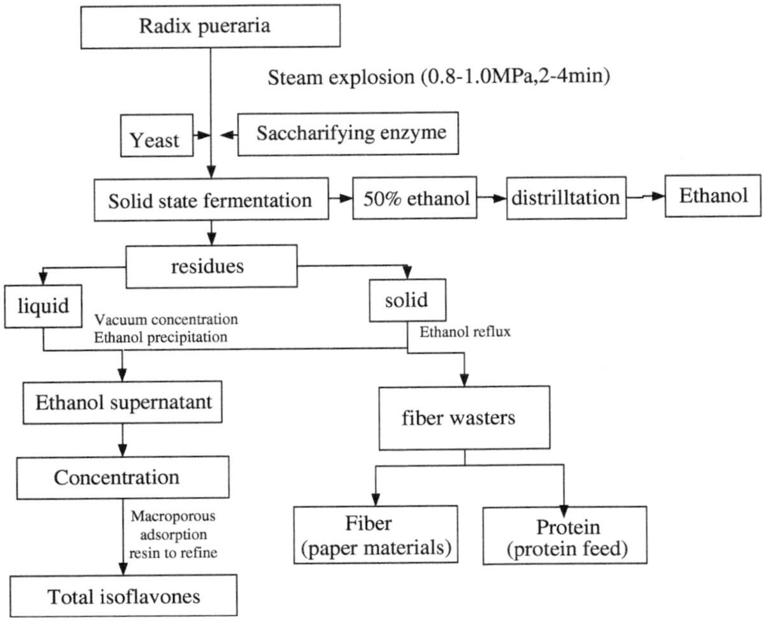

Fig. 6.17 Production of ethanol and isoflavones from steam pretreated *Radix Pueraria* by solid-state fermentation

3.5 min. Under this condition, ethanol yield after Kudzu fermentation reached 8.01 %, and flavonoid extraction yield reached 0.8917 %. The condition of simultaneous saccharification and solid-state fermentation of steam-exploded Kudzu was optimized. The extraction process of Kudzu flavonoids from fermentation residues was studied, and the comprehensive utilization of solid-state fermentation residue was discussed.

(3) Features of Kudzu eco-industrialized chain

This chain is based on Kudzu characteristics, and it realizes the fractionation conversion of Kudzu components and clean utilization. It has the following characteristics:

① Novel and unpolluted steam explosion pretreatment of Kudzu

Fresh Kudzu, directly going through steam explosion pretreatment without the addition of excess water, would reduce the water consumption of the production process.

By a short-time (2–4 min) steam explosion technology to pretreat Kudzu, the thermal chemical effect and physical tearing effects of high-temperature steam make the cell walls of plant tissue break down, undermining the solid structure of Kudzu and eliminating the unfavorable factors of fibrous tissue for starch and flavonoids utilization. Therefore, they increased the starch gelatinization rate and realized the direct fermentation of pretreated Kudzu to produce fuel ethanol.

The steam explosion pretreatment of Kudzu helps to eliminate the lengthy cooking process of starchy feedstock (30–120 min), thereby reducing the energy consumption of ethanol fermentation, shortening the production cycle, and reducing production costs.

② Simultaneous saccharification and solid-state fermentation of Kudzu

Simultaneous saccharification and solid-state fermentation of ethanol just need to add a small amount of water to make greatly reduction of fermented mash and increase ethanol content. Meanwhile, it reduces energy consumption of distillation and the subsequent wastewater treatment process. This method realized the clean production, reduced production costs, and laid the foundation for the second utilization of fermentation residues, which is conducive to Kudzu utilization.

③ Continuous solid-state fermentation method for producing ethanol

To solve the problem that the solid-state fermentation of Kudzu for ethanol process cannot continuously undergo, we proposed an ethanol fermentation method of Kudzu with continuous solid-state fermentation equipment. The fermentation and separation can be coupled by the continuous fermentation equipment, and CO_2 is used as a circulating carrier gas to separate produced ethanol from fermented feed. This method can reduce the influence of heat generated during fermentation and the inhibition effect of ethanol.

④ Coproduction of fuel ethanol and flavonoids

Simultaneous saccharification and fermentation of Kudzu for producing fuel ethanol need to destruct the fiber structure of Kudzu, release starch from Kudzu, and utilize starch to ferment fuel ethanol. The lack of utilization recognition of Kudzu flavonoids from fermentation residues after producing fuel ethanol not only means a waste of resources but is likely to cause environmental problems. To extract Kudzu's total flavonoids from fermentation residues is conducive to the comprehensive utilization of Kudzu, the improvement of economic effects, and the industrial production of kudzu.

⑤ Utilization of fermentation residual fibers

As a result of the new solid-state fermentation process, fermentation residue is of low water content (60–70 %) and easy to be utilized. It can be directly used as feed, with the low protein content and high crude fiber content. After drying by hot air to a moisture content of about 25 %, it can be divided into two parts of fibers and proteins by mechanical grading. For the fiber fraction, its fiber content is about 18 % and the maximum fiber length is 2.4 mm. The minimum length is 0.75 mm, and the mean length is 1.59 mm, which can be used as paper or textile materials. The solid powders after improving the protein content (21.8 %) can be used as protein feed.

6.2.4.2 Ecological Industrial Chain Model of Sumac Fruits

(1) Gas explosion treatment of Sumac fruits and oil extraction

Sumac is widely distributed in China and is rich in amount, while it is always left alone, receiving no reasonable development and utilization. According to statistics, there is about 500,000 ha of wild sumac in the west of Anhui Province. If each plant can harvest at least 2 kg of fruits every year, the total yield is very abundant. Sumac is an oil-rich plant with the oil content of 15–20 % in fruit. Oil in it mainly contains five kinds of fatty acids, including palmitic acid, stearic acid, linoleic acid, oleic acid, and linolenic acid. In which linoleic acid accounts for 40–48 % of the total amount and is recognized as one of the most important essential fatty acids. It can reduce blood cholesterol and prevent atherosclerosis. The absence of linoleic acid causes poor animal development, skin and kidney damage as well as infertility. In addition, sumac fruit is rich in flavonoids. About 2 kg of flavonoids can be extracted from 100 kg sumac fruit, most belonging to quercetin-3-O-rhamnoside, of which hydrolysis product is the quercetin. It has been proved that quercetin has a very wide range of physiological and pharmacological activity. It can expand the coronary blood vessels, lower blood lipids, and blood pressure and have antiplatelet aggregation effect. It has relieving cough, removing phlegm, and anti-inflammatory, antiviral, antiallergic, and antioxide free radical effects. It also has the significant prevention and treatment effects of tumor. Thus, sumac fruit is a good medicine resource, which has great value to develop.

Since oils and flavonoids are present in the cell of sumac fruit, fruits need to be crushed before extraction. Traditional pretreatment method of sumac fruits is mechanical pulverization to facilitate the extraction of effective constituents. As oilseeds have large resistance to exogenic action, the treatment effect on material is limited. All oil-containing herbs have problems of crushing. On the one hand, the toughness of the plant cell wall is strong. To achieve a higher crushing degree needs to consume large amounts of mechanical energy, thus increasing the processing cost. On the other hand, the oil leakage forms material bonding, which is unfavorable for solvent immersion and decreases extraction effect.

To solve the above problems, the author uses gas explosion technology to treat sumac fruit. Before gas explosion, the peel of sumac fruit should firstly be removed. The peel and seed of sumac fruit are exploded separately, in order to obtain oils with different fatty acid compositions. The seed oil has high linoleic acid content, which can be used as edible health oil, while the peel oil contains more C16–C18 fatty acids (more than 92 %) and is a good raw material for biodiesel production.

Compared with the mechanical crushing, the sumac fruit after gas explosion has incompact structure and small particle size. Under the same conditions, the oil extraction rate of crushed sumac fruit after 6–8 h can reach more than 95 %. After 3–4 h, the extraction rate of exploded sumac fruit can also reach 95 %, which saves about 50 % time. This is because the gas explosion process combines cooking and crushing processes. Cooking can passivate lipase in seeds and make protein denaturation, which promotes the condensation of grease and improves the oil extraction yield. Crushing can increase the specific surface area of the material, which is beneficial to accelerate solvent extraction process and reduce residual oil content.

The conditions of sumac fruit gas explosion treatment were then optimized. When the gas explosion pressure was less than 1.5 MPa, pressure-maintaining time was less than 5 min, and the breaking efficiency of seeds was low. Complete seed was contained in gas explosion material, extraction solvent was hard to immerse, and the oil extraction rate decreased. High gas explosion pressure and long maintaining time led to the waste of steam and increased the unnecessary energy consumption. Kinetics study showed that for the oil extraction from sumac fruit, 1.5 MPa and 5 min is optimized conditions of gas explosion processing.

It should be noted that when the pressure of saturated steam is 1.5 MPa during the gas explosion process, the temperature could reach about 200 °C. The high temperature and pressure change the partial properties of oil, such as enhancement of transparency, decrease of acid value, and viscosity. The content of neutral oil and unsaturated fatty acid in the oil increases. This may be due to the fact that through gas explosion with saturated vapor, hydrophilic phospholipids will swell, coagulate, and precipitate from the oil. The increase of neutral oil and unsaturated fatty acid is helpful for the reduction of subsequent refining cost, and the composition of fatty acid in the oil does not change greatly.

(2) Flavonoid extraction from residue after oil extraction

Flavonoid extraction solvent is generally water or ethanol, and extraction methods include microwave extraction, ultrasound extraction, and reflux. The results showed that after gas explosion treatment, the main flavonoid in the sumac fruit, quercetin glycoside, was converted to quercetin, which is insoluble in water and shows better solubility in hot ethanol. Thus, ethanol is used as extraction solvent, and the extraction experiments are carried out by heating.

According to orthogonal experiment analysis, the results show that temperature has significant effect on flavonoid extraction rate, followed by ethanol concentration, while extraction time and solid–liquid ratio have little influence. Based on the various factors analysis, the optimal condition for sumac flavonoid is extracted with 70 % ethanol of 20 times mass of dry materials under 80 °C temperature for 3 times with 1 h for each time. Under these conditions, the flavonoid extraction yield from the sumac fruit residue after oil extraction reached above 95 %. The obtained quercetin had above 95 % purity based on HPLC determination. Use HPLC to detect the method to get the quercetin purity of more than 95 %.

(3) Preparation process of activated carbon from residue of extraction

The residue of sumac fruit after oil and flavonoid extraction could be activated by activator soaking and high-temperature carbonization to prepare activated carbon. The sumac residue is mixed with activator according to certain ratio for a certain time. After that, the mixture is then placed in the pyrolysis reaction for carbonization and activation. After the reaction, the activated carbon samples are washed with hydrochloric acid solution and then with hot water to neutral pH. The washed samples are dried at 105 °C to obtain the activated carbon particle. The determination of iodine adsorption value is according to GB/T 12496.8 1999, and the determination of methylene blue adsorption value is according to GB/T 12496.10 1999.

Through orthogonal experiments, the optimum experimental conditions of activated carbon preparation by $ZnCl_2$ activation method are determined. The $ZnCl_2$ concentration is 30 %, solid–liquid ratio is 1:4, the activation temperature is 600 °C, and the activation time is 5 h. Under the preparation conditions, methylene blue adsorption value and the iodine adsorption value of activated carbon are 125 and 724 mg/g, respectively, which are equal to the commercial activated carbon product.

Extracting oils from steam-exploded materials would enhance the permeation of the solution in the porous structure of solid materials, thereby increasing the extraction efficiency and yield with the shorter extraction time and decreasing the residual oil left in the oil cake. In addition, steam explosion treatment can achieve the effects of heat–moisture treatment and material crush and avoid some complicated, energy-consuming, time-consuming problems caused by cracking, flaking, heat–moisture cooking, and other conventional steps. This improves production efficiency and saves equipment investment, thus reducing production costs. According to some studies, quercetin-3-O-rhamnoside could be hydrolyzed to quercetin during steam explosion process. So quercetin is directly extracted from steam-exploded materials, which saves the trouble of hydrolysis process of quercetin-3-O-rhamnoside [30]. Finally, residues after oil and flavonoid extraction can be produced to activated carbon by a simple heat treatment, realizing the comprehensive utilization of sumac fruit. Its process is shown in Fig. 6.18.

Sumac fruit ecological industrial chain has the following characteristics. (1) The introduction of steam explosion technology simultaneously achieves the crush and heat–moisture treatment process in the traditional oil extraction industry and establishes a novel and high-efficiency oil material processing technology, making oil extraction time decreased by 50 %. (2) The establishment of clean quercetin production process achieves the conversion from quercetin glycoside to quercetin without addition of acid and alkali and reaches the conversion rate of 90 %. (3) The construction of Sumac fruit ecological industrial chain through technical integration and innovation fulfills the comprehensive utilization of Sumac fruit and also provides a reference template to the development of a large number of medicinal plant resources containing oil-rich seeds or fruit.

As the application field of gas explosion expands unceasingly, it could be effectively used to extract the active ingredients of medicinal plants, such as flavonoids, alkaloids, and grease. Gas explosion can lead to significant structural change of plant cells. The cell wall is damaged to form holes. The hemicellulose and pectic substances in cell wall decrease significantly after explosion. The gas explosion treatment is more intense than mechanical crushing, by which plant tissue structure appears larger crack. The damage of plant cell wall is helpful to reduce the extract resistance caused by cell wall. The degradation of hemicellulose and pectin also reduces the viscosity of extracted liquid, which is conducive to the separation

Fig. 6.18 Process route of comprehensive utilization of Sumac fruits

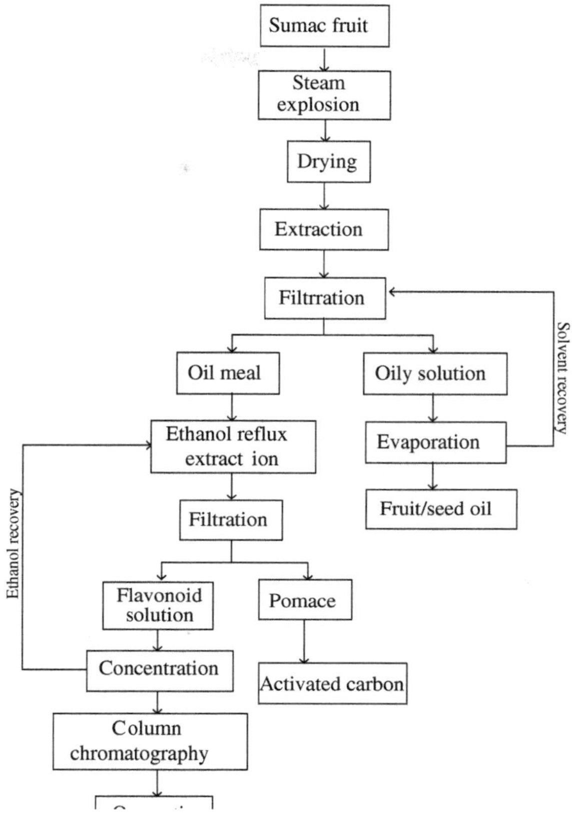

and purification of product. Besides, the high-temperature cooking during gas explosion could promote the reactions of chemical components of TCM, and thus, gas explosion could be developed into a modern TCM processing technology. The TCM processing by gas explosion could shorten the processing time and enrich the theory and range of products. With the deepening of the processing technology of medicinal plant research, the gas explosion technology can be flexibly applied to the processing of TCM extraction process and has wide development prospects in the specific field.

6.3 Application of Gas Explosion Technology in Bioenergy

6.3.1 Pretreatment of Feedstock in Bioenergy

Biomass [31] refers to get energy from biomass. There are many kinds of biomass feedstock. The main kinds of plant biomass include wood, crop straw (rice straw, wheat straw, the bean stalk, cotton stalk, chaff, etc.), weeds, and algae. Non-plant biomass mainly includes animal feces, dead animals, and organic composition of wastewater.

The plant biomass forms a tight structure in the levels of organs, tissues, cells, and cell wall. Cellulose, hemicellulose, and lignin are intertwined in the cell wall, and the pretreatment is necessary to destroy the physical and chemical structures of the cell wall and utilize the cellulose and hemicellulose components for bioenergy production. For the non-plant feedstock, such as living garbage and production waste, the primary premise of utilization is fractionation. To use the organic matter and grease in the non-plant feedstock for bioenergy production, more targeted pretreatment technology is required. Therefore, feedstock pretreatment technology has become the key to the development of biomass industry [28].

6.3.2 Advantages of Gas Explosion for Bioenergy Feedstock Pretreatment

Since 1986, the gas explosion technology is considered as a potential pretreatment technology [32, 33]. At present, the gas explosion technique has been proved to be an effective pretreatment technology [28, 34]. In nearly 20 years of researches and applications, Chen Hongzhang and his coworkers [15] summarize the advantages of the gas explosion technology as follows:

1. The straw pretreated by gas explosion has realized the fractionation at the cellular level. Due to chemical autocatalytic effect, hemicellulose is degraded in the pressure-maintaining process, resulting in a certain degree of fractionation on the component level.
2. In the gas explosion process, the steam is released instantly to destroy the plant tissue and cell wall, to loosen the close plant tissues. Thus, after gas explosion process, the feedstock forms porous structure. The specific surface area is increased, and the mass transfer rate for the subsequent solvent extraction is also increased by the enhancement of contact area.
3. After the separation of hemicellulose and water-soluble impurities, the purity is improved and further degradation and aggregation of the components are reduced, which avoids the dispersing of the product molecular weight and improves the activity for further transformation.
4. The gas-phase blasting process is clean and efficient without the emission of chemical pollutant, and the processing efficiency is high.
5. The operation of gas explosion technology is simple and easy to promote.

Therefore, the biomass feedstock after gas explosion, especially lignocellulosic feedstock, is suitable for the subsequent conversion by physical, chemical, and biological methods. Thus, gas explosion technology becomes the core of integration technology for bioenergy preparation.

6.3.3 *Typical Applications of Gas Explosion in Bioenergy*

6.3.3.1 Ethanol

Ethanol is the main raw material of fuel ethanol and ethylene preparation. The ethanol production by hexose fermentation by yeast is a very mature technology. When the lignocellulose is used as feedstock for ethanol production, the pretreatment process is necessary to separate cellulose, hemicellulose, and lignin and destroy the crystalline structure and polymerization degree of cellulose for the adsorption of cellulase on the substrates. The gas explosion technology could satisfy the industrialization requirements of cellulosic ethanol production.

When wheat straw after diluted sulfuric acid-catalyzed steam explosion is used for ethanol production by simultaneous saccharification and fermentation, the ethanol concentration and yield were 22.7 g/L and 65.8 %, respectively, under the conditions of reaction temperature 35 °C, substrate concentration 100 g/L, pH 5.0, and cellulase loading 30 FPU/g [35].

Lespedeza stalk was pretreated by steam explosion at 210 °C for 2, 4, and 6 min and was then used for ethanol preparation by simultaneous saccharification and fermentation (SSF). The ethanol yields were 59.3, 72.8, and 62.2 % of theoretical yield (the ethanol yield without steam explosion pretreatment is 16.4 % of theoretical yield). The studies indicated that the utilization rate of Lespedeza stalk after steam explosion was enhanced significantly and the ethanol yield after steam explosion increased by 4.65 times compared with that without steam explosion [36].

Owing to the rich content of cellulose and flavonoids in Kudzu [37], low-pressure gas explosion pretreatment could replace gelatinization process and the pretreated Kudzu could be used for ethanol preparation by SSF and the fermentation residues could be used for flavonoid extraction. The results showed that after gas explosion at 0.8 MPa and 3.5 min, 100 g Kudzu (dry weight) could produce 27.47 g ethanol and 4.43 g flavonoids under the conditions of glucoamylase loading 65 U/g, cellulase loading 1.5 U/g, fermentation time 60 h, and fermentation temperature 35–37 °C. In this process, the utilization rate of Kudzu starch is as high as 95 % and achieves the clean conversion and utilization of Kudzu, which provides a new way for the ethanol fermentation of non-food starch resources.

The process of ethanol preparation by SSF and gas explosion of citrus peel could obtain D-lemon essential oil, galacturonic acid, and citrus peel residues [38]. The separation of D-lemon could improve the ethanol yield to 50–60 L/1000 kg. The results [39] indicated that gas explosion could decrease the essential oil content in citrus peel to 0.025 % and significantly reduce the usage amount of cellulase. The gas explosion of olive tree pruning branches [40] showed the ethanol yield by gas explosion at 240 °C, and SSF could achieve 7.2 g/100 g feedstock, while the theoretical ethanol yield is 15.9 g/100 g feedstock. In order to improve the sugar yield and decrease the content of inhibitors, hydrolysis of rice straw is firstly carried out at 165 °C for 2 min, and then, the steam explosion is performed at 180 °C. Compared with acid hydrolysis, the sugar content of hydrolysate from rice straw after gas explosion enhanced 1.5 times [41]. When tape grass is used for ethanol production by enzymatic hydrolysis and fermentation after steam explosion, the soluble-sugar yield after hydrolysis is 5.06 g/100 g gas-exploded feedstock and 52.9 g/100 g insoluble cellulose. The fermentation ethanol yield is 243 g/kg insoluble cellulose [42].

Prof. Hongzhang Chen had industrialized the technology of enzymatic hydrolysis and ethanol fermentation of cornstalk by gas explosion in 2006 [43] and established industrialization demonstration project of 3000 ton/year cornstalk enzymolysis and fermentation, which included 5 m^3 gas explosion system, 100 m^3 cellulase solid-state fermentation, and 110 m^3 reaction system coupling solid-state enzymolysis and fermentation and separation. This industrialization demonstration project has provided a production technical route for straw enzymolysis and ethanol fermentation.

The Inbicon A/S Corporation from Japan used integrated biomass utilization system to convert lignocellulosic feedstock into ethanol and other by-products (shown in Fig. 6.19). This process was in pilot scale in 2003, and the demonstration factory was built at Kalundborg, Denmark, in 2009 [44].

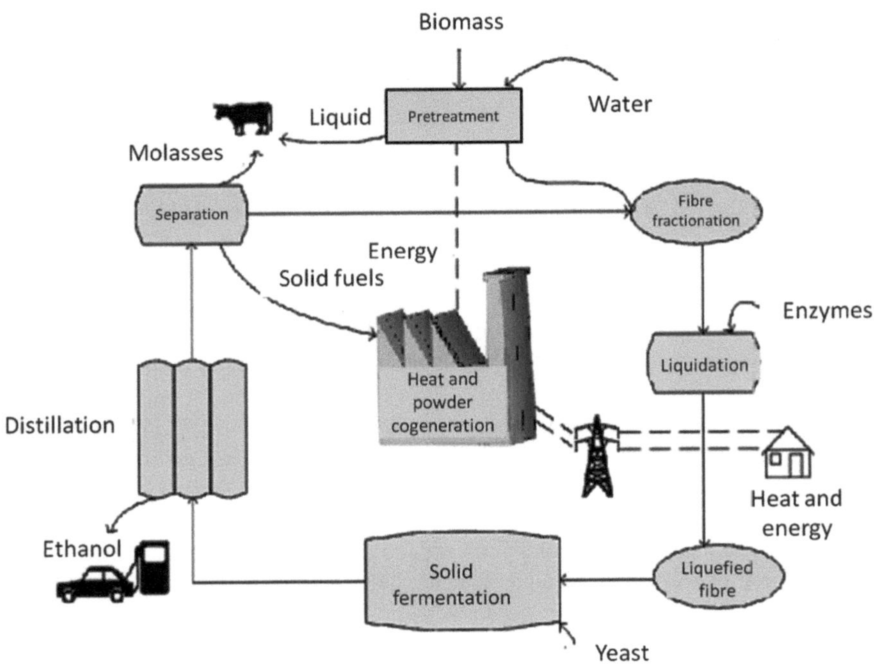

Fig. 6.19 Process of integrated biomass utilization system [44]

6.3.3.2 Acetone–Butanol

Acetone–butanol is good organic solvents and important chemical raw material, which is widely used in chemical, plastic, organic synthesis, paint, and other industries. The heat value of butanol is approximately equal to gasoline and higher than ethanol. With the shortage of oil resources, butanol shows the practical values in terms of energy and the use of renewable resources for acetone–butanol fermentation is highly valued.

The team of Prof. Chen Hongzhang studied the acetone–butanol fermentation by membrane recycling enzymolysis coupling fermentation system of gas-exploded cornstalk [45]. Under the dilution rate of 0.075 h^{-1}, the butanol yield is 0.14 g/g cellulose and hemicellulose. The maximum butanol yield is 0.31 g L^{-1} h^{-1}, and the solvent compositions of butanol/acetone/ethanol are 65.3, 24.3, and 10.4 (volume ratio). The conversion rates of cellulose and hemicellulose are 72 and 80 %, respectively. In this system, the enzymatic hydrolysis and fermentation are performed at their own optimal conditions and the cellulase usage amount is reduced. The inhibition effect of enzymatic products on cellulase is effectively relieved, the effect of solvent products on the activity of microbes is alleviated, and the fermentation cycle is prolonged.

The previous study [46] showed that hydrogen peroxide oxidation could remove the lignin in gas-exploded straw and then improve the enzymatic efficiency and the ethanol fermentation performance. Thus, the pretreatment of straw by the coupling of gas explosion and hydrogen peroxide oxidation could achieve the fractionation of cellulose, hemicellulose, and lignin, which provides technical support to the high-value applications of straw. The lignin and hemicellulose contents of cornstalk after the coupling treatment of gas explosion and hydrogen peroxide oxidation decreased from 22 and 33.5 to 8 and 24 %, respectively [47]. The cellulose content increased from 25.4 to 63 %, which improves the utilizability of cellulose component in cornstalk. In general, the sugar content in butanol fermentation medium is less than 60 g/L [48].

The total sugar content of enzymatic hydrolysis after 1 % NaOH and 4 % H_2O_2 treatment is about 45.24 g/L, which basically meets the requirements for butanol fermentation. The soluble lignin content in the concentrated enzymatic hydrolysate is merely 1.2 g/L, which would not produce inhibition effect on the butanol fermentation. After 72-h fermentation, the total solvent content is 12.1 g/L and the yield is 0.17 g L^{-1} h^{-1}.

This technology has been industrialized in Songyuan, Jilin Province, in China by the successful establishment of 300, 000 t/year cornstalk biorefinery industrialization production lines in September 2010 [21]. The process is based on the technology from Prof. Hongzhang Chen at Institute of Process Engineering, Chinese Academy of Sciences. The produce routes of 300,000 t/year cornstalk biorefinery is to use cornstalk hemicellulose for butanol, acetone and ethanol fermentation, long fiber for papermaking, short fiber and lignin for polyether glycol and phenolic resin synthesis. The multiple biobased products could be applied in energy, plastic, polymer, and chemical industry, which provides new routes for the high-value application of cornstalk.

6.3.3.3 Hydrogen

Hydrogen is an ideal clean energy. Biohydrogen production plays an increasingly important position in the study of new energy. The cost of biological hydrogen production technology is currently high. To use low-price and rich feedstock is an important way to reduce the cost. The use of biomass, especially lignocellulosic biomass, is the new development direction of hydrogen production. The straw is pretreated by gas explosion to destroy the natural crystalline structure of lignocellulose and partially degrade hemicellulose and lignin for easier decomposition of straw by microorganisms. The use of organic matter from low-cost straw is the effective means to solve the energy crisis, realize the waste utilization, and improve the environment.

The hemicellulose hydrolysate from gas explosion of cornstalk could be used for hydrogen production by submerged fermentation [49]. The comparison results of the acidic and neutral gas explosion show that the hydrogen yields per mole of hexose were 2.84 and 3.00 mol. If the gas-exploded cornstalk is used for hydrogen fermentation by SSF, its production rate and yield were 126 mL/g VSS d and 68 mL/g gas-exploded cornstalk [50]. Compared with the two-step enzymatic hydrolysis and hydrogen fermentation, the lag period of SSF can be shortened and the hydrogen yield is increased [51].

6.3.3.4 Biogas

Biogas is an inexhaustible bioenergy and extensively studied in the world as a clean alternative of fossil fuels with limited reserves. Due to the degradation recalcitrance of natural straw, in order to enhance the conversion and utilization rate of straw, many physical, chemical, and biological pretreatment methods are adopted in the studies of straw biogas fermentation. However, these methods have the disadvantages of environmental pollution and long processing cycle, which cannot meet the clean and effective conversion of biomass. Gas explosion is a widely used physicochemical pretreatment in the straw biogas fermentation.

When gas-exploded rice straw is used for biogas fermentation, the biogas yield increased by 20 % compared with that of untreated rice straw [52]. The highest biogas yield is 331 L/kg volatile solid. Meanwhile, the gas-exploded rice straw could first be used for ethanol fermentation and then for biogas fermentation. After the gas explosion at 200 °C and 10-min pressure-maintaining time, the ethanol yield is 0.2 kg/kg gas-exploded feedstock and the biogas yield of ethanol fermentation residue is 183 L/kg dry rice straw. Finally, the routes of cyclic utilization are proposed. The biogases from ethanol fermentation residue are used to generate steam, and steam is used for the ethanol distillation.

Compared with the untreated straw, the anaerobic fermentation biogas yield of the straw after gas explosion increased by 34–67 %. Under the gas explosion conditions of 3.0 MPa and 90 s, the maximum biogas amount of anaerobic fermentation per gram dry straw is 304.72 mL and the starting time and fermentation period are shortened after gas explosion pretreatment [53].

The straw after gas explosion pretreatment is used for biogas production under high-temperature conditions at 50 °C, and the methane production reached 1382 mL/g total solids (TS). In experimental conditions of the solid–liquid ratio of 1:7, initial pH 7.5, inoculation amount 35 %, added amount of NH_4HCO_3 0.04 g/g dry gas exploded straw, cellulase loading 30 IU/g dry gas exploded straw, fermentation temperature 50 °C, methane production of gas exploded straw was increased to 153.0 mL/g TS, which is 2.9 times of untreated straw. After fermentation, straw cellulose and hemicellulose degradation rates were 59.86 and 67.22 %, respectively [54]. Therefore, gas explosion pretreatment improves gas production and degradation rate of straw. High-temperature solid-state fermentation can shorten the fermentation lag phase and increase gas production efficiency and does not produce a lot of wastes after fermentation.

When gas-exploded switchgrass is used for biogas fermentation, the biogas yield improved 50 % compared with control samples [55]. When the gas-exploded switchgrass is mixed with cow dung, the methane yield is 230 mL CH_4/g VS under the C/N 31/56. 40 % volatile content showed the fastest rate of gas production and higher yield.

The Cambi A/S Corporation from Japan adopted gas explosion technology to treat the sludge in the wastewater and improve the biogas yield by organic matter fermentation [56]. The process of gas explosion on sludge treatment is shown in Fig. 6.20.

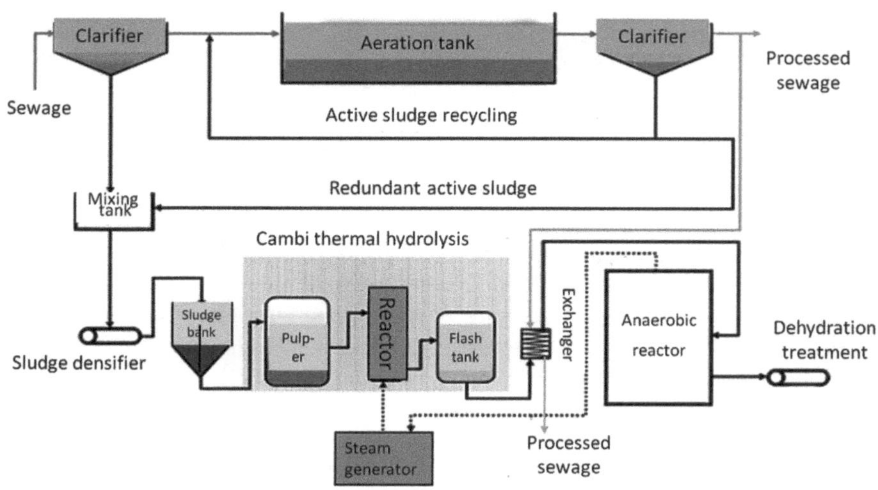

Fig. 6.20 Cambi gas explosion processes [57, 58]

The sludge from wastewater is firstly dehydrated by pressing with filter and then transferred into steam explosion reactor [56, 57]. The gas explosion of pretreated slurry is then performed at temperature 165–170 °C, and the treatment time is about 20–30 min [58, 59]. The steam in the gas explosion reactor is released slowly and reused.

6.4 The Applications of Steam Explosion Technology in Biomaterial Field

The biobased products take biomass as raw materials, utilizing the transformation technologies such as physics, chemistry, and biology to manufacture various kinds of products. These kinds of biobased products are numerous, including biobased chemicals such as xylitol, furfural, levulinic acid, and oxalic acid; biobased energy such as ethanol, butanol, hydrogen, biogas, and biodiesel; and biobased materials [60].

Human has used biomass materials (such as cotton, linen, wool, silk, and wood) for thousands of years. However, chemical materials developed from oil, coal and other fossil resources promote the civilization and economic development of human much greatly. The utilization of biomass resources has decreased gradually. Currently, the increasing depletion of fossil resources has trapped the development of chemical materials into a serious crisis of resources. Meanwhile, the non-biodegradable petrochemical materials have caused serious pollution on the living environment of humans. Facing the dual pressures of resources and environment, people need to urgently look for renewable resources to replace fossil resources. Biomass is a kind of renewable organic materials, including agricultural products and agricultural waste, wood and waste, and animal waste. Therefore, biobased materials based on biomass resources have become a research hot spot [61, 62].

Biobased materials belong to the new material category, and material industry is the main content of strategic emerging industries. Use of abundant agriculture and forest biomass resources for developing environment-friendly and recyclable biobased materials and replacing plastic, steel, cement and other materials is the important direction for the international industrial development of new materials. Since the twenty-first century, biobased materials have attracted extensive attention, showing a momentum of rapid development in agriculture and forestry biomass as feedstock into bioplastic manufacturing, energy-saving insulation materials, wood–plastic composite materials, thermosetting resin material, functional polymer materials such as biobased materials and biobased monomer compounds, biobased additives, and surface active agents. The rapid increase of biobased bulk fine chemicals has gradually increased the economical efficiency of these products. Bayer, BASF, Exxon Mobil, Samsung Total, Teijin, and DuPont have made long-term commitment to the development of biobased materials and promote the commercialization of the world's biobased materials.

During the period of "the 11th Five-Year Plan" of China, the biobased material industry technology has gained obvious improvement, forming a large number of technologies with own proprietary such as biobased biodegradable plastics, wood-based plastics, polymeric macromolecular polylactic acid, and agricultural film. Wood–plastic heat is gradually rising nationwide with annual sales of more than 200,000 tons, and the annual growth rate is higher than 20 %. Biobased material, as an upgraded replacement for petroleum-based materials, is moving to green resource utilization for efficient, high value-added features, directional transformation, functional utilization, environment-friendly, standardization, and other directions. Compared with the international advanced-level technologies, there are still gaps in product performance, manufacturing costs, key technologies, technology integration, and industry-scale aspects. So we must accelerate the technologies of biosynthesis of biobased materials during manufacturing processes, chemical modification and synthesis of resin-based composite molding and other key technologies to facilitate the low-cost large-scale production and demonstration of biobased materials. Therefore, it would enhance the science and technology innovation capability of enterprises for biobased materials to achieve effective alternative to fossil resources, which will provide technology support for the cultivation of biobased material industry [63].

6.4.1 Natural Textile Fiber Extraction Using Steam Explosion Technology

6.4.1.1 The Extraction of Cannabis Sativa Using Steam Explosion

Cannabis sativa is a kind of industrial crops with long cultivation history, which is widely distributed and has various utilization aspects. In 1990s, with the intensification of global environmental pollution, the lifestyle and living concept of people have changed. This ancient textile hemp fiber as raw material wins back the people's favor for its unique fabric performance. Hemp fabric is stiff, smooth, antimicrobial, hygroscopic, and quickly dry with good ventilation and can efficiently block the ultraviolet rays, which is most suitable for summer clothing and bedding. In recent years, as a healthy, environmentally friendly "green fiber," it is increasingly popular in the international market. However, there are still many problems affecting the further improvement of its product quality concerning the hemp textile processing technologies. Among them, the degumming process is the bottleneck affecting the cannabis hemp textile processing quality.

(1) Cannabis sativa degumming technology using steam explosion

For the spinnability of marijuana, degumming is first needed, and the degumming performance is a direct impact on the quality of yarn. Currently, of all the

Table 6.12 Comparison of chemical composition of hemp and ramie

Composition(%)	Hemicellulose	Lignin	Waxiness	Hydrotrope	Pectin	Cellulose
Hemp	17.25	7.27	2.02	9.71	6.55	57.21
Ramie	13.29	1.19	0.54	7.35	4.04	73.59

degumming processes for hemp crops, those of ramie and linen are the most mature. The difficulty of degumming increases because of the chemical composition and structural characteristics of hemp.

Although the chemical composition of hemp fiber is related to species, growing area, harvest time, storage period, stuffing method, retting methods, and many other factors such as the high content of lignin and hemicellulose and high content of pectin and low content of cellulose are the features of the hemp fiber. These features increase the degumming difficulty of marijuana, leading to low yield of fine fiber. This can be seen from the comparison of the chemical composition of ramie and hemp fiber (Table 6.12). The single fibers of hemp form a net with the bonding of the intercellular substance, and ramie fiber cells are then neatly arranged in close proximity to aggregates. Furthermore, hemp fiber cells are bonded with hemicellulose through chemical bonds, which also increases the difficulty of degumming. More critically, the single fiber hemp is too short, which is usually 12–25 mm, and the fiber uniformity is poor. If all substances between cell layers are taken off (i.e., fully unglued), it is bound to result in short fibers without spinnability. Therefore, adhesive residue must be made of a single fibronectin fiber (fiber technology) spinning, which is called the moderate degumming process. Due to the characteristics of marijuana itself, it causes greater difficulty in degumming.

For a long time, the development of hemp fiber both at home and in abroad stays on the chemical degumming methods that are mainly referred to the more mature technology for chemical degumming of ramie. The chemical degumming process has disadvantages of high energy consumption, high water consumption, and severe pollution, seriously affecting the development of hemp textile industry. Microbial retting had been carried out abroad since the 1950s, and such studies began in the 1970s in China. Although microbial retting has gained great progress, it still cannot meet the requirements of industrial production, with disadvantages of high processing cost, requirement for chemical supplement, and the environmental pollution [64].

To overcome the shortcomings of high costs, enzymatic degumming pollution, and the low efficiency of degumming, Prof. Hongzhang Chen from Institute of Process Engineering developed a new and clean marijuana degumming technology using steam explosion [28]. Steam explosion can break and degrade 80 % of the hemicellulose and pectin in marijuana and partially degrade lignin. Marijuana after steam explosion opening [65] and carding [66] can directly be used in spinning. The specific procedures are as follows:

1. Soak marijuana to adjust the water content

Hemp fibers are soaked in water for 40–80 min to adjust the moisture content of 60–100 %.

Table 6.13 The influence of different water contents on marijuana steam explosion effect

Moisture content/%	10	30	40
pH	7.0	5.6	7.0
Color	Partially coking	Dark puce and uniform	Not change
Shape	Almost not separated	Mostly filiform	Still wet and not separated

Presoak is very important to the steam explosion results of marijuana, and different initial moisture contents of materials affect the rate reaching the maximum temperature. Steam explosion works on the fiber structure and separation of fiber bundles through water (including liquid water, water vapor, and hot steam) as a medium to achieve. Presoaking hemp increases water content, and both partially water-soluble materials can be removed. Because the specific heat of water is greater than that of fiber at high temperature and pressure conditions, steam explosion can alleviate damage to the fiber. On the other hand, the fiber presoak moisture content is not too high; otherwise, it will increase the time of water absorbing heat. The absorption of excessive heat results in insufficient pressure. According to the experimental analysis, when fiber moisture content is about 30 %, the vapor blasting effect is ideal (Table 6.13).

2. Steam explosion

The hemp fiber soaked is put into steam explosion tank at a pressure of 1.3–1.7 MPa for 3–8 min. Different conditions of steam explosion impact the effect of cannabis degumming.

a. Effect of steam explosion on weight loss rate of hemp fiber

Figure 6.21 shows that with the increase of steam explosion pressure, gas cooking temperature and the weight loss rate of the test sample increase. At conditions of high temperature and high pressure, the majority of fat wax, pectin, hemicellulose, and other substances are decomposed or softened, which partially degrade lignin and convert them to dye substances. Therefore, hemp color deepened after steam explosion. The greater the pressure treatment is, the darker the color of the aqueous solution is (Table 6.14). Steam explosion changes the material in hemp fiber, which is more soluble in water.

b. Effect of steam explosion treatment on hemp fiber component

Ingredients' comparison of steam explosion and not marijuana is given in Table 6.15 below. As is shown in Table 6.15, cellulose content of hemp fiber without steam explosion is only 52.94 %, which contains higher non-cellulose content. But after steam explosion treatment, cellulose content of raw cannabis hemp increased up to 84.37 %, significantly lowering the lignin content. In order to achieve the degumming of raw materials, it can be directly used in textile. If further

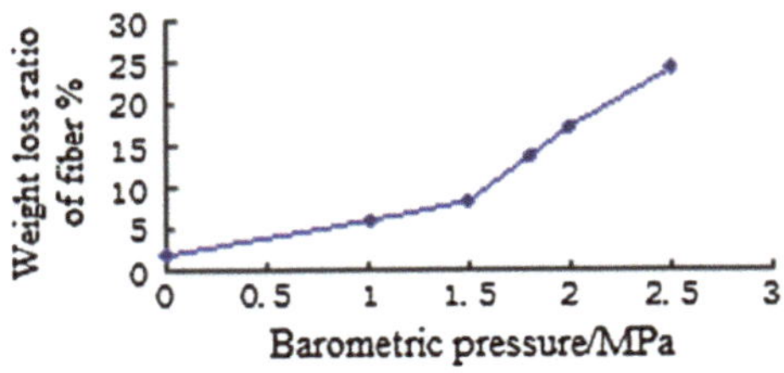

Fig. 6.21 The relation of steam explosion pressure and weight loss rate

Table 6.14 Hemp fiber morphological characteristics under different steam explosion pressure

Sample	A	B	C	D	E	F
Pressure	0	1.0	1.5	1.8	2.0	2.0
Color	Light yellow	Brownish yellow	Brownish yellow	Brownish yellow	Brown	Dark brown
Shape	Hemp peel	Filiform partially	Filiform mostly	Filament	Filament	Filament with some breakage

Table 6.15 Cellulose and lignin content analysis of raw hemp and marijuana with steam explosion

Sample	Cellulose content/%	Lignin content/%	Other/%
A	52.94	7.15	39.91
B	61.31	6.47	28.45
C	70.44	5.73	23.83
D	80.84	5.25	13.91
E	83.08	4.56	12.36
F	84.37	3.91	11.72

unglued, the time and reagent consumption unglued can be reduced. It is shown in Table 6.15, and with the increase of the pressure of the steam explosion treatment, the corresponding cellulose content increases and the corresponding lignin content reduces. But the change of the pressure weakened after reaching 2.5 MPa in this case. It shows that the higher pressure does not result in the better efficiency.

c. The effect of steam explosion treatment on hemp fiber gum content, unglued filtration rate, and the residual gum

Lye stew method is the main process for chemical degumming. In order to prove steam explosion efficiency of gum removal, chemical degumming process is chosen to do parallel processing of unglued contrast experiments using marijuana without steam explosion and explosion at 1.5 MPa, and the results are shown in Table 6.16. The gum content rate, unglued rate, and residual gum content rate with steam explosion are lower than those with untreated one. The higher the pressure is, the

Table 6.16 Degumming contract experiments

Sample	Time/min	Temperature/°C	Degumming rate/%	Liquid color
Untreated hemp	90	100	11.67	Brown
1.5 MPa steam explosion	90	100	6.62	Dark brown

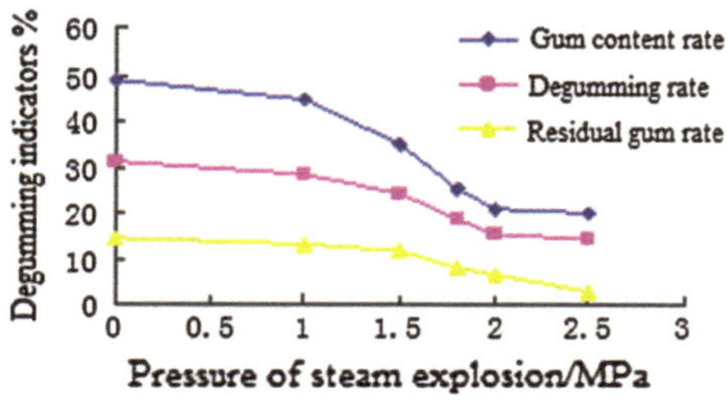

Fig. 6.22 The relation of degumming index and steam explosion pressure

lower the rates are. It showed that the higher the pressure, the easier the non-cellulose components in marijuana removed (shown in Fig. 6.22).

3. Washing by water

Cellulose and other hemicellulose, lignin, and pectin without spinnability during steam explosion degumming process are adsorbed on the hemp fiber surface, and separation of steam explosion-treated hemp fiber and epidermal tissue and other solid impurities can be achieved using water recycling, thus promoting extrusion technology and equipment.

In order to further improve the quality of hemp fibers, hemp after steam explosion is treated by microbiological degumming. Hemicellulose and pectin can provide the necessary nutrients for microbial fermentation, destroying the natural structure of marijuana to reach the purpose of hemp degumming and avoiding contamination by chemical supplementary methods.

(2) Bleaching of hemp by steam explosion

Lignin content of hemp fiber in general is higher than that of other hemp fibers, which may be figured out by comparing the chemical composition of hemp fiber and ramie fiber, respectively (Table 6.16). High lignin content has brought great difficulties to degumming process. By trial-and-error analysis, it is found that the fiber is white if lignin content is less than 0.8 %, meeting the requirements of textile printing and dyeing. When lignin content is more than 1.5 %, fiber color is brown yellow, bringing great difficulties to post-processing, especially on printing and dyeing. Hemp bleaching is to further remove residual lignin in hemp cellulose fibers and destroy other pigments with minimizing damage. Therefore, hemp bleaching is a necessary step in cannabis degumming.

Hydrogen peroxide is widely used, which can be used in a variety of fiber bleaching, with good stability of the product whiteness and brightness and no environmental pollution problems. Therefore, hydrogen peroxide is chosen for steam explosion of hemp fiber bleaching. In addition that the natural pigment will be destroyed in the bleaching process, the hemp fibers themselves may be damaged. Therefore, the bleaching process conditions must be controlled to the desired whiteness as much as possible. The quality of the fiber is preserved satisfactorily, so that inherent quality and appearance quality are reached.

① The effect of pH value on the bleaching effect

In H_2O_2 bleaching process, pH of bleaching solution is one of the important factors in bleaching quality. Hydrogen peroxide from acidic to weakly alkaline, i.e., pH < 9, is relatively stable within the range, the decomposition rate is small, and the decomposition rate is relatively high in the basic condition of more alkaline. It is particularly more obvious when pH is 10 or more. If the addition of stabilizers or other additives is appropriate, bleaching solution pH can be improved.

Na_2SiO_3 is a commonly used stabilizer. It is shown in Table 6.17, when the bleaching solution is within the pH range of 9–13 and whiteness of hemp fibers is between 38 and 46 %. When the pH is 10 and 11, the degree of whiteness is of 51.5 and 53.6 %. When the pH value is 6, almost no bleaching effect occurs. When pH was 13, whiteness of hemp declined. Therefore, after Na_2SiO_3 was added as a stabilizer, hydrogen peroxide bleaching at pH of 10–11 gives the best effect.

② The effect of temperature on whiteness results

Temperature is an important factor affecting the bleaching effect. Test found that when hydrogen peroxide bleaching is at higher temperatures, the hemp fiber whiteness increases significantly (Table 6.18). Ionization constant due to excessive hydrogen peroxide increases with increasing temperature (Table 6.19). Therefore, it can be expected to increase the bleaching temperature and bleach effect. Hydrogen peroxide decomposition rate increases as the temperature increases (Table 6.20). When H_2O_2 is used as a stabilizer, the dissociation constant K (lg residual H_2O_2 % $= kt/2.303$) was 3.02×10^{-3} at 70 °C, while it was 10.44×10^{-3} at 90 °C. Of course

Table 6.17 Bleaching results in different pH values

pH value	6	9	10	11	13
Hemp whiteness (%)	22.5	28	51.5	53.6	46

Table 6.18 Whiteness result at different temperature conditions

Temperature	55–65 °C	65–75 °C	75–85 °C	85–95 °C
Hemp whiteness (%)	43.1	52.4	55.1	49.2

Table 6.19 The effect of temperature on H_2O_2 ionization constant

Temperature (°C)	$K = \frac{[H^-][HO^-]}{[H_2O_2]}$
15	1.39×10^{-12}
20	1.78×10^{-12}
25	2.24×10^{-12}
35	3.55×10^{-12}

Table 6.20 The effect of temperature on H_2O_2 decomposition rate

Temperature (°C)	H_2O_2 content (%)		
	Initial	1 h later	2 h later
20	0.69	0.69	0.69
40	0.69	0.69	0.65
60	0.69	0.53	0.39
80	0.69	0.39	0.18

only by the speed of decomposition of H_2O_2, it cannot say whether it is effectively bleaching. It also contains a side reaction for H_2O_2 oxidation of fibers and other invalid decomposition. Many experiments show that in the case of the correct use of stabilizers, fabric whiteness and fiber extent of the damage are only concerned with the H_2O_2 decomposition rate. The impact of rate of decomposition speed on them is smaller.

It is shown in Table 6.20, and as the temperature rises, hemp whiteness gradually increases. As the temperature successively rises to about 90 °C, the hemp fiber whiteness declines. Therefore, hemp bleaching should control the optimal temperature in the range of 65–85 °C.

③ The effect of time on whiteness results

It was found that under the same conditions, the time required for bleaching solution at a concentration of 10 % hydrogen peroxide is shorter with rapid changes in marijuana whiteness. When the bleaching time before 35 min is reached, fiber whiteness rapidly increased. After 35-min subsequent time, whiteness is not enhanced significantly. Bleaching time used in the bleaching solution by hydrogen peroxide concentration of 5 and 2 % increased, and cannabis whiteness did not change significantly. Bleaching before 50 min with a concentration of 5 % hydrogen peroxide, and hemp whiteness is enhanced quickly. After 50 min, whiteness change is very obvious. With a concentration of 2 % hydrogen peroxide bleaching to 75 min, the hemp fiber whiteness has increased almost to the maximum.

④ The effect of hydrogen peroxide dosage on whiteness results

As is shown in Table 6.21, with the reduction of the amount of hydrogen peroxide, the degree of bleaching decreased. When the concentration of hydrogen peroxide is 5 %, improvement in whiteness is greater. If the concentration of hydrogen peroxide is greater than 10 % or less than 2 %, the whiteness improvement is small.

Table 6.21 The effect of hydrogen peroxide dosage on whiteness results

H_2O_2 dosage (30 ml)	Concentration of 10 %	Concentration of 5 %	Concentration of 2 %
Hemp whiteness (%)	54.4	50.0	40.5

Meanwhile, the study also proved that under the same bleaching conditions, if marijuana steam explosion is prior to pickling and boiling water for some time, it can significantly improve the whiteness. The reason might be that marijuana in the boiling process removes part of the pigment.

⑤ The function of stabilizer

In H_2O_2 bleaching process, H_2O_2 is vulnerable to some of the catalytic materials, and violent decomposition occurs. Although some of these also accelerate fabric bleaching decomposition effect, some do not have a bleaching effect, and some will accelerate cellulose degradation. Therefore, the proper use of stabilizing agents is of great significance.

Water, medicine, and some special reason can make bleaching solution introduce some catalytic metal or metal ion impurities outside. The fabric often contains these ions, which has accelerated the decomposition of H_2O_2. After fabric pickling, the metal content decreased, and thus, H_2O_2 decomposition rate was reduced accordingly (Table 6.22).

As is shown in Table 6.22, pickling and adding stabilizer can both reduce H_2O_2 decomposition rate.

In summary, before hemp fiber bleaching, in addition to be fully cleaned as much as possible to reduce metallic impurities on the fabric, to make the full use of H_2O_2 and quality assurance of bleaching, an appropriate amount of stabilizers are usually added in bleach solution. The most commonly used stabilizer is sodium silicate, whose stabilizing effect is shown in Table 6.23.

Na_2SiO_3 actually has a dual role. On the one hand, its basic role is to accelerate the decomposition of H_2O_2. On the other hand, it has a stabilizing effect. As is shown in Table 6.23, with the increase of Na_2SiO_3, H_2O_2 decomposition rate is increasing compared with other alkali agents. Na_2SiO_3 has a lower decomposition

Table 6.22 The effect of pickling on H_2O_2 decomposition rate

Sample	Initial H_2O_2 concentration (%)	H_2O_2 decomposition rate constant $K \times 10^3$
Fabric without pickling	1.84 (without stabilizer)	21.3
	1.96 (with stabilizer)	10.4
Pickling fabric (0.1 N HCl for 1 h)	1.97 (with stabilizer)	2.42

Table 6.23 Stabilization of sodium silicate

Items	2 V H_2O_2 (80 °C for 2 h)							
Na_2SiO_3 (g/l)	0	2	5	10	40	0	0	7
Na_2CO_3 (g/l)	0	0	0	0	0	1.7	0	1.7
NaOH (g/l)	0	0	0	0	0	0	0.5	0.5
Initial pH	6.8	9.6	9.9	10.3	11.0	10.2	10.2	10.3
H_2O_2 decomposition rate	1.0	12.5	19.0	25.0	54.2	79.2	82.5	38.5

H_2O_2 concentration of 1 V is equal to 0.3 %

rate, and even if the pH is up to 11.0, H_2O_2 decomposition rate is only 54.2 %. Why sodium silicate will have such a good stabilizing effect, so far it is not very clear. It is thought to be capable of combining with catalytic metal ions. However, the stabilizing effect of sodium silicate must have the right amount of calcium or magnesium salts when it is more significant. One of the important reasons why the liquid has a stabilizing effect is that the catalytic colloidal silicate adsorption of metal ions is hydrogen peroxide bleaching silicate. In H_2O_2 bleaching process, one can use hard water containing 300–1000 ppm $CaCO_3$. If soft water is used, 0.1–0.2 g/L of magnesium sulfate must be added. Alkali of bleaching solution is not entirely provided by Na_2SiO_3, but another adjustment is made with an alkali agent. When the hemp fiber absorbs part of alkalis, pH bleaching solution may reduce, or even precipitated, so that the fabric becomes stiff. In addition to sodium, many other compounds can be used as H_2O_2 bleach stabilizers. Phosphate is used as a stabilizer, such as sodium silicate, needed for calcium and magnesium ions in order to be fully effective. In the current industrial production, hydrogen peroxide bleaches still use sodium silicate or mixed with other stabilizers.

(3) Steam-exploded hemp fiber morphology

Hemp morphology is shown in Fig. 6.23 after steam explosion. In raw hemp about 15–30 fibers are gathered into a fiber bundle as shown in Fig. 6.23a. As is shown in Fig. 6.23b, most pectin substance on the bundle surface is removed after washing with water and steam explosion, which reduced fiber in fiber bundles by 2–5. After gas explosion and washing, the fibers extracted with 2 % NaOH could be well separated as shown in Fig. 6.23c. In Fig. 6.23d, bleaching hemp fibers are subjected to a certain degree of damage after the extraction of alkali, and they are partially fibrillated. The microfibrils are arranged in parallel along the fiber axis, rather than staggered [67].

The amplification time of hemp scanning electron microscopy in Fig. 6.24 is higher than that in Fig. 6.23. From Fig. 6.24a, it can be seen that hemp fiber surface is not smooth after washing and steam explosion, and it is covered with small lignin particles. The hemp fiber surface of Fig. 6.24b is smooth, mainly due to the alkali extraction wiping off residual lignin and resin material. Figure 6.24c shows that the hemp fiber is no longer smooth, but it is full of ravines, in which the internal microfiber filaments [67] can be clearly seen.

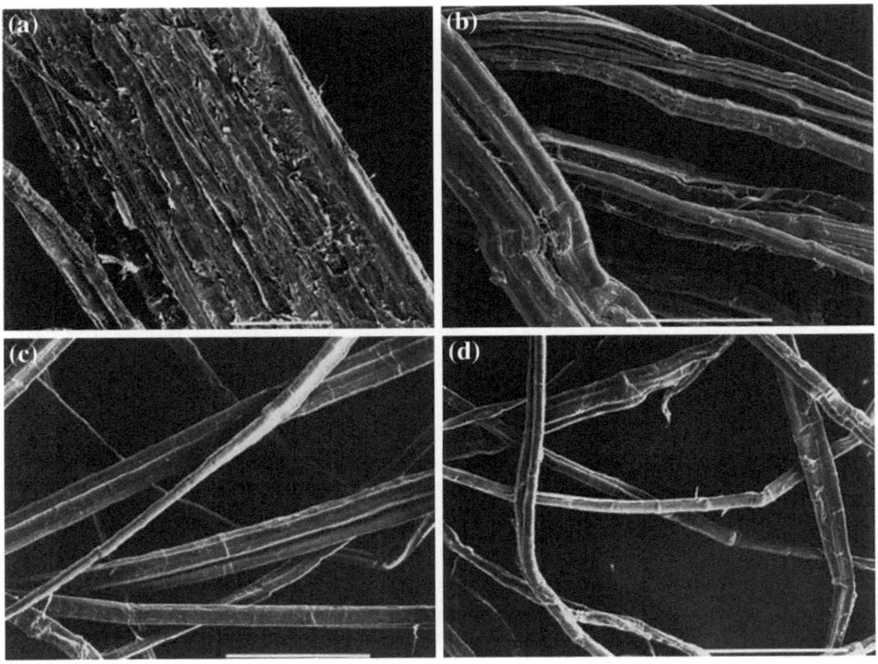

Fig. 6.23 Scanning electron microscopy pictures of hemp. **a** is fiber bundle of raw hemp; **b** is fiber bundle by steam explosion and water washing; **c** is fiber bundle by steam explosion, water washing and alkali extraction; **d** is fiber bundle by steam explosion, water washing, alkali extraction and bleaching. The plotting scale is 100 μm

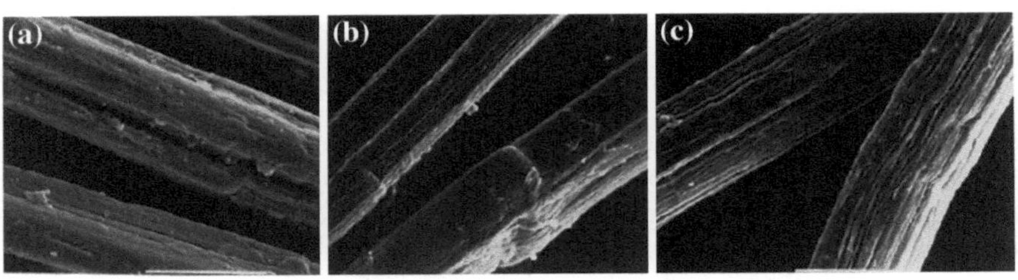

Fig. 6.24 Scanning electron microscopy pictures of hemp. **a** is to Fig. 6.23b; **b** is to Fig. 6.23c; **c** is to Fig. 6.23d with larger multiples of amplification. The plotting scale is 10 μm

6.4.1.2 Flax Fiber Extracted by Steam Explosion

Flax fiber is an excellent textile fiber and popular in consumers, which has good heat absorption, well permeability, comfortability and other styles [68]. Back in the 1930s, Charles V. Rowell had applied for relevant patents, using steam explosion technique to extract agricultural waste fibers [69]. After steam explosion it can

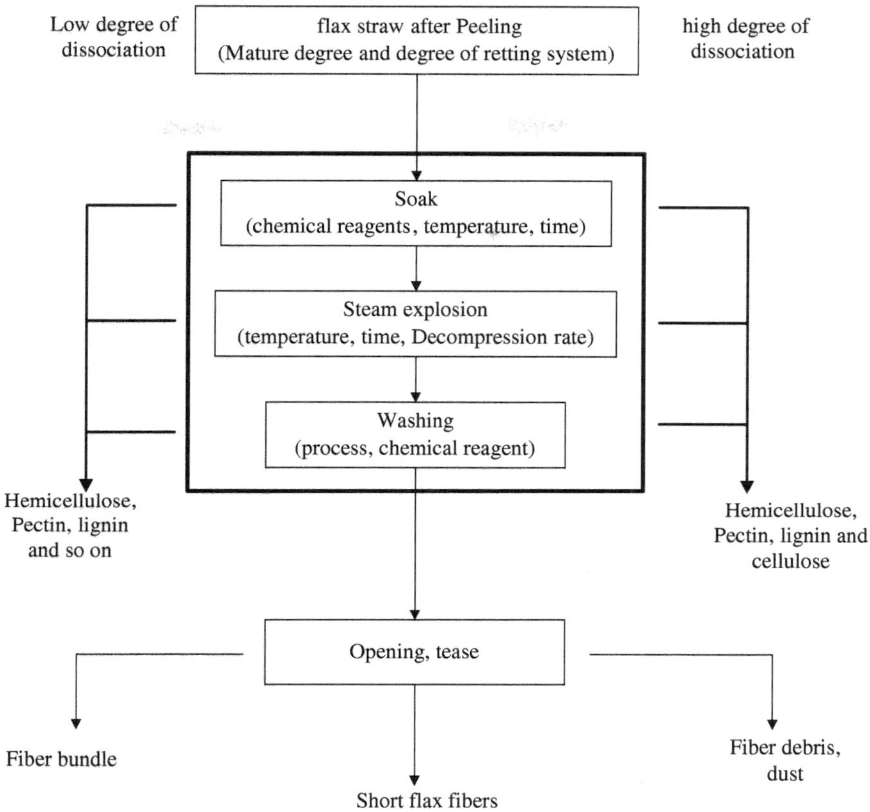

Fig. 6.25 Technology schematic diagram of steam explosion treating flax fiber

obtain useful short flax fibers for the preparation of textile yarns. The optimum condition for steam explosion treatment is 30–60 s at 1.5–3.0 MPa. The steam explosion process can significantly shorten the refining cycle. In 1986, German in Reutlingen carried out steam explosion tests to produce short flax fibers. The produced short flax fibers can be blended with cotton, viscose or polyester fibers for the preparation of fabric textile. Technology schematic diagram of steam explosion treating flax fiber is shown in Fig. 6.25. Peeled flax is soaked in 0.1 to 0.5 % NaOH solution at 20–120 °C, after taking off the excessive alkali solution, the flax is then put into steam explosion tank, and gas phase conditions can be adjusted depending on the raw material. By steam cooking and mechanical tearing action, high purity and good dispersion of short flax fibers can be obtained. Pectin and hemicellulose produced during steam explosion can be removed by alkaline extraction, and fibers are then dried in room temperature after washing. Finally, flax fibers are prepared through opening and carding [70].

Table 6.24 The impact of steam explosion strength on flax fibers

Property	$\log_{10} 2.5$	$\log_{10} 4.5$
Fiber loss (%)	15	30
Tension (cN/tex)	70	90
Average fiber length (mm)	25	15
Short staple component (%)	25	40
Long staple length (mm)	70	40
Water holding capacity (%)	16	12
Kappa number	25	15
DP (%)	1800	2500

The impact of steam explosion on flax fibers is shown in Table 6.24. When steam explosion severity is low, non-cellulosic components are more in flax fiber with good separation. The high pectin and hemicellulose content make flax fiber have high water absorption. After opening and carding by steam explosion, fiber section and undissociated fibers will be produced, resulting in the loss of fibers. High steam explosion severity resulted in the degradation of most pectin and hemicellulose, and such fibers are clean and suitable for industrial applications. But fiber fragments will be produced, resulting in the loss of fibers. Therefore, it is necessary to select the appropriate steam explosion conditions, to meet the needs of the textile.

6.4.2 *Preparation of Natural Cellulose Nanofiber by Steam Explosion*

Fiber from natural cellulose fibers or obtained by the conventional spinning methods is of above micron diameter. It is possible to increase the specific surface area of fibers by reducing fiber diameter, thereby expanding the contact area of reinforcing fibers and the resin matrix and reinforcing fiber/resin interface interactions in a certain extent. Natural cellulose nanofibers is separated constituting component of plant fibers-cellulose microfibrils into nano fibers with the number of units. Cellulose microfibrils constitute of about 30–50 cellulose molecules on the straight line. Several microfibrils of about 4 nm width combine together, which may form nanofibers with a width of about 20–100 nm.

Cellulose microfibrils are basic components of cellulose unit of plant cell walls, and the strength and hardness of natural cellulose depend on the cellulose microfibrils. Microfibrils having a diameter of 5–30 nm form crystals through hydrogen bonding between hydroxyl groups with a high crystallinity. Such a stable structure has excellent mechanical properties, along with the axial direction of the fibers. Young's modulus of microfibrils is up to 138 GPa with a tensile strength of 1.7 GPa and a low coefficient of thermal expansion.

At present, the microfibrils with high purity are prepared by a series of chemical treatments and mechanical processing of plant cell walls. Steam explosion coupled with chemical treatment can simplify microfibril preparation method and reduce the amount of chemicals and energy consumption, which improves the yield and productivity of microfibrils.

6.4.2.1 Preparation of Banana Nanofibers

Banana fibers are uniformly chopped to 10 cm and soaked in 2 % NaOH, and pressure is instantaneously released with a pressure of 0.9 MPa at a temperature of 110–120 °C for 1 h. The banana fibers after steam explosion are washed with water of ~pH 7.0 and then dried at 70 °C for 2 h. After washing and drying, banana fiber undergoes two-phase bleaching. The first bleaching solution used is NaOH and acetic acid (27 and 78.8 g, respectively) for 1 h, and the second is sodium hypochlorite solution for 1 h. It is washed with distilled water after bleaching for six times, followed by dried. Banana fiber after steam explosion and bleaching is treated with oxalic acid for 3 h with pressure of 0.9 MPa in explosion tank, and then, pressure is immediately relieved. Banana fiber is washed with water vapor blasting. Finally, banana fibers are suspended in water at 8000 r/min with mechanical stirring for 4 h, and the suspension is then dried at 90 °C [71].

6.4.2.2 Analysis of Banana Nanofibers

The change of banana fiber composition before and after treatment is shown in Table 6.25. During the steam explosion process, part of hemicelluloses depolymerizes and the degradation product is solved in water after washing. The lignin and hemicellulose content reduced, while cellulose content increased. The bleaching lowers the content of lignin and hemicellulose further.

SEM photographs of different banana fiber processing are shown in Fig. 6.26. As shown in Figure B, banana fiber is dissociated after steam explosion. C and D illustrate banana fiber becomes short after steam explosion bleaching, and the fibers are broken down into single small fibers. Fiber diameter changes from 25 to 10 μm. To further reduce the fiber diameter, acid treatment of banana fiber is required. As shown in Figure E, after acid treatment, fiber diameter reduces from 10 to 1 μm.

Table 6.25 The banana fiber composition change before and after treatment

Material	α-cellulose/%	Hemicellulose/%	Lignin/%
Untreated	64.0 ± 2.8	18.6 ± 1.6	4.9 ± 0.7
After steam explosion	82.4 ± 2.5	13.9 ± 0.4	3.6 ± 0.5
After bleach	95.9 ± 0.6	0.4 ± 0.02	1.9 ± 0.4

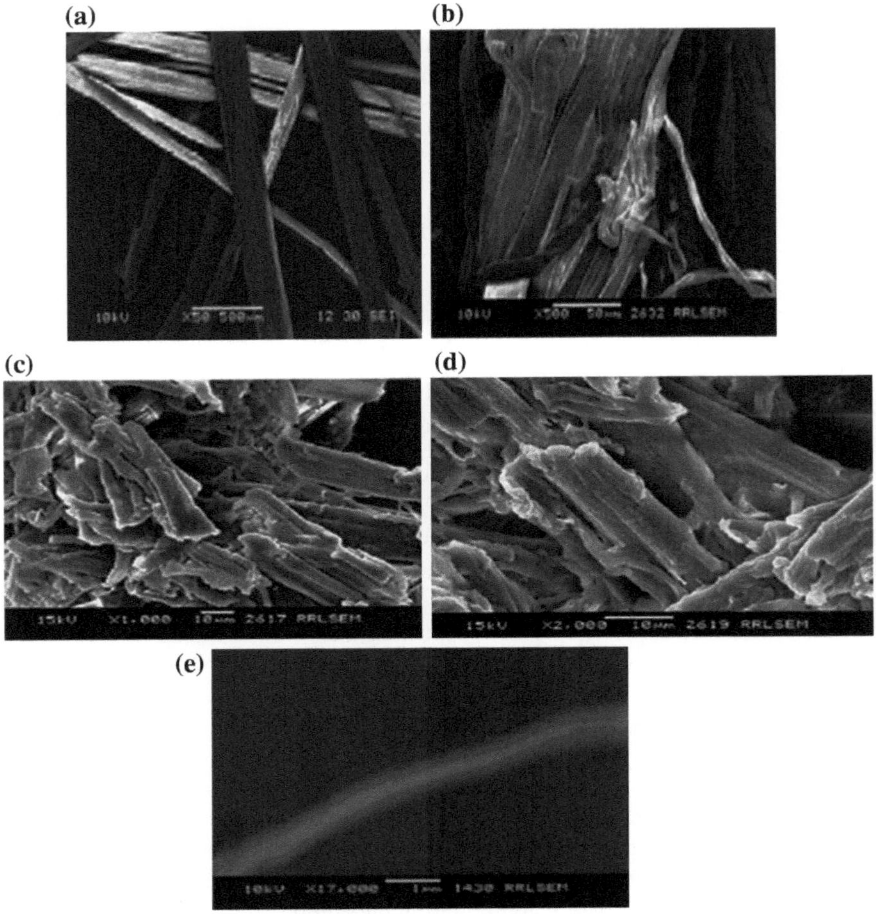

Fig. 6.26 SEM photographs of different banana fibers. **a** is untreated banana fiber (×50); **b** is banana fiber treated by steam explosion (×500); **c** is banana fiber by bleaching (×1000); **d** is banana fiber by bleaching (×2000); **e** is banana fiber by bleaching acid (×17,000)

6.4.3 Wood-Based Panels Made by Steam Explosion Corn Straw

Agriculture and forestry biomass resources include timber forest resources and crop straw. Compared with developed countries, forest resources in China are low per capita. The consumption contradiction between the demand for wood and wood-based panel products and the supply of wood has been therefore a long time. While China is a large agricultural country, the annual crop straw yield is around 700 million tons, but it is now generally not effectively utilized in many areas and even is the source of contamination. If the rich straw resources are used for wood-based panel industry, it will greatly ease the shortage of supply of raw material-based panels' contradiction. However, according to the features of the high content of hydrophobic plastic on the surface of straw material, the use of adhesives like Strawboard is greater than that of wood-based raw materials. Higher costs of binder are important bottleneck restricting the development of straw-based panels' industry.

Method to solve the above problem is to find Strawboard no gluing techniques. No gluing technique mainly relies on straw's three components, namely cellulose, hemicellulose, and lignin. It is used in the reaction to form insoluble resin at high temperature and pressure, and then, the straw fibers are glued together and pressed into a plate. Due to the high-density structures of straw material and the low content of the active group in three major components, there is need for activating the process of straw, destroying the cell wall structure, and improving its reactivity.

Steam explosion process is performed by steam heated to a certain temperature, and pressure is maintained for a certain time. It is then released suddenly to produce secondary steam. The role of the material structure is destroyed by the mechanical force. This method can damage the structure of straw cell wall so as to obtain fibers between wood shavings and the thermal wear. So that the number of hydroxyl groups, carbonyl groups, and other reactive functional groups of the fiber surface is significantly increased, while the cell wall structure is destroyed, resulting in the increase of lignin content. This can be eluted at a lower concentrated alkaline solution. Steam explosion activates lignin in plant fiber material and degrades hemicellulose to produce sugar and dries the material to produce self-adhesive role in pressing process, which can be applied in fiberboard case without the chemical adhesive [72]. The process is shown in Fig. 6.27.

Chen Hongzhang from Institute of Process Engineering realized the dissolution of lignin in steam explosion-treated straw by hot lye, during which the active groups of lignin are increased at high temperatures after activation and lignin itself can be dehydrated and have condensation reaction to form a similar adhesive effect. The steam-exploded straw is of thermoforming, preparing high-strength sheet without glue environmental ecology. Specific steps are as follows:

① Preparation of steam-exploded straw: Straw feedstock is chopped to 2–5 cm and transferred into steam explosion tank at pressure of 1.2–1.7 MPa for

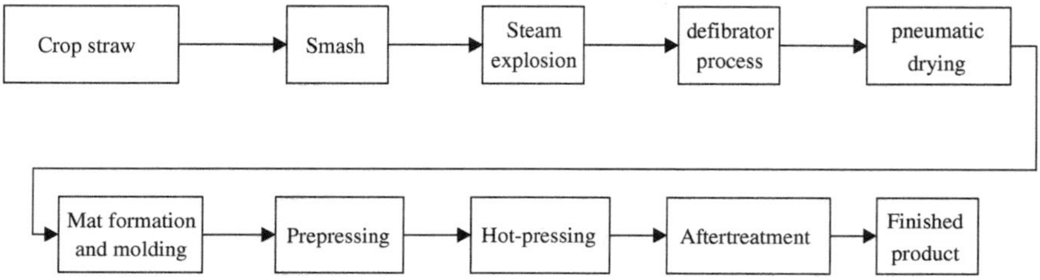

Fig. 6.27 Flowchart of no plastic fiberboard by steam explosion preparation

5–10 min. After instantaneous release of pressure, steam-exploded straw is obtained.

② The steam-exploded straw from the step ① is dried to a moisture content of 5–10 %. The steam-exploded straw is uniformly mixed after drying with 1–3 % alkaline solution by solid-to-liquid ratio of 1: 0.5–1.

③ The steam-exploded straw from step ② is covered evenly on top of the pavement in the press machine with pressure of 0.1–0.2 MPa, and pressing temperature is controlled at 90–110 °C for 8–10 min. Then, the pressure is increased continuously to 0.8–1.5 MPa at temperature of 170–190 °C for 5–10 min.

In step ③, material is preloaded under a pressure of 0.1–0.2 MPa and a temperature of 110–130 °C for 5–8 min. The main purpose of the prepress is sufficiently to escape water vapor, reduce the water content, improve the heat transfer efficiency of straw, and reduce energy consumption. It also eliminates internal stresses and increases flapper performance.

The treatment of straw material by steam explosion technique can improve the wettability of biomass material, while it can destruct the cell wall structure. The lignin of raw material is easily dissolute in alkaline condition. The lignin dissolution process at high temperature by pressing the feedstock lignin and hemicellulose has condensation reaction to form the adhesive effect, achieving glued straw materials without glue. It not only saves the adding cost of the adhesive, but also simplifies the process and production lines and helps to reduce the environmental pollution caused by synthetic resin adhesives and reduce production costs.

6.4.4 Dissolving Pulp Produced by Steam-exploded Straw

Viscose fiber has good moisture absorption capacity and permeability, which is soft and smooth fabric. It is comfortable to wear. With the improvement of people's living standards, dress requirements of people turn from synthetic fiber to the plant fiber. Viscose textile has become a new favorite in market. But material development process of cellulosic fiber is slow; the production of raw materials is relatively simple. Main raw material is currently available for viscose fiber, and solvent-spun cellulose fibers are wood pulp and cotton pulp, which limit the arable land resources. The contradiction between supply and demand of the cotton linters and pulp is serious. Lack of raw materials has larger constraints on regenerated cellulose fiber industry.

The first nationwide special survey of crop straw resources was completed which is organized by the Ministry of Agriculture of China in 2010, and "National Crop Straw Resources Survey and Evaluation Report" had been published [73]. According to the report, China's crop straw can collect resources of 687 million ton, of which maize straw is 265 million ton, rice straw is about 205 million ton, and wheat straw is 150 million ton. Straw contains about 30–49 % cellulose, and therefore, it is a potential cellulose material in the use of viscose pulp.

Fiber of crop straw resources is short and has inhomogeneity; fiber content is less and miscellaneous cells are more; the ash content and silicon content are high, which are important factors in the preparation of crop straw-dissolving pulp. Chen Hongzhang, from Institute of Process Engineering, proposed the strategy that to start from characteristics of crop straw resources, the ideas of process engineering are used to achieve straw component separation, classification directional transformation, preparation of viscose fiber with pulp, and various high added products through cross-cutting and integration of various technological processes.

For raw material defects, the use of steam explosion and water washing is proposed to remove most of the hemicellulose and inorganic salts and small amounts of lignin. Long fiber and short fiber are separated through mechanical comb treatment process. The process makes use of cornstalks, rice straw, wheat straw, and other crop residues for the viscose fiber pulp preparation, broadens material scope of artificial dissolving pulp fiber, and achieves the full utilization of biomass straw resources. Specific process steps are as follows [74]:

(1) Preparation

The straw is crushed to 3–5 cm, and the leaves and spike are removed. It is sorted using dilute acid for 30–60 min, and the moisture content of straw is adjusted to 30–50 %. Because hybrid cells and ash are mainly in the straw leaves, spike, and other parts of the ear, in the biomass process preparation, leaves and spike are first removed by sorting. The sorted leaves, spike and other biomass are sent to boilers for combustion heat; dilute acid solution can increase the concentration of hydrogen ions in the reaction system, which is benefit to the degradation of hemicellulose, thus speeding up the reaction rate.

(2) Steam explosion

Straw is put into the steam explosion tank, and the pressure is maintained at 1.4–1.7 MPa for 5–15 min. The steam explosion can damage the structure of strawlike filiform, which is conducive to the penetration of cooking liquid and subsequent operation. Steam explosion enables degradation about 80 % of hemicellulose and about 10 % of lignin, while the steam explosion can make about 72 % of inorganic ion elution.

(3) Three levels of countercurrent washing

Liquid ratio is 1:10–1:20, temperature is 50–90 °C, and hydraulic retention time is 15–60 min.

Three levels of countercurrent washing can increase the organic content of the water wash. Washing purposes are as follows: First is to remove hemicellulose degradation products and soluble lignin and reduce chemical reagent consumption in the subsequent cooking operation; second is to remove the hybrid cells and short fibers generated in the process of steam explosion, because the thin-walled structure is loose and very easy to tear into tiny pieces in the process of steam explosion. The material can be separated from fibrous material through water, reducing the amount of hybrid cells and ash; and third is to remove approximately 72 % of inorganic ions dissoluted in the process of the steam explosion, reducing the impact on recovery of ash.

(4) The separation of the short and long fibers

The separation of the short and long fibers is achieved by mechanical carding. The heteroatom cells and ash contained in short fibers are more than those in long fibers. It is possible to remove short fibers by mechanical carding, enrich long fibers, and reduce fiber unevenness, while further reducing the ash content.

(5) Kraft pulping

Take long fiber pulp as raw material, and the present invention takes a base amount of 8–12 % (in terms of NaOH), curing degree of 8–12 %, liquid ratio of 1:5–1:8, the cooking temperature of 130–170 °C, and cooking time of 1–3 h. Pulp prepared in this way has low hemicellulose content, high α-cellulose content, high viscosity, degree of polymerization, and so on.

(6) Slurry separation

By slurry separation, isolated cooking pastes and cooking liquor are obtained.

(7) Washing and screening

The crude pulp is obtained after cooking, and the black liquor is obtained by washing. This has access to get clean slurry, thereby reducing the subsequent bleaching process for bleaching solution consumption. It is filtered by CX sieve (aperture diameter of 1.8 mm) in order to screen the fines further, and the quality of the slurry is improved.

(8) Two phases of alkaline hydrogen peroxide bleaching

The first paragraph of alkaline hydrogen peroxide bleaching conditions: 0.5–2 % (w/v) NaOH, 3–6 % (w/v) H_2O_2, 0.1–0.2 % (w/v) EDTA or DTPA, 1: 6–1: 8 for liquid ratio, 50–80 °C and 1–2 h for bleaching time. Condition for secondary stage alkaline hydrogen peroxide bleaching: 0.5–2 % (w/v) NaOH, 3–6 % (w/v) H_2O_2, 0.1–0.2 % (w/v) EDTA or DTPA, liquid ratio is 1:6–1:8, 50–80 °C, and is 1–2 h for bleaching time. Alkali-oxygen bleaching is a kind of non-chlorine method, which could reduce the damage to the cellulose and prevent environmental pollution.

(9) Copy pulp board

The bleached pulp is washed, followed by pulp copy board so as to get finished pulp. A kind of finished pulp has cellulose content of 88–92 %, white of 85–90 %, ash of ≤0.50 %, iron content of ≤50 mg/kg, and pentosan content of ≤4.0 %.

In order to reduce costs and achieve the full utilization of straw biomass resource, hemicellulose and fiber fines are also utilized as well as the recovery of high-purity lignin.

(1) Utilization of hemicellulose and fiber fines

Washing liquid in step 3 contains hemicellulose hydrolysate monosaccharides, oligosaccharides and other carbohydrates. They can be used directly (as well as the fibers fines in steps 4 and 7) for common temperature methane fermentation at medium temperature without any treatment.

(2) Utilization of lignin

Cooking liquor is obtained after Step 6 by membrane filtration grade, pH adjustment, and acid precipitation, and it is washed with water and dried to obtain high-purity lignin with different molecular weights.

Advantages of this technique are as follows:

① About 80 % of the hemicellulose and 10 % of lignin can be degraded by steam explosion and then removed by washing with water. Fibrous tissue is disrupted, which is conducive to the subsequent cooking operation and reduces the amount of alkali.

② 72 % of inorganic ions are eluted through steam explosion and removed by washing with water to reduce the effect of ash.

③ The long and short fibers are separated by mechanical combing. Long fibers for the production of dissolving pulp are enriched, and the uniformity of the fibers is improved to enhance the quality of the slurry.

④ Non-chlorine bleach reduces the pollution of the environment, reducing the loss of the fiber and improving the pulp quality.

⑤ Hemicellulose washing liquid isolated by steam explosion and fiber fines by mechanical combing and screening can be used in biogas fermentation; black liquor grade and acid analysis by membrane filtration are used to get high-purity lignin with different molecular weights. This process also achieves separation of long fibers, short fibers, hemicellulose, and lignin. Classification directional conversion also achieves the full and high-value utilization of biomass straw resource, which is conducive to reduce the dissolved pulp costs.

6.4.5 Polyurethane Foam Produced by Steam-exploded Straw Liquidation

6.4.5.1 Polyurethane Foam Produced by Steam-exploded Straw Polyol Liquidation

Polyurethane is an important polymer material, having a wide range utilization in furniture, packaging, automotive, aviation, and shipbuilding industries. Polyol is a required raw material in synthesis of polyurethane, from the petrochemical industry. It has a strong dependence on the oil, and the volatility of international oil prices directly affects their prices, leading to rising production costs. In addition, due to the difficulty in decomposition of polyurethane plastic, making it difficult to automatically degrade polyurethane waste, the decomposition rate is not to 1 % in 100 years. If it is stored in air, the supplement in it will permeate into the ground with the rain, polluting groundwater. Only solved by the construction of large-scale landfill, it will cause a great financial burden. Lignocellulose containing a large amount of reactive hydroxyl groups is represented. Under certain conditions, it can quickly liquefy in the polyol, in which liquefied products can substitute chemical products for resins and polyurethane plastics. Straw mainly contains 50–55 % of cellulose, 15–25 % of hemicellulose, and 20–30 % of lignin, but also contains a small amount of proteins, oligosaccharides, and inorganic salts. Cellulose, hemicellulose, and lignin are rich in hydroxyl groups, which can be degraded by chemical means. Thereby, polyurethane plastics substituting polyol can be synthesized, which not only has all the general mechanical properties of polyurethane plastic, but also has a unique biodegradability that rapidly degrades in natural environment. This use of crop straw can not only alleviate the dependence on oil in modern society, but the development of renewable biomass resources can also turn waste into treasure and as much as possible reduce the environmental pollution. It is a promising student substance use patterns. After treated by steam explosion, fibrous tissue becomes porous. Liquefaction agents have easier access to the fiber interior, while the hemicellulose and lignin also undergone some degradation when cellulose is exposed. It increases the liquefaction efficiency [75, 76]. Take wheat straw as example, and the preparation ways are the following:

(1) Steam explosion

The straw is chopped to about 5 cm, and moisture content is adjusted to 30 %. The saturated steam is injected into it and is then maintained at 1.5 MPa for 4 min. The straw is exploded instantaneously, and the steam-exploded straw is obtained.

(2) Polyol liquefaction

Liquefaction agent is mainly composed of polyethylene glycol and glycerol, while an organic acid is added as a catalyst of liquefaction reaction. Firstly, wheat straw and liquefied reagent are mixed uniformly, and then, the mixture is poured into 250-mL three-necked flask and placed in an oil bath and heated by a continuous stirring and reflux condensation system (Fig. 6.28). After reaching the reaction time, the flask was removed and placed in water at room temperature to complete the reaction.

Liquefaction time is an important factor which affects wheat straw liquefaction. Degradation reactions predominate at the beginning of liquefaction, making the residue rate decreased rapidly. At late liquefaction stage, reunited function is gradually strengthened, making residue rate decreased slowly. Hence, it has limited effect on increasing liquefaction rate to extend the liquefaction time excessively and the appropriate time is 2 h.

Higher temperatures and liquid–solid ratio, adding an appropriate amount of glycerol as auxiliary reagent, and using sulfuric acid as a liquefaction catalyst can improve the effect of liquefaction. The optimum value of the above-mentioned

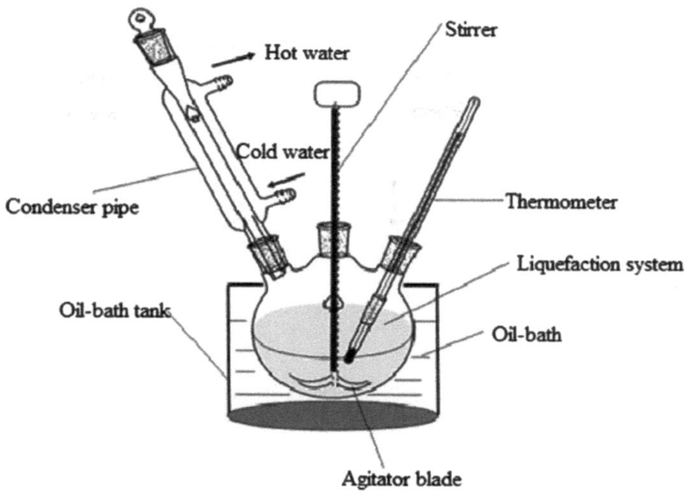

Fig. 6.28 Polyol by steam-exploded straw liquidation equipment

experimental parameters was 140 °C, 6: 1, glycerin in an amount of PEG/glycerol = 5, and 4 % sulfuric acid.

The presence of an appropriate amount of water is conducive to liquefaction. The moisture content of wheat straw is at 100 %, the liquefaction is the best, and wood liquefaction effects are not ideal after thoroughly dried, indicating that the hydrolysis reaction as a liquefaction is very important for degradation of wheat straw macromolecules.

When the straw particle size varied within the range of 20–100 meshes, the residue was almost not changed, indicating that smaller particles did not improve liquefaction straw effect. Because the straw is used as powder, its structure is porous. The relative amount of liquefaction is enough for wood flour combined with supporting catalyst. The liquefaction reaction is relatively intense at the beginning, when most components are degraded in a very short period, without reducing the particle size of wheat straw to improve liquefaction efficiency.

(3) The preparation of polyurethane foam

The biomass-derived polyols, catalysts, water, and other additives are mixed uniformly according to formulations in Table 6.26, followed by the addition of 4,4' diphenylmethane diisocyanate (MDI). After mixing was poured into 20 cm × 20 cm × 20 cm mold appropriately, the reaction is conducted at room temperature until the foam solidifies (Table 6.26).

Liquefied straw can be directly used for the synthesis of polyurethane foam, and Fig. 6.29 is the synthetic polyurethane foam. It is shown in Table 6.27 that apparent density, tensile strength, elongation, and resilience rate were 15 kg/m^3, 80 kPa, 30, and 160 % of the polyurethane foam, respectively, based on the straw polyol. In the

Table 6.26 Formulations of polyurethane foam

Formulations (%)	Liquefied straw product as material	Polyols on the market as material
Polyol	100	100
4,4′-diphenylmethane diisocyanate (MDI)	69.8	45.8
Water	4	4
Triethylene diamine	0.125	0.125
Stannous octoate	0.125	0.125
Tween-80	2	2

Fig. 6.29 Polyurethane foam produced by liquefied product of steam-exploded straw

control group, it was foamed plastic used by the synthesis of polyethylene glycol, and parameters of these indicators were 30–60 kg/m^3, 70–85 kPa, 180–300, and 30–35 %, respectively. It can be seen that the difference is small, indicating that the synthesis of polyurethane foams by this method has good mechanical strength to meet industry needs.

From Table 6.27, it can also be seen that water absorption of polyurethane foam based on straw polyol is 6 %, which is much greater than 0.2 % in the control group. This is due to the fact that liquefaction product has a lot of straw hydrophilic materials and the hydrophobicity of foam surface can be changed, thus improving water absorption rate.

6.4.5.2 Phenolic Resin Prepared by Phenol Liquefied Steam-exploded Straw

Phenol liquefaction is another important biomass liquefaction process, and biomass liquefaction product can be directly used to synthesize phenolic resin. Chen

Table 6.27 Property of polyurethane foam

Items	Liquefied straw product as material	PEG as materials
Performance density	35	30–60
Tensile strength	80	70–85
Ductility	160	180–300
Disability	30	30–35
Water absorption	6	0.2

Hongzhang and other studied liquefaction behavior of wheat straw in phenol, and the liquefied product is directly used for the synthesis of phenolic resin. The liquefied products are shown in Fig. 6.30.

Compared with phenolic resin obtained by the reaction of the traditional method, the color of resins from liquefaction straw products that reacted with formaldehyde is deep, which is due to the fact that the used liquefaction straw is steam explosion-treated wheat straw. Wheat straw after steam explosion is sepia, and small molecules are oxidized when having liquefaction within phenol in high temperature. The color is even deepened, and the liquefied product is dark so that the synthetic resins are also dark.

As is shown in Table 6.28, the performance of various aspects of phenolic resin based on biomass is close to conventional phenol resin, and it has good biodegradability which conventional phenol resin does not possess. Although the hardness of the phenolic resin is large, its structure is too dense, porosity is not enough, and water absorption is very low. It is not suitable for the utilization as a carrier in solid-state fermentation.

The features of phenolic resin prepared by liquefied steam-exploded straw are as follows.

① Steam explosion pretreatment can improve the effect of the straw of liquefaction. This is because during the process of steam explosion, very drastic physical and chemical changes occurred. The destructive effects of

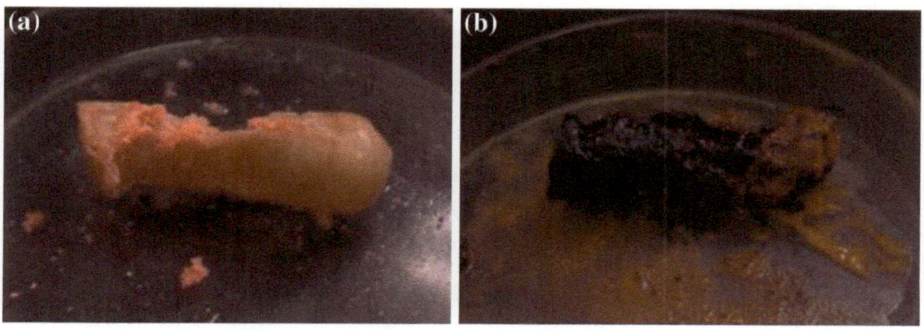

Fig. 6.30 Synthetic phenolic resin. **a** Synthesis phenolic resin of phenol and formaldehyde; **b** Resins from liquefaction straw products reacted with formaldehyde

Table 6.28 The performance comparison of two kinds of phenolic resin

Items	Density (g/cm^3)	Tensile strength (MPa)	Bending strength (MPa)	Compression strength (MPa)	Water absorption (%)	Biodegradability
Phenolic resin based on biomass	1.7	40	83	176	1.0	Good
Phenolic resin based on chemicals	1.64	49	85	156	0.5	Poor

high-pressure air on the fibers make it porous. Liquefying agent is easier to enter the interior of the fibers, thereby enhancing the liquefaction effect. Secondly, the component of the wheat straw can be degraded by high temperature and pressure during steam explosion. Hemicellulose chain especially macromolecules was broken, so as to provide favorable conditions for further liquefaction.

② The amount of phenol, liquefaction temperature, catalyst, particle size, and moisture content of the straw will affect the liquefaction effect. Within a certain range, the greater the amount of phenol, the better the liquefaction and the higher the liquefaction temperature is in favor of liquefaction; sodium hydroxide and sulfuric acid have the effect of promoting the liquefaction with two different mechanisms of action with better catalytic effect of sulfuric acid; straw particles have little effect on liquefaction; proper moisture content of wheat straw is in favor of liquefaction. In this experiment, the optimal values of the parameters affecting the above are liquid–solid ratio of 7:1, temperature of 130 °C, moisture content of 150 %, and 5 % sulfuric acid as a catalyst, respectively.

③ During the process of liquefaction, macromolecule is of continuous degradation, and the viscosity of the reaction system decreases; weight average molecular weight in the liquefaction process does not change much, which is maintained at about 800.

④ The performance of various aspects of phenolic resin based on biomass is close to conventional phenol resin, and it has good biodegradability which conventional phenol resin does not possess. Although the mechanical properties of the phenolic resin are very good, its density is too large, the structure is too dense, and water absorption is low. It is not suitable for use as a carrier in solid-state fermentation. But it is still an effective method to use straw resources and also has a strong inspiration to take advantage of other agricultural wastes.

6.4.5.3 Adhesive Prepared by Phenol Liquefied Steam-exploded Straw

Phenol liquefaction is an important means of lignocellulosic liquefaction. Lignocellulosic biomass is composed of three main components of cellulose, hemicellulose, and lignin, each of which having different molecular structures and reactive groups. The three liquefaction reaction processes vary greatly. In addition, due to the liquefaction of lignocellulosic environment in which there is some differences in liquefaction, the liquefied lignocelluloses are very different. Lignocellulosic feedstock is uneven, and completely liquefied study treats it as a "single" raw material. Chen Hongzhang took straw as raw material to solve this problem, using a selective liquefaction approach to carry out liquefaction. The applied researches were carried out for a solid product and a liquid product [77].

Utilizing the characteristics of elective liquefaction of phenol, it is taken as a means of enhancing the straw fractionation and enzymatic hydrolysis of cellulose substrate, in order to achieve an effective separation of the components of the straw and to improve the effect of cellulase enzymatic hydrolysis of substrate. Selective liquefaction of phenol makes a lot of straw lignin and hemicellulose degraded, which retained the cellulose. Under the low temperature (about 100 °C), H_2SO_4 concentration of 3–4 %, and phenol/straw amount of 3–4, selective liquefaction of phenol can remove the hemicellulose and lignin (lignin removal rate ≥70 %) in straw quickly within 20 min. While it retained the cellulose, cellulose recovery is ≥80 %, in order to achieve the effective separation of straw components. Pretreated straw obtained from selective liquefaction of phenol has good effect of cellulose hydrolysis, under the conditions of 100 °C, H_2SO_4 concentration of 3 %, phenol/straw amount of 3, and liquefaction time of 60 min. The enzymatic rate of phenol selective liquefaction residue obtained is ≥65 %.

In order to investigate the practicality of elective liquefaction products of phenol, Chen Hongzhang also studied the properties of the products and synthesized resin adhesive. The results showed that the binding phenolic content of elective liquefaction products of phenol increases in0–30 min when amount of acid is 3 % and phenol/straw amount ratio (w/w) is 3 at 100 °C. The combined phenol content is 100 % at 30 min, after which the combined phenol content increased slowly, and the combined phenol is over 120 % at 60 min. The synthesis of resin adhesive using selective liquefaction product is obtained at 30 min and the property of products reached standard of GB/T 14732-2006.

6.4.6 *Protein Fiber Processing*

6.4.6.1 Modified Wool Fiber Protein

Wool fiber is a kind of high-quality protein, which is widely used in the manufacture of high-quality textile material. Currently, people have developed new usage of wool, such as wool and wool protein powder film preparation. Preparation of wool protein powder includes physical and chemical methods. In order to obtain superfine wool protein powder, special chemicals are used to break chemical bonds and reduce the crystallinity of the woolfibers. This can improve productivity when wool and wool fibers of protein powder were crushed. Steam explosion can be not only used to separate plant fiber, but also to separate cotton, hemp, and other modified cellulose fibers. At present, steam explosion is also successfully applied to proteins such as quality of wool material [78].

Flake wool fiber surface can protect the wool fibers from damage, while scales also can affect other important characteristics such as gloss and shrinkage properties of wool. Figure 6.31a, d shows the processing of wool fiber surface features, and scaly surface of wool fibers is arranged in clear and compact. In Fig. 6.31b, c, after the wool under conditions of 0.4 and 0.8 MPa steam explosion, scales are still clearly visible, but one can clearly see that the scales have been damaged at a higher magnification (Fig. 6.31e, f). This shows that the after steam explosion of wool, small fragments are detached from the scales. After steam explosion, scaly surface appeared gully.

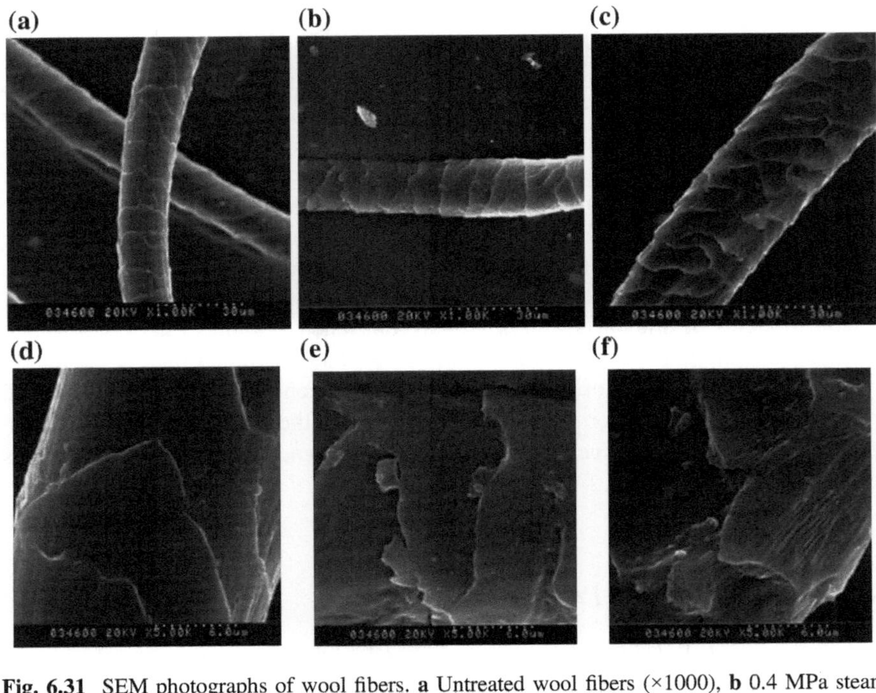

Fig. 6.31 SEM photographs of wool fibers. **a** Untreated wool fibers (×1000), **b** 0.4 MPa steam explosion wool fibers (×1000), **c** 0.8 MPa steam explosion wool fibers (×1000), **d** Untreated wool fibers (×5000), **e** 0.4 MPa steam explosion wool fibers (×5000), **f** 0.8 MPa steam explosion wool fibers (×1000)

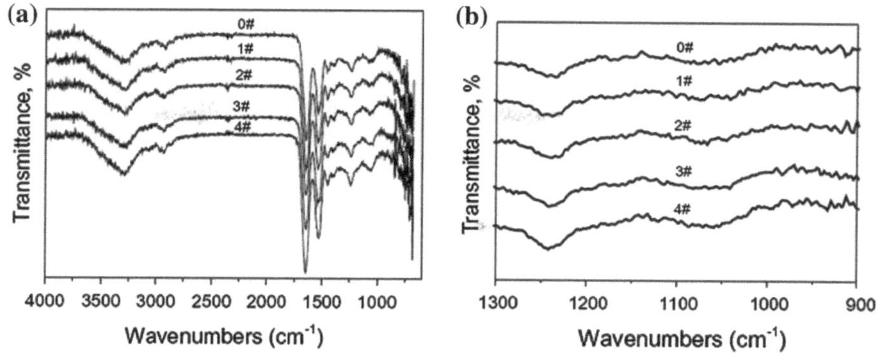

Fig. 6.32 Infrared spectra of wool. The wave number range of **a** is from 900 to 4000 cm^{-1}, the wave number range of **b** is from 900 to 1300 cm^{-1}. 0 # 1 # 2 # 3 # 4 # samples were untreated wool fiber, 0.2, 0.4, 0.6, 0.8 MPa, respectively

It can be seen in the Fourier Transform Infrared Spectroscopy that absorption peaks are consistent for all the samples, reflecting that the steam explosion treatment did not produce new functional groups and chemical bonds. Disulfide bond of wool fiber affects the physical and chemical properties of wool protein and its absorption peak typically occurs within the wave number range of 1300–1000 cm^{-1}, and the strength of the absorption peak reflects the different sulfur chemical groups in the wool. Further spectral scanning is showed in Fig. 6.32b, there is a difference in the absorption peak at 1250 cm^{-1} among the samples. The absorption peak intensity increases along with the increase of explosion strength. This may be explained as that the variation of some sulfur-containing group took place during the steam explosion process.

After steam explosion, the crystallinity of the wool fiber has significant changes. As shown in Fig. 6.33, typical diffraction peak of wool fiber α-keratin has two. A main peak at 2θ is 22°, and a sub-peak at 2θ is 10°. After steam explosion, the

Fig. 6.33 Wool fiber X-diffraction pattern. 0 # 1 # 2 # 3 # 4 # samples are untreated wool fiber, 0.2, 0.4, 0.6 MPa steam, 0.8 MPa, respectively

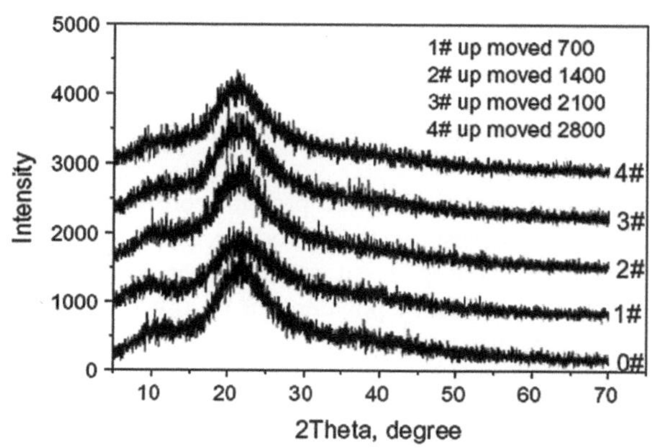

Table 6.29 Properties of wool fiber

Sample	0#	1#	2#	3#	4#
Moisture regain/%	14.76	14.36	13.84	12.08	11.76
Lysis time/min	31	35	43	47	45
Break load/cN	6.07	5.76	5.80	3.93	3.71
Elongation at break/%	52.47	53.30	51.96	45.71	33.09
Fault power/MJ	0.23	0.20	0.20	0.14	0.09

absorption peak of the X-ray diffraction of wool fiber dropped. Compared with the untreated wool (3.2), absorption peak of wool fibers at 22° has changed after steam explosion. They are changed into 2.57, 3.14, 3.07, and 2.94 (1 # 2 # 3 # 4 #), respectively. In conditions of high temperature and humid, most hydrogen bonds, some of the crystalline region, and the amorphous region of the wool fiber are destroyed. When steam explosion strength is further enhanced, some crystalline regions are completely destroyed, leading to the decrease in the degree of crystallinity of wool fibers from 52.1 to 42.3, 35.1, 30.5, and 25.9 %, respectively. Along with the increase of the explosion strength, the crystallinity of the wool fiber samples significantly reduces.

Wool has a hydrophobic surface, but due to the presence of non-crystalline region and amino and carboxyl (hydrophilic) groups, the wool has regained high moisture. As shown in Table 6.29, with the explosion strength increased, the hydrophilic of wool fibers reduced. Dissolved time of wool fibers increased in 2.5 % NaOH. This is mainly due to the fact that the rearrangement and macromolecular chains of polar groups reduced during steam explosion process. This makes the water absorption of wool and swelling of wool. With the increase of steam explosion strength, the mechanical properties of wool decrease because disulfide bond is broken and crystal structure is reduced during the steam explosion process. All of the changes reduce the energy consumption at the time of pulverizing for preparing the wool powder.

6.4.6.2 Cocoon Processing

Silk fibroin powder is pure protein, containing 18 kinds of amino acids and trace elements. Because of its fine rodlike shape and homogeneous dispersion, it can be used as dispersing agent and softener for dyes, paints, and leather polish. In addition, silk fibroin powder can be used as fundamental materials for cosmetic because hydrophilic factor exists in the structure, which can absorb and release moisture according to the change of temperature and humidity [79]. However, current production methods are still fibroin powder using an acid, alkali, and other chemicals. The first of fibroin embrittlement is removed after repeated washing with chemicals, drying, grinding, and other processes. However, acid or alkali embrittlement is usually conducted in current production methods of silk fibroin powder production, followed by the removal of chemical by washing, drying, grinding, and other processes. Too much water and chemicals are consumed in this process, which will lead to environmental pollution. In addition, it also has the disadvantages of much loss, complex, low yield, and high cost.

Production method of silk fibroin powder is as follows: (1) Put silk fibroin which had taken off the sericin into a closed container and seal explosion outlet with a cap using rupture disk. (2) Dock diffuser box and seal container. (3) Inlet saturated steam of 2.5–3.0 MPa into the explosion tank and maintain its pressure for 6–15 min. Silk fibroin that had taken off the sericin is composed by region of crystalline and non-crystalline. In crystalline region, the gravitation is formed by β-folding-layer structure and the peptide chain arranges orderly. The gravity and hydrogen bond between adjacent peptide chains make peptide chain closely packed, which endows the peptide chain with a high degree of crystallinity and orientation. However, the non-crystalline regions of fibroin peptide chain actually were irregular bend and have sintered arrangement. Therefore, under the effect of high-temperature and high-pressure saturated steam, silk fibroin will be loosened and softened. In addition, the degree of orientation of macromolecules will also reduce, followed by thermal motion which will lead to deorientation of crystalline and amorphous regions. Then, sticking point of fibroin fibers is released and degree of orientation is reduced. In addition, the macromolecular chains in amorphous region arrangement are prone to disorder and force between molecular decreases. (4) Explosion membrane is forced to rupture through spearhead, resulting in steam explosion, and the fibroin high is pushed into the diffuser box. During this process, fibroin silk fibroin is crushed into powder under the joint action of tear, shear, and condensed energy. (5) Separate the diffuser box and seal container and collect the fibroin powder box. (6) Dehydrate the fibroin powder.

Modest amount of urea (1–5 % of the silk fibroin) is added into the closed container, while the silk fibroin is put into the container. Urea will be decomposed into ammonia and carbon dioxide under the high-temperature steam. Ammonia is alkaline, and it may cause force damage of the silk fibroin molecules. This will lead to decrease of the fiber intensity which will make fibroin more likely to be crushed into powder fibroin during steam explosion process. The test proved that adding urea number from 1 to 5 % by weight of silk fibroin is more appropriate.

No large amount of chemicals such as acid and alkali are used in this method to pretreat the silk, which eliminates the environmental pollution. In addition, closed container and diffusion box are used to collect all the silk grain powder in this method. Therefore, this method has the advantages of simple, less equipment, and high yield. All of these will contribute to reduce the cost significantly.

This technology has revolutionized the traditional silk spinning process method and solved the problem of environmental pollution and the huge loss of water. With this technology, the properties of fibroin have been modified. Its physical indicators are superior to those produced by old technology. It becomes a new fiber. The spun silk that is made from this fiber can be green or natural. Recycling of amino acids, sericin, and other valuable products in the refining industrial wastewater enriches the product structure, which greatly improved the economic and environmental benefits.

6.4.6.3 Waste Leather Processing

In recent 10 years, China has become the world center of leather production, processing, and trade. However, with the rapid development of the leather industry, environmental pollution problem is worsening. Collagen containing chromium (leather waste) during the process of shaving and trimming of the tanning is one of the main pollutions. According to statistics, this kind of solid waste each year has reached 30 million tons every year. Chromium-contained leather waste contains about 90 % collagen protein and 3–6 % Cr_2O_3 in dry waste. It causes serious pollution problems because this waste is hard to be degraded. Massive researches have been carried out in order to find a reasonable utilization of these wastes. The most promising approach is to extract collagen and its degradation product from chrome shavings with a methodology of dechromisation. Therefore, the key to recovery and utilization of waste chrome shaving is the removal of Cr^{3+}. Conventional dechromisation methodology includes acid, alkali, alternating, enzymatic, and oxidation. H_2O_2 and other oxidants are used in the method of oxidation for chromium shaving treatment, during which Cr^{3+} is oxidized to water-soluble Cr^{6+}, making chrome leather get rid of the tan. Then, after rinsing and filtration, collagen and chromium are separated. This approach is mainly carried out in an alkaline medium. Compared with other dechromisation methods, oxidation method has the advantages of higher dechromisation speed, fine color, and less damage of the collagen structure. Therefore, with this method, we can obtain collagen product with higher application value. However, oxidation method has the disadvantages of long chromium removal time and low dechromisation rate.

Steam explosion of the chromium oxide can be a good solution to the above problem. Moderate NaOH (1:5–20) and water were added into the waste leather, followed by explosion in the high steam explosion tank. The operation conditions are concluded as follows: 1.3–1.5 MPa for pressure and 3–10 s for maintaining time. Appropriate amount of H_2O_2 (0.6–1.5-fold of the dry mass) was added into the steam-exploded leather. Oxalic acid and sodium chloride are also added as stabilizer, and chromium in the leather will be removed after a few minutes of stirring. The removal rate can reach 95 %. The treated leather can be used in the preparation of gelatin and animal protein feed. Steam explosion technology can significantly reduce the time for chromium removal.

The main component of leather is collagen, and chrome tanning process is the combination process of Cr^{3+} and carboxy which exists in the contained one in the side chains of the collagen molecule, i.e., cross-linking. The cross-linked chromium complex has high stability after the tanning process. Therefore, it is difficult to separate proteins and Cr^{3+}. In fact, it is the reverse reaction of tanning to separate proteins and Cr^{3+}, which is to break the Cr^{3+} from cross-linked protein and make the latter converted into free. Under the effect of high-temperature and high-pressure saturated steam, senior structure of collagen in leather will change. The force between molecules is reduced or destroyed. Macromolecular chain gets into disorder or even broken down into small molecular chain, which is accelerated by sudden steam discharge. Cr^{3+} falls down from the peptide chain under the condition of CaO, NaOH, and other alkaline substances.

6.5 Application of Steam Explosion Technology in Chemical Industry

With the rapid development of chemical industry in nineteenth and twentieth centuries, chemicals have undergone several stages such as coal chemical and petrochemical. Particularly, the later has played massive role in boosting human social economic development. However, petroleum tends to be exhausted for its non-renewable feature in the process of continuous development and utilization, leading to the development of newly replaced raw materials to be the new focus of current chemical engineering research [80]. There is about 20 billion tons of plant biomass generated through photosynthesis every year, making biomass become the most abundant renewable resource. Plant biomass is a complex compound composed of cellulose, hemicellulose, and lignin, accounting for 40, 25, and 20 % of the total weight of raw materials, respectively. The compositions mentioned above are platform chemicals which can be made into relative chemicals. Therefore, many states have put the development of biomass-based production to the strategic level and plugged into massive human and financial resource; for example, the USA had a plan that 10 % chemical production would be produced by lignin biomass in 2020, which would increase to 50 % in 2050. Chemical composition of biomass is complex, so the primary task in efficient biomass conversion is to separate each composition and degrade the macromolecule of biomass so that the small molecular product will be obtained. Then, it would be used as platform compound which will be modified or converted into certain chemicals and serve the humans. Chen Hongzhang, research fellow of Institute of Process Engineering, Chinese Academy of Sciences, focused on separation fraction and established steam explosion separation technology. He fully absorbed new ideas of molecular biology and industrial ecology [81] combined with mature technology in traditional chemical industry, conducting further research on biomass-based chemical production (Fig. 6.34), and finally gained sound result. For example, many biomass-based productions have realized industrialization [82].

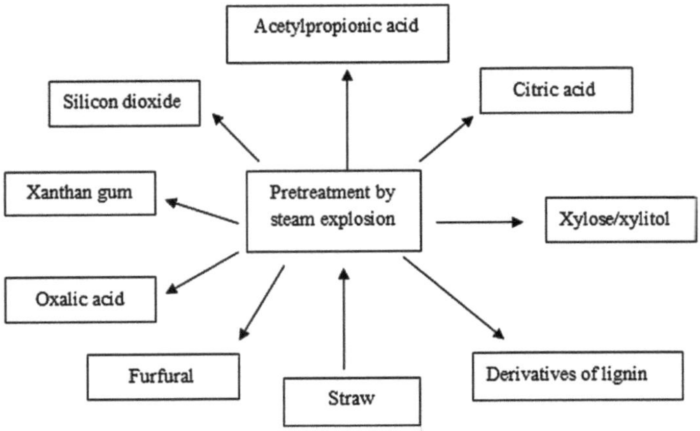

Fig. 6.34 Preparation of chemicals with biomass by key technology of steam explosion

6.5.1 *Oxalic Acid*

6.5.1.1 Introduction of Oxalic Acid

Oxalic acid, also called ethane diacid, is one of the simplest organic dibasic acids with the molecular formula of $C_2H_4O_2$. The oxalic acid usually exists in the form of oxalate, which is a colorless and transparent crystal and widely spread in the natural world. Almost all the plants contain the oxalate, such as the sheep hoof grass and the creeping oxalis.

Oxalic acid is widely used in different areas. In the chemical industry, it is used in the starch hydrolysis to produce pure dextrin and glucose, or various oxalate reagents, oxalate and glyoxylic acid. In the pharmaceutical industry, it is used to produce antibiotics, such as chlortetracycline, tetracycline, vitamins (vitamin B), and pantothenate. In the textile dyeing industry, it is used as the mordant or detergent of the cotton and wool, the fire suppressor of the textiles. Besides, it is also used in the tanning and bleaching of the leather, and the bleaching of the paper pulp, cork, and plywood. In the metallurgical industry, it is used to epurate high rare earth metal purity and make carbon sticks. What is more, the high-purity oxalic acid can be also used in the electronics industry, synthetic resin, production of the ink, the printing ink and the coating, and the preparation of the catalyst.

6.5.1.2 Traditional Preparation Technology of Oxalic Acid

The traditional preparation technology of oxalic acid mainly includes the oxidation of carbohydrate, CO coupling, and sodium formate methods [83].

The oxidation of carbohydrate method: The starch is putted into the aqueous solution which contains 10 % of the oxalic acid, and the mixture is then heated and the acid is added; reflux reaction is for 6 h, and the degradation product, glucose, is obtained. Then, the nitric acid is added, iron–vanadium catalyst is added at 63 °C to catalyze hydrolysis, and the oxalic acid is made. This method is easy, and the reaction conditions are mild. But the product yield is low, and there is a great deal of nitrogen oxides in the tail gas, which are of high toxicity. It takes grain as the raw material, which makes the cost high and thus is restricted to the development and applications.

CO coupling method: Oxalate is obtained by coupling reaction, which takes place among the substrates of carbon monoxide, oxygen, alcohol and dilute nitric acid at the condition of 8–11 MPa, 90–100 °C with the catalysts of palladium and copper. The oxalate is heated to get oxalic acid and the corresponding alcohol. The catalytic system in this method is single, and the catalytic activity is high. Besides, the product is very pure. However, the disadvantages are that it requires high purity of the carbon monoxide, which is high in the energy consumption and has much investment cost.

Sodium formate method: The CO is washed by water and alkali and boosted and it is heated in high concentration of NaOH solution. They are then added into the reactor to get the dilute acid–sodium formate solution. Condensing the solution and dehydrogenation followed by melting of the obtained solid, finally, the solid sodium formate is distributed into suspension. After washing and removing the soluble impurities, oxalic acid solution is obtained after acidification. Coagulating sedimentation by the addition of barium carbonate and polyacrylamide can remove impurities. Finished product can be finally obtained after cooling crystallization and drying. This technology is mature and has the advantages of short production cycle and high yield of the production. However, lead ions in this technology process can pollute the environment.

Other methods of oxalic acid production include ethylene glycol–nitric acid oxidation, propylene oxidation, and glyoxal oxidation.

6.5.1.3 Preparation Technology of Oxalic Acid Based on Steam Explosion

Chen Hongzhang, research fellow of Institute of Process Engineering, Chinese Academy of Sciences, proposed a new technology of oxalic acid production by alkali melting and oxidation steam-exploded straws in recycling system (Fig. 6.35). Basic process is described as follows: Add 40–60 % strong alkaline solution into the exploded straws; keep the mixed system under high temperature to get the alkali fusion gas-exploded straw solution; collect the filtrate and add calcium oxide into it to get calcium oxalate and calcium hydroxide; add 20–30 % sulfuric acid into calcium oxalate and keep this mixed system under the temperature of 200 °C for certain period of time; acidulated solution is condensed and crystallized to get oxalic acid crystal [84].

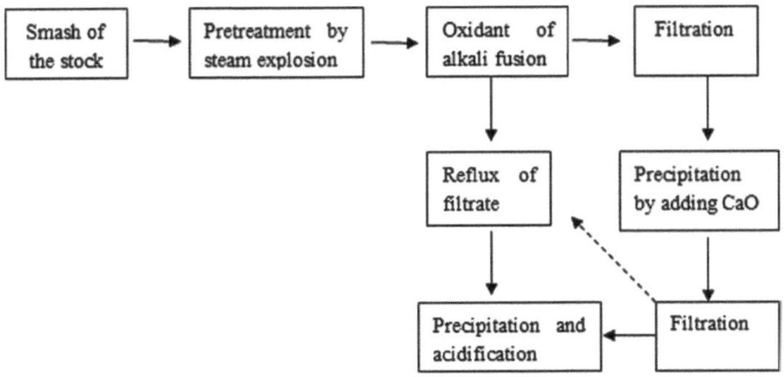

Fig. 6.35 Technology of oxalic acid preparation by steam explosion pretreatment of the biomass

After washing the gas-exploded straw by water, hemicellulose exists in the water solution in the form of xylose and xylooligosaccharide. Therefore, water washing solution can be used to cultivate the brown rot fungus to produce oxalic acid by fermentation. Brown rot fungus is one member of the wood-rot fungus. They mainly degrade cellulose and hemicellulose in the timber and leave the lignin. Timber is divided into small part and is fragile. They play the role of redox in the forest ecology system and are the important parts of the matter recycle and energy flow in the forest ecology system. Research verified that oxalic acid provides proton donor for enzymatic hydrolysis or non-enzymatic hydrolysis process of the carbohydrate. Oxalic acid secreted by brown rot fungus is the primary metabolite, and its biosynthesis can be fined by cooperation of short TCA cycle, glyoxysome, and the pathway of acetate recovery. Carbohydrates in the gas-exploded straw washing solution are used by brown rot fungus and get into resource utilization.

6.5.2 *Furfural*

6.5.2.1 Introduction of Furfural

Furfural, also called furaldehyde, is a kind of important heterocyclic organic compounds with the formula of $C_5H_4O_2$. It is soluble in hot water and slightly soluble in cold water. It is also soluble in organic solution, including acetone, benzene, diethyl ether, acetic acid, isobutanol, trichloromethane, ethyl acetate, hexanediol, carbon tetrachloride, pyridine, toluene, and so on. Furfural has aldehyde group and dialkylene ether. It has the properties of aldehyde, ether, and dienes, and can participate in multiple chemical reaction. For example, furfural can generate maleic and furoic acid and furan carboxylic acid through oxidation, and it can generate furfuryl alcohol, methylfuran, and methyltetrahydrofuran by hydrogenation. Furfural can react with strong alkali to generate furfuryl alcohol and sodium furoic acid and generate furfuracrylic acid by condensation reaction with salts of fatty acids or organic alkali. It also can generate thermoplastic resin by condensation reaction with phenolic compounds and generate furfuryl acetone resin through condensation reaction with acetone.

Furfural is widely used from 1960s, and it has been applied to perfume synthesis and become an important kind of perfume. Perfume based on furfural has been applied to food, drink, and cosmetics broadly [85]. Furoic acid and furfuryl alcohol can be prepared using furfural as the material through disproportionation. Furfuryl can be prepared through DMAP or PPY/$NaHCO_3$ method using furfural alcohol and anhydride. Medicine and pesticides using furfuryl as the raw material are applied broadly, such as sterilizing agent, pesticides, and acaricide. Ferrous fumarate (cure iron deficiency anemia), dimethyl fumarate (mold proof and antiseptic), and benzyl fumarate (deodorant) are currently used. Furfural and its derivative furoic acid and furfuryl alcohol can be used as antiseptic. In addition, they are all the raw materials for advanced preservative synthesis. For example, furfural can be used to produce xylitol which can be added into chewing and candy to prevent decayed tooth. In synthetic resin, furfural can be used to synthesize resin with the advantages of high-temperature resistance, good mechanical strength, insulated, strong acid resistant, and corrosion resistance. Furfural resin, furfuryl acetone resin, and furfur alcohol resin are applied to plastic, coating, daub, and adhesive. Furan resin synthesized with furfural has the advantages of corrosion resistance and good stability and can be used as corrosion resistance coating. It improves production efficiency when used as adhesive for its fast hardening speed and high core strength. Furan resin can bring convenience to construction because it can improve temperature resistance and chemical resistance and has slower hardening speed when used as epoxy glass fiber-reinforced plastic. Furfural resin synthesized by furfural instead of formaldehyde has the ability of good mechanical physical quality, low cost, and non-pollution.

6.5.2.2 Traditional Preparation Technology of Furfural

Furfural is generated by the hydrolysis of pentosan in acid medium followed by dehydration. Catalysts for furfural preparation include sulfuric acid, phosphoric acid, and hydrochloric acid. Furfural in reaction system is separated by gas stripping and solvent extraction operation. Currently, methods for furfural preparation are one-step method and two-step method [86].

One-step method is used by most industries, and hydrolysis of pentosan and dehydration of pentose happen in one reactor so as to get the furfural. With the development in recent several decades, technology for furfural preparation has been improved a lot, from single cooking to multi-cooking and continuous preparation. The following technologies are used widely, such as Quaker Oats technology, Agrifuran technology, petrale-chimie technology, Escher Wyss technology, Rosenlew technology, and RRL-J technology. All those technologies adapt steam stripping to separate the furfural. One-step method demands much steam (18–25 t steam for 1.0 t furfural) and low yield (60 %) and can produce much residue which is composed of cellulose, lignin, and hemicellulose. At present, the method for treatment of the waste residue is to burn it with coal for steam production. Two-step method is to carry out the hydrolysis of pentosan and dehydration separately.

6.5.2.3 Preparation Technology of Furfural Based on Steam Explosion

Chen Hongzhang combines the steam explosion pretreatment and washing to divide rice and cornstalk into washing part and solid part. The technology process is shown in Fig. 6.36. Raw materials are cut into 5 cm and put into the explosion tank; followed by inletting steam and keeping the working pressure 1.5 Mpa for 3 min. Then, discharge the pressure immediately and get the exploded materials by open the outlet pipeline. Moisture of the exploded straw is about 50 %, adding water at the ratio of 1:3 to prepare washing solution. Hydrolysate of hemicellulose in the washing solution is condensed to 13–18 % for preparation of furfural. The condensed solution is transported into reactor and 98 % sulfuric acid is added at the ratio of 5:100 (sulfuric acid: condensed solution) to obtain furfural. Collecting furfural by reflux condensation and adding modest water to get 6 % furfural solution; distillation column was exploited to remove wastewater and organic acid to get crude furfural (Fig. 6.36).

Chen Hongzhang develops an integrated technology for furfural, polyether polyol, and nanosilicon dioxide preparation with exploded straw (Fig. 6.37). Basic technology process is concluded as follows [87]: ① Put straws into explosion tank followed by water washing to extract hemicellulose; ② add solid acid or inorganic acid to prepare furfural; ③ straw air classification to get parenchyma cells and fiber cells; ④ burn the parenchyma cells to prepare nanosilicon dioxide; ⑤ cook fiber cells to separate cellulose and lignin; ⑥ solid lignin is obtained by acid education; ⑦ PEG and glycerinum are added as liquefier, and sulfuric acid or hydrochloric acid is added as catalyst in fiber solution to prepare polyether polyol; ⑧ ethylene

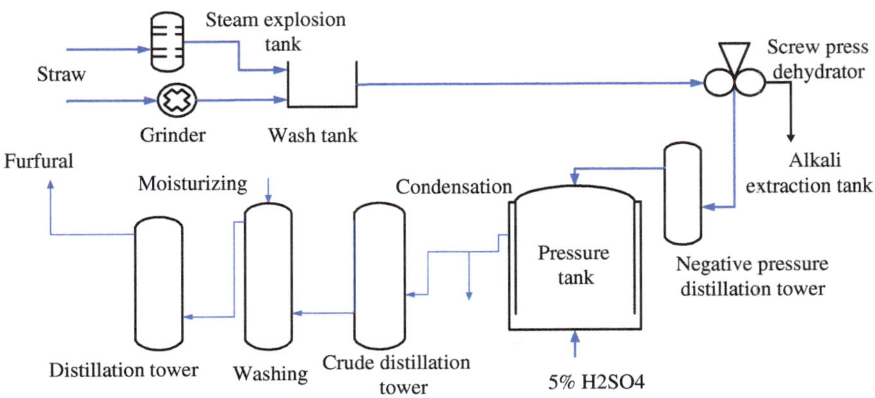

Fig. 6.36 Technology of furfural preparation by steam explosion pretreatment of the biomass

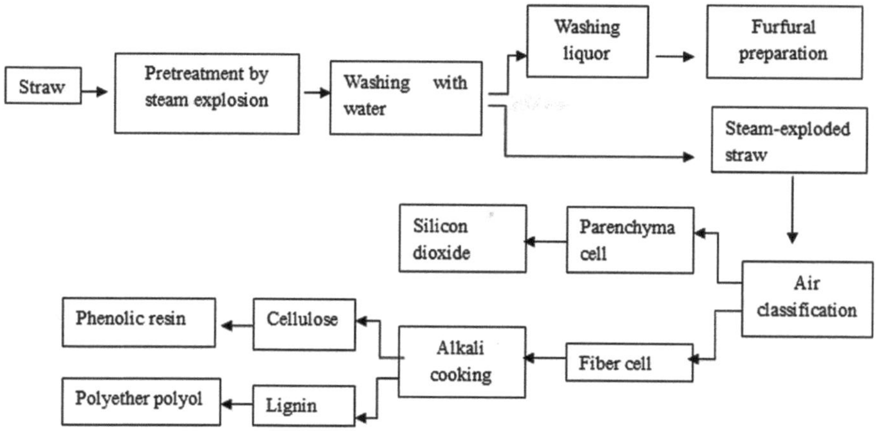

Fig. 6.37 Coupling preparation of polyether polyol and phenolic resin with steam-exploded straw

oxide and propylene oxide are added as liquefier, and NaOH or KOH is added as catalyst in lignin to prepare polyether polyol; ⑨ mixing lignin and phenol, liquefied by sulfuric acid to generate phenolic resin. All the cellulose and lignin are used in high value, and furfural, polyether polyol, and silicon dioxide are produced at the same time. This technology is promising in industrial application.

6.5.3 *Acetylpropionic Acid*

6.5.3.1 Introduction of Acetylpropionic Acid

Acetylpropionic acid is an achromic liquid with the formula of $C_5H_8O_3$. It has unique carbonyl group which can make it isomerized. It also has good reaction activity and can take part in hydrolysis, transesterification, addition, substitution, and redox reaction [88, 89]. In perfume industry, 5-valerolactone and ethyl levulinate, which have the flavor of fruit and flower, can be synthesized with platform compound of acetylpropionic acid and used in edible essence and fruit essence. Angelica lactone mixed with tobacco fragrance is a kind of good cigarette additive. In medicine industry, neocalcium is usually used as nutrition medicine; it is benefit to formation of bone and normal excitability of the muscle. In light industry, levulinic acid ethanol amine and levulinic acid guanidine can smooth and shine the hair. It also can be used in cosmetic to inhabit secretion of the sebum. Pentadiene is the derivative of levulinic acid, which is the raw material of rubber synthesis. In pesticide industry, 2-methyl-3-indoleacetic acid and hexyl levulinic, synthesized by levulinic acid, can be used as medicine intermediates, plant hormone, and insect repellant. New fertilizer of levulinic acid derivatives has advantages of broad application, non-toxic, and environment-friendly.

6.5.3.2 Traditional Preparation Technology of Acetylpropionic Acid

Traditional preparation technology of acetylpropionic acid is hydrolysis method. Furfuryl alcohol hydrolysis method: Furfuryl alcohol is used as raw material and hydrolyzed in acid medium, forming the acetylpropionic acid. Direct hydrolysis of polysaccharide: Cellulose and starch are used as raw materials, and inorganic acid is used as catalyst; polysaccharide can be hydrolyzed and generates monosaccharide in high temperature. Hydroxymethyl furfural can be generated by dehydration, and acetylpropionic acid can be generated by decarboxylation. Batch hydrolysis method: Polysaccharide is put into reactor at one time followed by the addition of inorganic acid for hydrolysis and separation of acetylpropionic acid. This method is simple, but the yield and purity are low. Biomass continuous hydrolysis: Raw materials are added continuously to get product followed by separation and purification. This method has the advantage of high efficiency and is the direction of acetylpropionic acid development [90].

6.5.3.3 Preparation Technology of Acetylpropionic Acid Based on Steam Explosion

Chen Hongzhang establishes component classification for the preparation of acetylpropionic acid from the respect of properties. Classify short and long fibers after steam explosion (Fig. 6.38). Washing liquid of steam-exploded cellulose and short fiber is used as materials for preparation of acetyl propionic acid and solid strong acid, which could be used as catalyst [91] (Fig. 6.39).

Microwave-assisted solid superacid preparation of acetylpropionic acid with gas-exploded straw: 800 W microwave power is used in this method; add water and solid acid into gas-exploded straw and keep this mixed system for 40–50 min, followed by pumping filtration and centrifugation (8000 r/min, 10 min).

Preparation of acetylpropionic acid by high-temperature solid superacid catalyst with gas-exploded straw: Add moderate water into gas-exploded straw; heat this mix up to 200 °C for 40–50 min; keep this mixed system for 5 min under the condition of 1.2 Mpa, 200 °C, and 180–200 r/min for rotational speed.

Preparation of acetylpropionic acid by high-temperature solid superacid catalyst with short fiber: Add cellulose into short fiber and keep this system for 2 h; put them into reactor along with inhibitor and solid acid catalyst; keep this system in high temperature for a period of time to get acetylpropionic acid.

This technology can improve acetylpropionic acid yield and has the advantages of non-environmental pollution, and safe and free equipment corrosion, compared with traditional method.

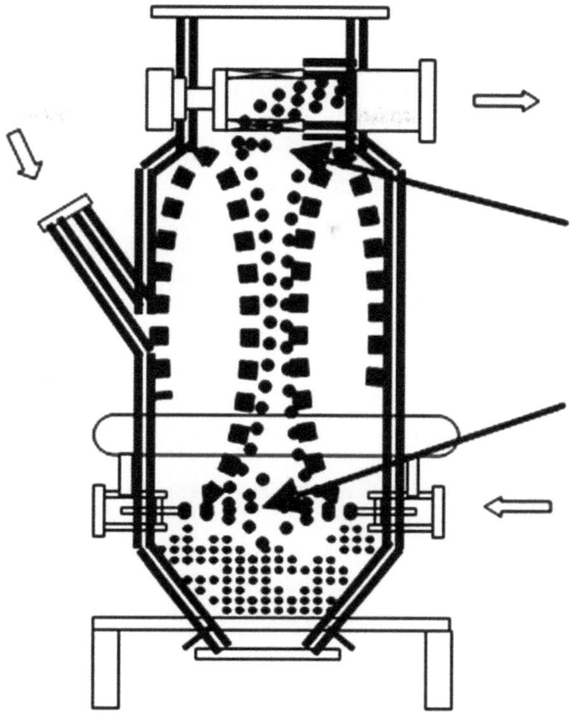

Fig. 6.38 Pulverizer of biomass

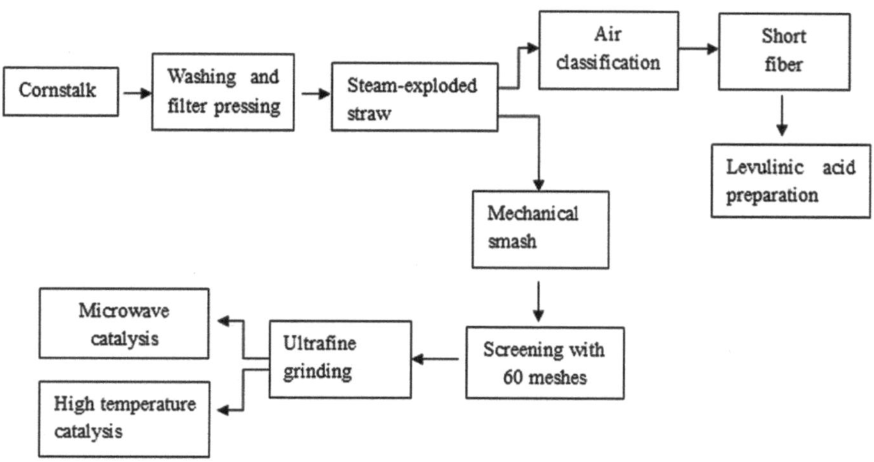

Fig. 6.39 Preparation of acetylpropionic acid with steam-exploded straw

6.5.4 Xylooligosaccharide/Xylose/Xylitol

6.5.4.1 Introduction of Xylooligosaccharide/Xylose/Xylitol

Xylose is a pentose sugars, soluble in water, hot ethanol and other organic solvents, and insoluble in ether. Molecular formula is $C_5H_{10}O_5$. The appearance characteristics of xylose are colorless or white crystal or powder. It is of sweet and refreshing taste. Xylitol can be produced by catalytic hydrogenation of xylose. In addition, it is edible for diabetes and has anti-caries function. Currently, it has been extensively used as a food additive. Xylooligosaccharide is consisted of 2–7 molecules of xylose, and they are connected by β-1,4-glycoside bond. Some also contain arabinose, glucuronic acid, and glucuronic acid side chains, which are mainly xylophone and xylophone. Xylooligosaccharide is white or pale yellow powder solid, with good processing characteristics and storage stability. Xylitol is derived from xylose. Xylitol is white powder or crystal form, its molecular formula is $C_5H_{12}O_5$, and it is widely found in fruits and vegetables. The sweetness of xylitol is similar to sucrose and has a unique sense of cool.

Xylose or xylooligosaccharide mainly used in food products [92]: Xylose and xylooligosaccharide are fermentable but indigestible sugars. They are hardly directly absorbed by the body, and thus, they will not be converted to fat. But when they enter into the intestine, they can contribute to the proliferation of intestinal probiotics or improve its physiological activity and improve the intestinal microbial environment, such as promotion of nitrobacteria and lactobacilli. What is more, they can inhibit the growth of harmful bacteria such as Clostridium, Escherichia coli, and Salmonella. In addition, they can reduce the formation of toxic fermentation products, improve human immunity, serve to reduce cholesterol, lower cholesterol, and prevent the role of colorectal cancer. Xylose is not easy to be fermented by streptococcus mutants, so the teeth cannot easily be corroded. When xylose and sucrose are used in combination, they can prevent the action of streptococcus mutants, form water-insoluble polymer of glucose, and have anticaries effect. When xylose and calcium are used, they can promote the body's absorption of calcium. In addition, xylose can also be converted to xylitol, and xylitol is a new sweetener. Xylose is almost as sweet as six-carbon sugar, and it has excellent characteristics similar to glycerol and other polygons. Therefore, it is widely used in national defense, pharmaceutical, chemical, leather, paint, food, and other industries. As a sugar substitute, xylitol is widely added to chewing gum and hard candy, this will not only keep the candy sweet but also effectively prevent and inhibit the occurrence of dental caries. It serves as food additives for diabetes, or added to white wine to increase liquor fragrance. We can obtain carbon fatty acid ester if we synthesize xylitol and xylitol, and it can serve as a heat-resistant plastic plasticizer and leather greasing agent. When it is condensed with propylene oxide, we can obtain polyether resin and the resin can be manufactured with foam.

6.5.4.2 Traditional Preparation Technology of Xylooligosaccharide/Xylose/Xylitol

Traditional preparation technologies of xylooligosaccharide include dilute acid hydrolysis, hot water extraction, and enzymatic hydrolysis. Dilute acid hydrolysis: Separate xylan by alkali, followed by hydrolysis and dilute acid to get xylooligosaccharide. This method requires too much of the equipment and investment. It has not been put into production for its disadvantages of large investment at a time, and it is hard to control. It is also harmful matter production and complex. Hot water extraction: Steam is used to degrade hemicellulose to prepare xylooligosaccharide. However, this method can produce many by-products and is complex for further steps. Enzymatic hydrolysis: Hydrolyze xylan with endo-xylanase followed by separation and purification to get xylose. There are little by-products in this method because of the selectivity of endo-xylanase. Therefore, it is benefit to separate and purify the xylose for further steps. Microorganisms for xylanase production include germ, streptomycete, aspergillus, penicillium, and trichoderma. Xylanase is often produced coupling with amylase and cellulase which increases difficulty for xylanase separation because of their similar properties. This affects xylose yield [93].

Traditional preparation technologies of xylitol include extraction, chemical catalysis, and bioconversion (Fig. 6.40). Extraction is used hardly for low content of xylitol in fruits and vegetables. Chemical catalysis demands nickel as catalyst to catalyze xylose for xylitol preparation. However, this method demands multi-step purification for hydrolysis solution and large amount of steam consumption in hydrogenation. In addition, there are lots of impurities in the solution and hard to recover. Bioconversion is to convert xylose into xylitol by xylose reductase in the

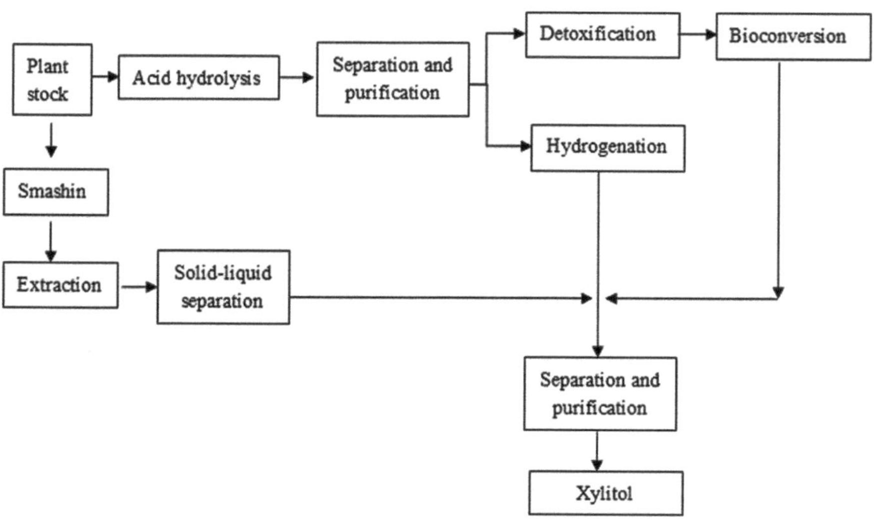

Fig. 6.40 Traditional preparation technology of xylitol [94]

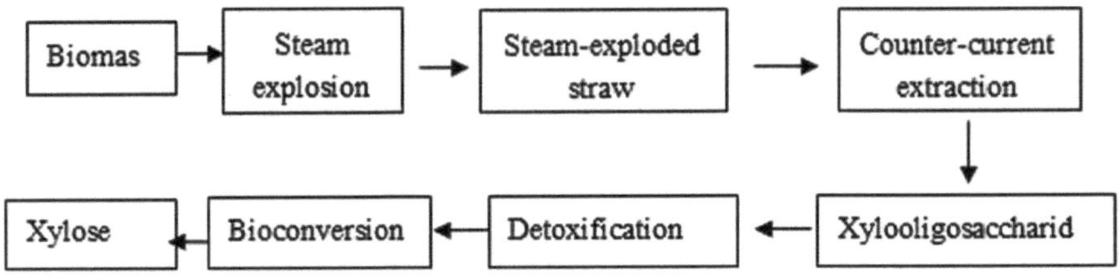

Fig. 6.41 Preparation of xylose with steam-exploded straw

microorganism. This method is moderate, simple, and easy to control. However, the yield is low and there are too many inhibitors in the hydrolysate. They are harmful to microorganism.

6.5.4.3 Preparation Technology of Xylose Based on Steam Explosion

Chen Hongzhang establishes steam explosion method for xylan extraction [95], followed by countercurrent extraction and fermentation to prepare xylose. The concentration can reach up to 30.12 g/L, and the yield is beyond 80 %. Basic process can be described as follows: Smash the biomass and explode it to get exploded straw; recover xylan by countercurrent extraction; remove inhibitors such as formic acid, acetic acid, and furfural; cultivate microorganism to produce xylanase and hydrolyze xylan to get xylose (Fig. 6.41).

6.5.5 Citric Acid

6.5.5.1 Introduction of Citric Acid

Citric acid, having scientific name 2-hydroxy-1,2,3-propane tricarboxylic acid, belongs to ternary acid, and it is intermediate metabolites of the TCA cycle and plays an important role in physiological processes of the body. It can be divided into anhydrous citric acid and citric acid monohydrate. Anhydrous citric acid is white crystalline powder, and relative molecular mass is 192.14. While heating, citric acid can be decomposed to various products which can be transformed into each other. In 1875, citric acid was first isolated from lemon juice and Swedish chemist Scheel prepared the crystals, so it is called citrate. The artificial preparation of citric acid began at 1913; Zahorski produced citric acid by using black Aspergillus, in 1919. The shallow tray fermentation technique of citric acid fermentation process was established, making industrial production come true. In 2007, the global production of citric acid was nearly 1.6 million tons.

Citric acid is known as the largest organic acids and safe and has non-toxic side effects. It can be directly metabolized by organism and has a pleasant acidity, so it is widely used in all walks of daily life. Food industry: Citric acid is widely used in the production of fruit juices, soft drinks, canned food, snacks, cakes and biscuits, and other foods, and the market share is more than 70 %. As for beverage production, citric acid can play the role of solubilization and antioxidant and enrich flavor of taste products. In jelly production process, citric acid meets the requirements of narrow range of pH. In the wine production process, it can make up for subacidity when added to ice cream and margarine, can increase stability, and prevent oxidation. Because citric acid can be combined with calcium, zinc, and iron ions which human body needs, then it formed salts, contributing to the body's absorption. Chemical industry: Citric acid can be used in buffers, experimental analysis reagents, complex agents, and chromatographic reagents. For example, citric acid is often used as electroplating buffers and chemical reaction activator. When used in shampoo formulation, it can help hair styling. In the pharmaceutical industry, citric acid and its salts can promote the absorption of trace elements, and potassium citrate can treat inflammation caused by bladder. Copper citrate can used to sterilize, in the textile industry, and citric acid is used as mordant and more accelerant, which can effectively prevent fading. Wrinkle agent made by modified citric acid can effectively solve the problem that textile is wrinkle easily, and the cost of production is reduced. In environmental protection, citric acid–sodium citrate is mainly used in adsorption desulfurization. In the feed industry, citric acid is often used as an additive. Citric acid added to feed livestock can improve the utilization rate of feed and livestock immunity, increase the amount of litter and improve meat quality, reduce the week back fat thickness, shorten the feeding period, and so on.

6.5.5.2 Traditional Preparation Technology of Citric Acid

Citric acid is abundant in fruits and vegetables. In initial period, lime milk is added into fruit juice to extract citric acid in the form of calcium citrate. This method has the disadvantages of low yield, large amount of raw material consumption, high cost, and hard to apply. In 1880s, scientist established synthesis method for citric acid preparation with glycerinum. This method is complex, and the raw materials are expensive; therefore, it is not suitable for industrial production. Recent fermentation method began in 1971. American nutrition chemists prepared citric acid by Aspergillus niger fermentation. In 1919, Pfizer began to adapt surface fermentation industrial production and adapt submerged fermentation from 1950s to produce citric acid.

At present, industrial raw materials for citric fermentation include sugar beet honey, sugarcane honey, corn starch, cellulose, sugarcane, and sweet potato residue. Take *Aspergillus niger* fermentation as an example: Raw materials are hydrolyzed to produce cellulose; cellulose is converted to phosphoenolpyruvic acid through EMP or PPP pathway and finally converted to pyruvic acid; pyruvic acid is converted to acetyl coenzyme A by decarboxylation; reverse synthesis of citric acid by citrate synthase.

6.5.6 Xanthan Gum

6.5.6.1 Introduction of Xanthan Gum

Xanthan gum is yellow and white power, and it is the fermentation product from 1970s. It is a kind of anionic extracellular polysaccharide produced by *Xanthomonas campestris* with carbohydrates (corn, starch, and so on) as the raw materials, followed by ethanol extraction, drying, and smashing. Xanthan gum is composed by hexaose, and its main stain is similar to the cellulose. However, oligosaccharide side chain appears alternately between glucose units. Xanthan gum has strong hydrophilicity with no poison. In 1883, Wakker firstly recorded xanthan gum and its producing strain. In 1960s, American began to produce xanthan in semi-industrial scale.

Xanthan gum has broad application. In terms of food, xanthan gum has the functions of thickening, suspension, stable emulsion, and freeze thawing and it is a kind of good food additives. In daily chemical industry, there are amounts of hydrophilic groups in xanthan gum, making it to be the fine surfactant. Xanthan gum has the advantages of antioxidation and antiaging of the skin when used in cosmetics. In terms of medical, xanthan is the functional composition of micro-capsule for its hydrophilic and preserves water features. It plays an important role in drug delayed release. In petroleum industry, xanthan gum has unique technical advantages for its rheological property, salt tolerance, and thickening. In addition, xanthan gum can be used as flame retardant in fire extinguishing agent.

6.5.6.2 Traditional Preparation Technology of Xanthan Gum

Xanthan gum belongs to heterotypic polysaccharide and is more complex than homotypic polysaccharide when synthesized in cells by *X. campestris*. The main process is shown in Fig. 6.42 [96]. Firstly, hexose is absorbed to synthesize pre-cursor of nucleotidyl sugar, phosphoenolpyruvate, and acetyl-CoA, followed by synthesizing pentose and oligomer. Then, glucose phosphate is linked to lipid carrier, catalyzed by glucosyltransferase. Glucose and sucrose are usually used as carbon source, and the substrates are sugar content vegetable residue and corn syrup. Inorganic nitrogen source such as $(NH_4)_2SO_4$ and NH_4Cl is used in xanthan gum preparation. Research verified that high-concentration glucose can inhibit cell growth. Therefore, flow fed carbon source is benefit to cell growth and improves production. Viscosity of xanthan gum solution can affect the fermentation process and should be controlled properly. Viscosity of fermentation broth increases in anaphase and influences the process, for example, the ability of material mix and

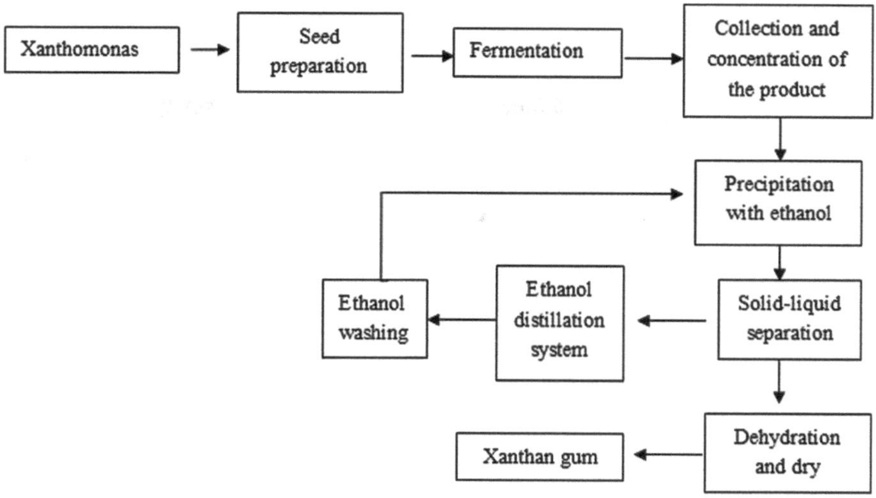

Fig. 6.42 Traditional preparation technology of xanthan gum

oxygen dispersion decreases, resulting in lower yield of xanthan gum and harder extraction process. Solution to the above problems is concluded as follows: Add chemical deformer which can bring in mixed bacterium; use immobilized cell to separate production of xanthan gum from fermentation broth and this can provide enough oxygen for the cell which can improve xanthan gum yield. Hydroxyl radical and hypochlorous acid are used as introducers by some scholars. They can promote formation of active oxygen and therefore provide oxygen source for cell growth and formation of xanthan gum, which can promote the formation process.

6.5.6.3 Preparation Technology of Xanthan Gum Based on Steam Explosion

Chen Hongzhang established the preparation technology of xanthan gum based on gas-exploded straw by component classification and solid-state fermentation [97, 98]. Inert carrier is the fixed phase in solid-state fermentation. Nutrient materials are adsorbed on the carrier surface, and microorganism cell grows on the surface. Matters and energy are changed through the carrier. The carrier is squeezed to get the broth when fermentation process finishes. Adsorbed material is porous material, containing nutrient liquid and providing huge space for microorganism growth. In addition, porous material is loose and air is the continuous phase. This solves the problem of oxygen distribution and overcomes disadvantage of transfer of heat and mass due to high-viscosity broth in fermentation anaphase. Besides, microorganism grows on the solid-state medium directly, and separation of solid medium and

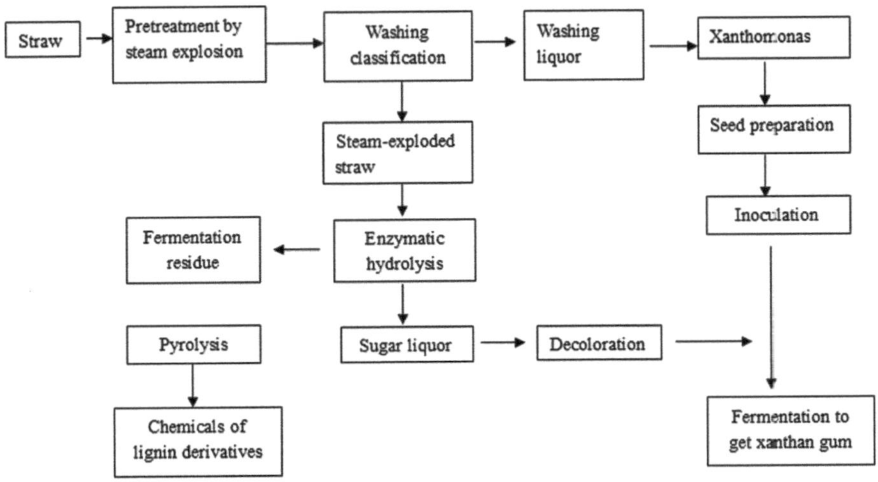

Fig. 6.43 Preparation of xanthan gum with steam-exploded straw

liquid product is easily realized, which reduces difficulty in microorganism separation in the following steps.

Preparation technology of xanthan gum based on steam explosion coupled with enzymatic hydrolysis and fermentation is shown in Fig. 6.43. Cornstalk is cut into 3–5 cm and exploded by steam; wash the exploded straw and detoxify it by water; add water by fixed ratio, pH 4.8; enzymatic hydrolysis is carried out for 48 h at 50 °C, yeast powder is used as nitrogen source and Mg^{2+}, and PO_4^{3-} are used as inorganic salts; polyurethane foam is cut into 0.3–1 cm^3; inoculate *X. campestris*; mix enzymolysis liquid and inoculated carrier in certain ratio; squeeze the carrier to get the liquid after fermentation; ethanol precipitation and separation are used to extract xanthan gum. The research shows that there is less xylose in enzymolysis liquid after the exploding the straw. This can reduce the inhibition to the microorganism. Higher glucose yield by enzymatic hydrolysis is very important to xanthan gum production. This process realizes utilization for high value of the cornstalk.

6.5.7 Phenolic Acids

6.5.7.1 Introduction of Phenolic Acids

Biomass is composed of cellulose, hemicellulose, and lignin. It means a lot to utilize lignin for high value. Lignin can be transformed into many matters, including ferulic acid, syringaldehyde, syringic acid, vanillin, and vanillic acid.

Ferulic acid is the derivatives of cinnamic acid and distributes widely in plants, which was firstly found in seeds and leaves of the plants. It plays an important role in the formation of secondary wall. Currently, ferulic acid is mainly applied in medicine and food industries [99]. For example, it can scavenge free radicals in human body so as to prevent cancer. Ferulic acid sodium can be used to induce platelet aggregation and release of thromboxane so as to cure cerebral thrombosis. In addition, ferulic acid sodium can prevent aggregation of neutrophilic blood cells caused by activated complement and organ damage caused by complement activation. It also can inhabit activity of tyrosine so as to reduce the formation of melanin and improve skin health. In terms of food industry, ferulic acid plays the role of antioxidation and bacteria inhabitation, such as lipid antioxidation in food processing.

Vanillin is also known as vaniline, which can be found in plants. Vanilla contains the highest dose of vanillin with a strong smell of vanilla orchid. It is white to light yellow in the form of needle crystal or crystalline powder and forms a colorless crystals in aqueous, aqueous–alcohol and an organic solvent. It is gradually oxidized in air and easily changes the color when encountering with alkali or alkaline substances. Vanillin is the largest output of synthetic fragrances in the world, which is widely used in food, washing cosmetics, and pharmaceutical and other industries. For example, it can be used as food flavors in cakes, soy milk, soft drinks, and candy, in which it played the role of antibacterial preservative. Vanillin can also be used in the electroplating industry polishes. In agriculture, it is used as production promoter, ripener, and herbicide. In industry, it can be used in leather tanning agent synthesis. Vanillin has capabilities of antibacterial and can be used in recipe of dermics. In medicine aspect, vanillin can be used in berberine synthesis and methyldopa synthesis which can cure hypertension.

6.5.7.2 Traditional Preparation Technology of Phenolic Acids

Technology for ferulic acid preparation includes lixiviating and chemical synthesis. Ferulic acid extraction from rice bran (Fig. 6.44) [100] has the disadvantage of low yield and is not suited for industrial production in large scale. Chemical method for ferulic acid synthesis is Klloevellagel condensation reaction of vanillin and malonic acid. The difference among the current method lies in catalyst and solution; for

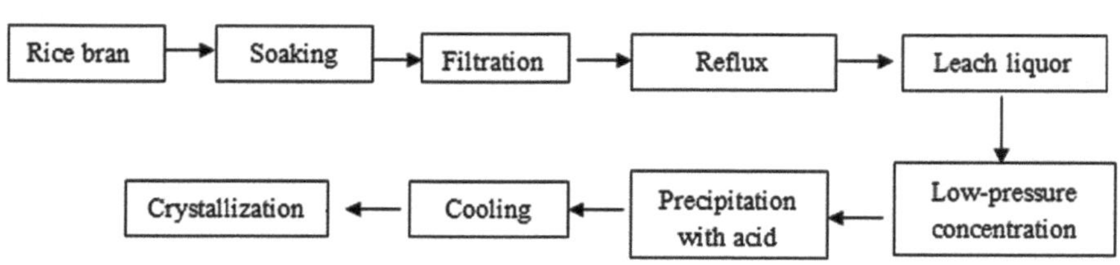

Fig. 6.44 Preparation of phenolic acids with methodology of lixiviating

example, some scholars prepare ferulic acid through Klloevellagel condensation reaction with microwave assistant.

Technology for vanillin preparation includes lixiviating method, chemical synthesis, and bioconversion [101] (Fig. 6.45). Lixiviating method has the advantages of non-toxic and solution residue, but it is high cost and low yield. In recent years, scholars focus on inducing plant cell to promote vanillin yield. Chemical synthesis for vanillin preparation is different in terms of different raw materials. For example, oxidation of clove finishing is used to prepare vanillin; hydrolysis of coniferin is used to synthesize coniferyl alcohol, followed by oxidation to produce vanillin. Lignin oxidation method is also the focus of many scholars. Details are concluded as follows: Add moderate alkali into the papermaking wastewater; pump air to oxidate and acidify the system under temperature of 160 °C. Bioconversion method is very moderate and less contaminated. Enzyme in microorganism metabolic process catalyzes the substrate, ferulic acid esterase releases ferulic acid on the cell wall, and then the vanillin is obtained. Current microorganism method focuses on two steps for vanillin preparation. Transfer ferulic acid to vanillic acid with one strain followed by transformation of the latter to vanillin with another strain (Fig. 6.46). Germany scholar Rabenhorst selected Amycolatopsis to produce vanillin, and the conversion rate is 77 % in 10 L scale.

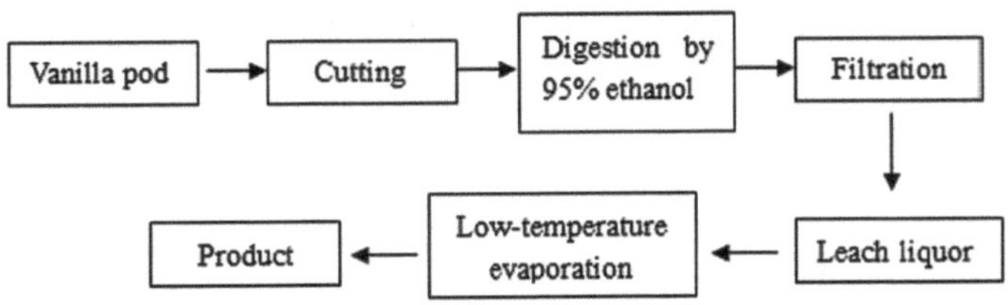

Fig. 6.45 Preparation of vanillin with methodology of lixiviating

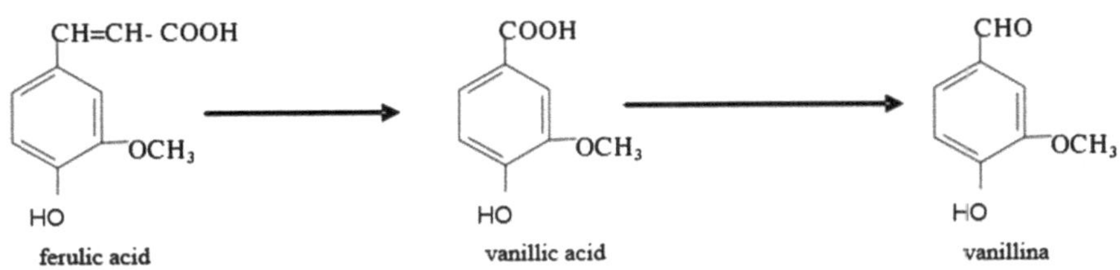

Fig. 6.46 Technology of conversion of phenolic acids to vanillin

6.5.7.3 Preparation Technology of Phenolic Acids Based on Steam Explosion

Chen Hongzhang established phenolic acid extraction technology from steam-exploded straw washing liquid based on steam explosion technology. In the explosion process, lignin breaks into small molecular with the increase of intensity. They are dissolved into the washing liquid after washing and can be separated for high-value utilization. Take syringaldehyde as an example [102–104], extraction 1 h (steam-exploded straw/water 1/10), condense the washing liquid (aldehyde compound concentration >5 g/L) and filter, adjust pH 6, and extract the target matters with ethyl acetate, followed by the removal of water in ethyl acetate with $MgSO_4$ and concentration; dissolve the condensed liquid in the butanol, extract for 1–5 times with saturated sodium bisulfite; extract liquid is acidified with 50 % H_2SO_4, pH 2–3, and extract aldehyde compound with chloroform; dry the extract liquid with vacuum evaporation to get yellow crystalline aldehyde compound followed by column chromatography separation (Fig. 6.47).

Lignin is the polymer of phenylpropane compound. It can be oxidized by lignin oxidase such as laccase to generate phenylpropane and phenoxy radical which can induce free radical reaction (Fig. 6.48). Lignin also can be degraded through

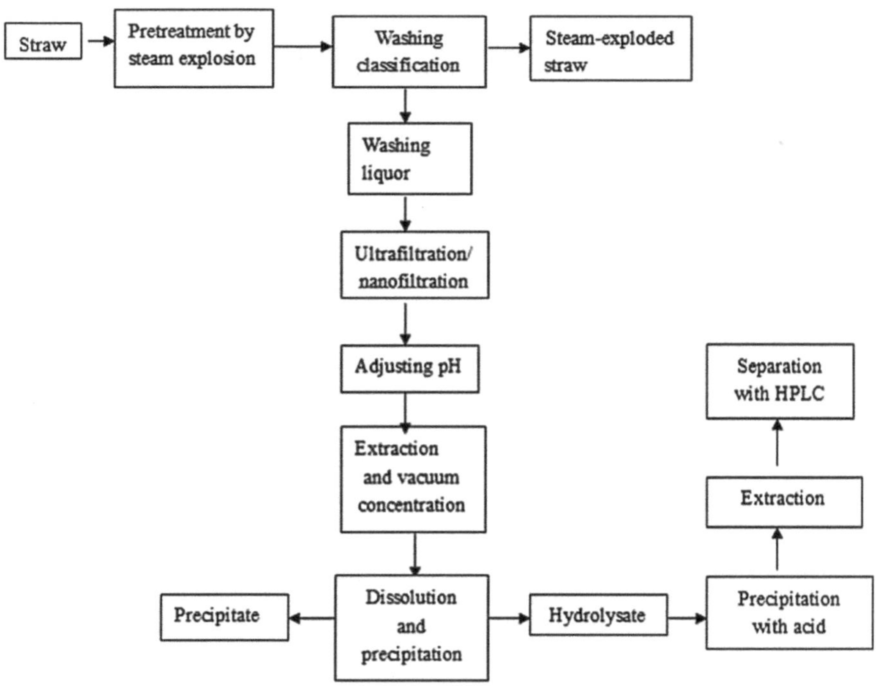

Fig. 6.47 Preparation of syringaldehyde with steam-exploded straw washing liquid

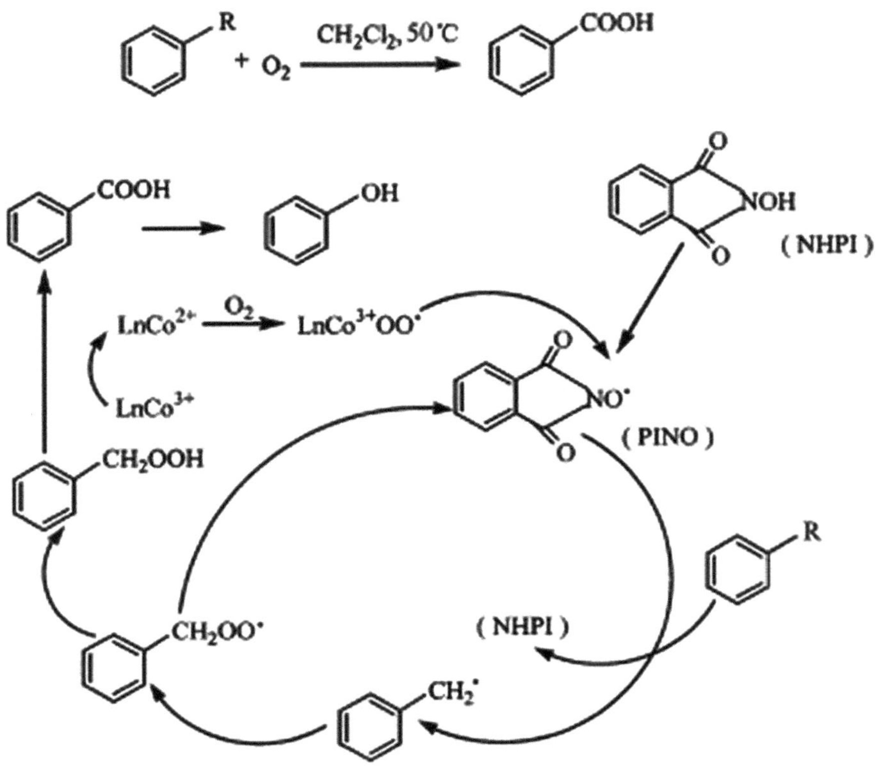

Fig. 6.48 Lignin and derivatives [105]

hydrogenation, oxidation, and high-temperature pyrolysis to get derivatives, such as ferulic acid and vanillin. Steam explosion lignin is obtained from steam-exploded straw through steam explosion and alkali cooking technology and can be further transformed into relative derivatives.

6.5.8 *Silicon Dioxide*

6.5.8.1 Introduction of Silicon Dioxide

Silicon dioxide is also called silica [106]. It is widely spread in natural environment and can be divided into crystalline silica and amorphous silica, such as quartz and silica sand. Silica dioxide is insoluble in the water but slightly soluble in the acid. It can react with molten caustic soda in the form of particle. It can be used as raw materials to produce glass, water glass, pottery, refractory, and monatomic silicon. Silicon dioxide belongs to acidic oxides. It is insoluble in water and cannot react with ordinary acids but can react with HF to generate SiF_4. It can react with hot strong alkali or molten caustic soda to generate silicate and water and with metallic oxide to generate silicate in high temperature. As a kind of good fortifier, silicon dioxide can improve tensile strength; therefore, it is widely applied to rubber industry. In papermaking industry, silicon dioxide can improve whiteness, intensity, wear resistance, and non-transparency of the papers. In pesticide industry, silicon can be used as anticaking agent and dispersing agent.

6.5.8.2 Traditional Preparation Technology of Silicon Dioxide

Physical method for silicon preparation is to use super-flow grinder or high-energy ball mill to multi-smash the silicon dioxide. This technology is simple, but the particles unevenly distributed and impurities are easily mixed. Chemical methods for silicon preparation include thermal vapor condensation, ion exchange, precipitation, and sol-gel method. At present, raw materials for silicon preparation are mainly from rocks and soil.

6.5.8.3 Preparation Technology of Silicon Dioxide Based on Steam Explosion

Research fellow Chen Hongzhang, according to different compositions of straw, establishes steam explosion and selective separation method to prepare silicon dioxide [107]. There is much silicon fiber in corn, rice, and wheat straw cells and can be used as materials for silicon dioxide preparation. The basic process is concluded as follows: Treat the straw by steam explosion to get fiber-rich cell part and parenchyma-rich cell part; burn the later in high-temperature furnace (600 °C) and recover the heat to dry materials; collect silicon dioxide particles after reaction and smash them with ball mill to get amorphous (Fig. 6.49).

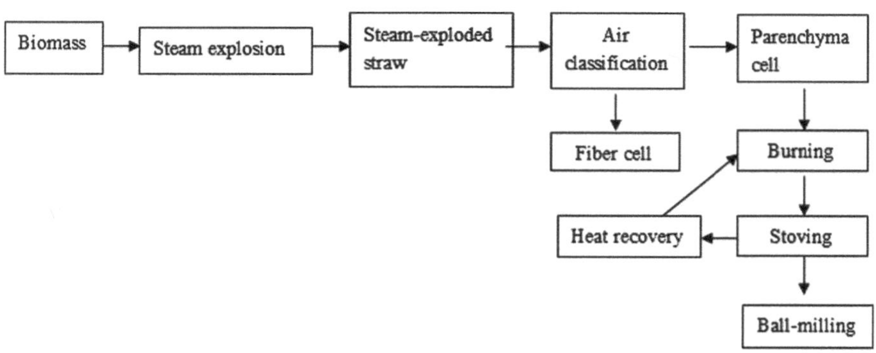

Fig. 6.49 Preparation technology of silicon dioxide with steam-exploded straw

6.5.9 *Chemical Production Examples Based on Steam Explosion Technology*

Institute of Process Engineering, Chinese Academy of Sciences, cooperating with Guangxi Yulin Corn chemical industry company, develops an industrial item of preparation of furfural with straw and comprehensive utilization of straws. Taking the unpolluted steam explosion technology as the core, the full use of lignocellulose compositions to produce biobased chemicals (such as furfural) has been realized and overall high-value and multi-level utilization of the straw resource has been achieved.

This item began in January 2012 and gone into production in June 2012. 100 thousand tons of rice straw and cornstalk was treated, and 8.6 thousand tons furfural was produced coupling production of 10.5 thousand tons of lignin and 36 thousand tons of fiber raw materials (Fig. 6.50).

The project can realize the total biomass utilization for high value and coupling. Soluble carbohydrates and hydrolysates of hemicellulose are used to produce

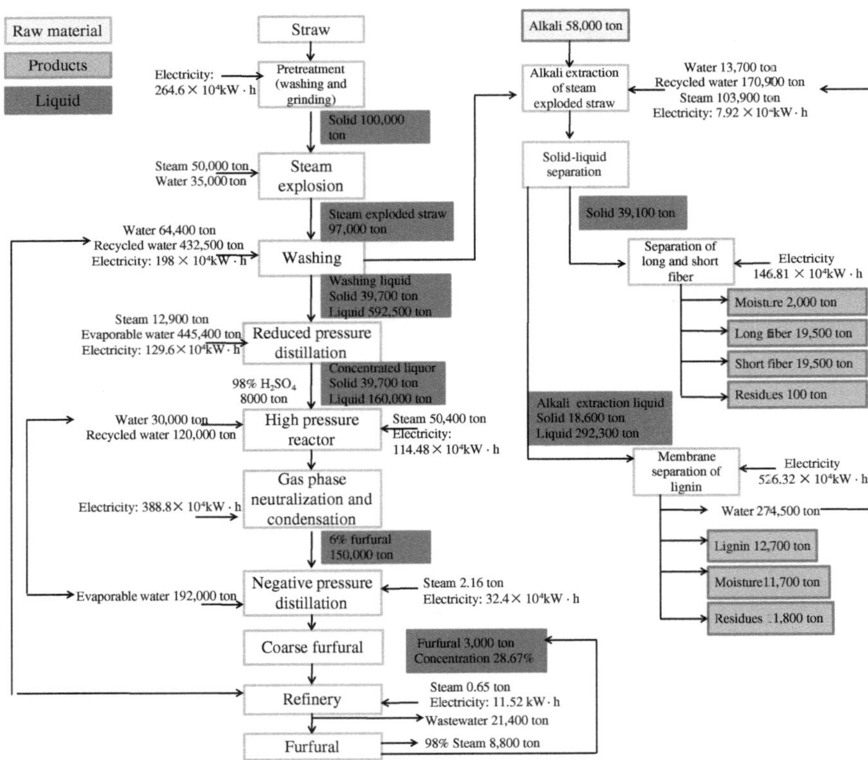

Fig. 6.50 Mass balance of furfural production from lignocellulosic biomass

furfural; the solid matters are extracted by alkali to get lignin or exploited for phenolic resin production; short and long fiber are separated and exploited to produce carbohydrates and polyether polyols respectively. The waste, which is produced during the process, is burned in boiler. Hence, the straws are utilized comprehensively without pollution while traditional two-steps method for furfural preparation is complex, which demands much energy. Pentosan in the straw can be hydrolyzed during steam explosion process and the washing solution can be exploited to produce furfural directly. There is no wastewater and residue in the process. The implement of this project is the sign of industrialization of steam explosion for chemicals production and lays solid foundation for its further utilization.

6.6 Application of Steam Explosion Technology in Environmental Protection

Ecology environment is not only the basic condition for living and development of human beings, but also the fundamental state policy for economy and social sustainable development. Our government attaches great importance to ecology environment and takes sustainable development as basic state policy. However, under the pressure of rapid increase of population and economy, environmental problem is still outstanding in the process of rapid industrialization and urbanization. It is closely linked with economy, society, policy, culture, technology, international relationships, and so on. The factors for environmental problem formation are complex, influencing and interacting with each other. In recent years, tendency of environmental problem deterioration has got controlled roughly but just in some areas and the overall tendency has not been controlled essentially; environmental problems are still under great pressure although it has not been on inflexion point.

It is our environment withes with Chinese characteristic that keeping rapid development, urbanization and industrialization under the limit of environmental bearing capacity. Pollution from consumption is increasing along with higher consumption level of people. Environment and resource are main bottlenecks of our development, which can be settled by developing green technology innovation positively and promoting development of green industries. We should master the key technology to tackle environmental problems by exploring new road with little cost, good benefit, little waste, and sustainable characteristics positively.

Steam explosion technology has undergone 84 years of development and has been applied in fields such as pulping papermaking, extraction of Chinese herbs, processing of fruits and vegetables, fiber processing, liquor production, tobacco expansion, and pretreatment of raw materials for bioresource utilization. Particularly, it shows unique advantages in settling the problems of solid waste addressing, unpolluted pulping and environmental materials of absorption and environment protection, showing enormous potentials.

6.6.1 Damage and Management of Solid Wastes

In recent years, solid wastes, produced in the process of production and consumption, are increasing along with the rapid development of economy and urbanization process. It takes amount of land and pollutes the underground water and air. These put cities under more serious environmental pressure, lead to more complex ecology problems, and eventually damage production and life of people [108].

6.6.1.1 Damage of Solid Wastes

The damage of solid wastes to human and environment can be concluded as follows [109]:

① Taking a lot of land: It must be stored because it cannot be used, which demands more space and even takes the farmland. This will put relative industry under great pressure.

② Contaminating soil: Harmful compositions of outdoor solid wastes can easily penetrate the soil through weathering, raining, and surface runoff, which will damage decomposition capability of the soil by killing the microorganisms and resulting in wastelands finally.

③ Contaminating the waters: Solid wastes will leach through runoff of natural rainfall, moving with the wind or draining into the waters and eventually contaminating the waters.

④ Contaminating the air: Solid wastes could pollute the air through power and poisonous gas. Currently, inhalable particles that influence air quality of cities are mainly produced by solid wastes.

⑤ Influencing environmental hygiene: The storage of industrial wastes in cities affects townscape as well as bacteria and mosquitoes breed, which can result in disease distribution.

The damage of urban solid wastes to ecology and environment is obvious and huge. However, in the prospective of materials, solid wastes are misplaced and increasing resource. The aims of solid waste management are quantitative reduction, harmless, and resource recovery. The essential is changing waste into valuables and realizing the reuse of resource. This has been always the direction of controlling solid wastes [110].

Many research institutes have conducted a lot of researches on resource recovery of solid wastes. Currently, the main technologies we develop and use are landfill [111], incineration [112, 113], composting, pyrolysis, and so on. Technology

Table 6.30 Comparison of management technologies of solid wastes

Methods	Target matters	Requirement	Production	Advantages	Disadvantages
Landfill	All matters	Compaction		Large throughput; simple; low cost	Land taking; waste resource; pollution; unsafe
Incineration	Organics	Detearing; separation; crushing	Thermal energy	Large throughput; harmless; recovery of heat	Large investment; energy consumption; pollution
Compost	Organics	Separation; crushing	Fertilizer	Low cost; simple; organics recycling	Long time; metal contamination
Pyrolysis	Organics	Detearing; separation; crushing	Fuel raw materials	Slight pollution; resource recovery	Complex; large investment
Gasification	Biomass	Separation; crushing	Biogas fertilizer	Non-pollution; biogas and fertilizer production	Small throughput; long time

application and requests are listed in Table 6.30. The aims of urban solid waste management are resource recovery (to recover useful materials and energy, and transform them into beneficial materials, such as fertilizers), quantitative reduction (to reduce the volume and quantity to the maximal degree), and harmless (to turn the wastes into harmless and nonpolluting material for human beings), and all the technologies are applied in terms of the three aspects.

6.6.1.2 Problems Remained in the Management of Solid Wastes

At present, comprehensive utilization of solid wastes is still in serious situation, and the total resource recovery and technology levels demand further promotion. In order to realize triple wins in economy, society, and ecological benefits, the problems listed as follows need to be solved.

① There is no emission standard of solid wastes, resulting in great variability in composition and characteristics of the solid wastes. Too much undetermined impurity cannot make the wastes meet the qualification for resource recovery unless they get pretreatment, which is high cost and hard to carry on. Too much emphasis is put on the single solid waste, lacking consideration and researches on resource recovery of multiple solid wastes within a certain area.

② Comprehensive utilization of resources in our state is affected by many factors such as regional economy and resource distribution. In addition, many resources may be reused, but it is not economical. Finally, finance, plugged into resource comprehensive utilization by our government, is not efficient. The backbone function of science and technology to resource comprehensive utilization must be promoted.
To get the utilization of solid wastes into industrialization, we must improve our comprehensive competition by strengthening technology innovation, sampling our technology, and reducing our cost in terms of market environment. There are lots of useful materials in solid wastes. We can get them into utilization for high value by extracting useful materials and energy through management and technology.
③ Taking national situation and plans of city development, we should focus on overall utilization and pay some attention to multi-functional and efficient utilization. Try to get the social and ecological benefits as well as economic benefit.

Solid wastes could be divided into municipal solid wastes, industrial solid wastes, and agricultural solid wastes according to the sources in our state. Besides, they also can be divided into organic and inorganic solid wastes in terms of their compositions.

Comparing with advanced technologies and rapid development of solid waste resource utilization in foreign nations, the development in aspect of application and research in China is insufficient. Industrial solid wastes are mainly used in construction materials such as sintered brick manufacturing and road construction [114]. Agricultural solid wastes are used in composting, and municipal solid wastes are applied to concrete production [115].

6.6.1.3 Treatment of Solid Wastes by Steam Explosion Technology

Steam explosion is the key technology for organic solid wastes utilization, which has the advantages of technology reliability, economic advantages and faster payback period.

Treatment of solid wastes by steam explosion has multiple functions listed as follows [15]:

① Comminuting. In the process of steam explosion, high pressure of steam becomes low pressure immediately inside the wastes and gets the wastes broken. This process is more effective than mechanical comminuting because steam can get into all voids around the wastes. The force of explosion makes all the wastes comminuted thoroughly, simplifying step of mechanical comminuting in the process of waste classification.
② Decomposition. Macromolecule substances (such as protein, fat, and cellulose) are partly decomposed in the wastes under high-temperature condition. For

Table 6.31 Dosage and function of deinking agents [141]

Deinking agents	Function	Dosage/%
Sodium hydroxide	Expansion; emulsion	1.0–2.0
Sodium silicate	Stabilization; dispersion	1.5–5.0
H_2O_2	Bleaching	1.0–1.5
Chelating agent	Prevent degradation of H_2O_2 by metal ions	1.0–2.0
Surfactant	Wetting; penetration; dispersion; foaming; trapping	0.3–1.0
Calcium salt	Trapping	Moderate

example, cellulose and lignin in horticultural wastes are partly hydrolyzed or become easier to be hydrolyzed in the process of steam explosion, because steam can get into all voids and play its role in molecular level. This can improve the anaerobic digestion conversion rate of the wastes and reduce the time of digestion.

③ Disinfection. Most harmful virus and bacterium will be killed in sealed steam explosion tank with 8–12 atm of steam pressure and temperature of 160 °C for 5 min. Workers will be safer in the process of the later treatment of solid wastes. In addition, in the process of steam explosion, steam condensates on dust, making the dust depositing and reducing the distribution of bad smell.

However, the process of fermentation will not be affected because high temperature mainly killed aerobic microorganisms and virus. In the following fermentation process, mixed bacteria will be added into the solid wastes in the tank.

④ Separation. In the process of steam explosion, the treated wastes will be jetted out of the tank along with the steam. Wastes can be separated due to their different density. The wastes with higher density will land a shorter distance comparing with the wastes with lower density.

Chen Hongzhang invented a new method of unpolluted steam explosion with low pressure for solid waste treatment. He conducted lots of researches on technology of steam explosion with low pressure in large scale and succeeded in getting it into industrial scale of from 5 L and 5 m^3, which has been applied to papermaking and spinning industries. This laid a solid foundation for the treatment of solid wastes in large scale [24].

The innovation of this the technology mentioned above can be concluded as follows: ① The characteristics of the solid wastes were changed during the process of steam explosion. For example, moisture content in the waste got higher, the plastics were dissolved, and organic compositions were decomposed. ② The structure of solid wastes was changed by steam explosion, making it easier to be degraded by microorganisms. This would improve the utilization ratio of organic solid wastes and transform them into feedstuff and fertilizer with low cost. ③ The steam disinfected the wastes in this process, making it convenient for operation.

6.6.2 Organic Fertilizer Manufacturing

6.6.2.1 Current Situation of Organic Fertilizer

Soil is not only the circulation origin of energy and materials in ecosystem and the origin of the food chain, but also the basic step in agricultural production. Fertilizer is the basic factor that affects the crop production. It is a guarantee to use organic or inorganic fertilizer in improving production with good quality when other conditions are consistent [116].

Fertilizers can be divided into organic fertilizer and inorganic fertilizer according to their characteristic and source. Inorganic fertilizer is usually called chemical fertilizers. It is inorganic compound containing high-nutrient elements and produced through industrial manufacturing. It is the basic method to use chemical fertilizer constantly and massively at home and abroad. However, along with high production, utilization of fertilizer leads to many problems, for example, degrading soil fertility, changing physicochemical properties of the soil, influencing the normal growth of crops, intensifying water and soil erosion, polluting the air and water, decreasing the production of food, and reducing the active organic matter of the soil. At present, fertilization structure in China mainly relies on chemical fertilizer. However, people of our governments and industries as well as the farmers have gradually realized that only the chemical fertilizer and organic fertilizer are mixed in proper ratio, and the fertility can be obtained and maintained. According to the latest statistics from Chinese Bureau of Statistics, chemical fertilizer production and organic fertilizer production were 66.198 and 14 million tons in 2010, respectively. Currently, organic fertilizer is mainly applied to green-food basement such as large farmland and orchards, urban forestry development, and flower cultivation. The production of organic fertilizer is promising in the market [117].

Organic fertilizer is the total name of natural fertilizer. It is produced by stacking of agricultural wastes. Traditional organic fertilizer is the normal stacking fertilizer. It is produced with wastes of animals by anaerobic fermentation in natural condition. However, the process of organic matter deposition in stacking fertilizer is very slow (more than a half year), and it takes large land. There are amounts of pathogen and worm eggs in this organic fertilizer. It can cause diseases and pests when added to the farmland, increasing the cost of pesticide and pesticide residue. The incubation of traditional organic fertilizer is very difficult. It will cause seeding injury and bad smell when it is added to the land and it is inconvenient to operate. Centralized treatment of organic materials by introducing advanced biochemical technology and relative equipment to produce commercial complex fertilizers containing much more organic compositions (commercial organic fertilizer) is the new field of organic fertilizer development [118]. After carrying out of plans and policies such as the non-pollution food plan, green food, and organic food, Chinese government has taken the food safety under control. This stimulates the organic fertilizer market to a certain degree. Demand of green food has been always exceeding its supply, which makes commercial organic fertilizer has large market at worldwide in the future [119]. Shandong Lin Jia Quan Organic Fertilizer Limited Liability Company is the biggest basement of organic fertilizer production in China. This company produces paper by extracting fiber in crop straw and uses the beneficial parts of by-product (lignin, fulvic acid, and microelement) to produce natural organic fertilizer by improving their technology. 1.0 million tons of green organic fertilizer can be produced in this company every year [120].

Commercial organic fertilizer is produced with organic wastes (animal wastes, crop straws, municipal waste, and sludge) by industrial centralized treatment, followed by deodorization, disinfection and sterilization, drying, mixing of inorganic fertilizer and organic fertilizer and packing. Then, it can be stored for a long time and transported in a long distance and finally came into the market. The technical process of fertilizer production is shown in Fig. 6.51, including smashing followed by stirring, fermentation, deodorization, dehydration, smashing, granulating, and drying. Different organic matters are made into basic smell-less and dry organic fertilizer by the technology mentioned above. It can be made into liquid fertilizer and foliar fertilizer for further steps.

The following problems must be solved in commercial organic fertilizer.

① Diversified strains. Production of organic fertilizer must undergo the process of fermentation and decomposition, and moderate beneficial microorganism needs to be added to or kept in the fertilizer to faster its incubation. The raw materials of organic fertilizer are complex and extensive. The effective stains need to decompose multiple wastes and organic materials such as crop straws.

② Mixed raw materials. Organic contains essential nutrient elements (N, P, K, and so on) for the growth of plants as well as multi-nutrient elements such as Ca, S, and Fe. In addition, it also contains B, vitamin, and antibiotics. They can stimulate and promote the growth of the plants. All of them provide the plants with nutrients together. Different amounts of nutrients with different effectiveness are contained in different organic materials including ignite, peat, weathered coal, animal wastes, multiple wastes, crop straws, and wastes of agricultural by-products and food industry. In terms of field specificity in China, collocating the raw materials scientifically and improving technologies of treatment, production, and implication can improve the utilization ratio of organic fertilizer.

③ Technology modernization. There are five problems (low nutrients, big volume, low benefit, low level of harmless, and high pollution) in utilization of

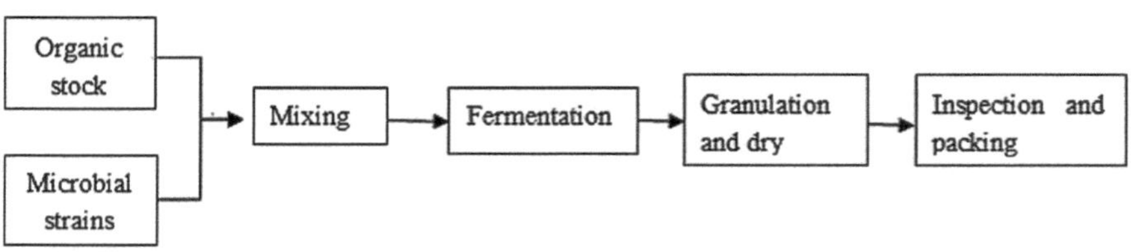

Fig. 6.51 Production process of commercial organic fertilizer

organic fertilizer resource. The developments of effective technology of organic fertilizer treatment are key ways to improve the utilization of organic fertilizer resource [121].

6.6.2.2 Application of Steam Explosion in Organic Fertilizer Manufacturing

Commercial organic fertilizer is the compost after fermentation in high temperature, which is produced through a series of technologies including steam explosion followed by composting fermentation in high temperature and smashing. Compared with other commercial organic fertilizer, the compost uses unique technologies of steam explosion and solid-state fermentation [122]. This can ensure good aeration and fermentation activity in high temperature (60 °C), controlling the ratio of C and N, moisture, and pH. In addition, artificial inoculation is applied in this process. This process makes the organic composition incubated faster in a shorter time (15–20 min). In addition, the high temperature can kill pathogens, worm eggs, and seeds effectively.

6.6.3 Application of Steam Explosion in Papermaking Industry

Papermaking is one of the four great innovations in ancient China. It has greatly promoted the development of science and culture around the world.

Papermaking is an important industry closely associated with development of national economy and construction of social civilization. It attracts increasing attention for its important role in modern economy. Papermaking is recognized as sustainable industry. Papermaking is linked to many industries including forestry, agriculture, machinery manufacturing, chemical industries, transportation, energy, and environment protection. The increasing need for demand of paper production will contribute to the development of upper and downstream economy [123]. Accelerating the development of papermaking is the liable steps to increase the employment and arrange the rural surplus labor. In addition, it will also be the growth point that promotes economic growth. Papermaking is an industry demanding lots of investment, energy and chemical materials and water. It also can cause serious pollution and be the primary target of control. The fact is that environmental pollution caused by papermaking has been the obstacle of paper-making development [124].

Modern papermaking technology includes two steps, pulping and papermaking [125]. The process of pulping can be concluded as follows: storage of or stock followed by cutting, removing skin, chipping, defibrination, cooking, washing, screening, bleaching, dipping, and defibrination. Finally, we get the natural board.

6.6.3.1 Pulping by the Method of Steam Explosion

Pulping is defined as the process that separates the fiber from the raw materials so as to get the natural board or bleached pulp with chemical and mechanical methods or combined method [126]. Pulping methods mainly include mechanical–chemical and chemical–mechanical methods. Chemical pulp, mechanical pulp, and chemical–mechanical pulp can be obtained, respectively.

(1) Chemical pulping

Chemical pulping is the process that separates timber organ into single fiber with chemicals (such as sodium hydroxide) so as to get the pulp. Alkaline pulping and sulfite pulping are two methods usually used in industrial production.

Wheat straw is the main raw material in Chinese pulping industries. In our traditional chemical pulping process, the black liquid is strong alkaline, which has much foam and high demand of oxygen due to wheat straw cooking mixed with sodium hydroxide and sulfite [127]. It not only pollutes the environment seriously but also restricts the recovery of lignin and humic acid in the black liquid. COD produced by wheat straw chemical pulping accounts for 90 % of the total pulping pollutes. Traditional process of wheat straw chemical pulping is shown in Fig. 6.52 [128].

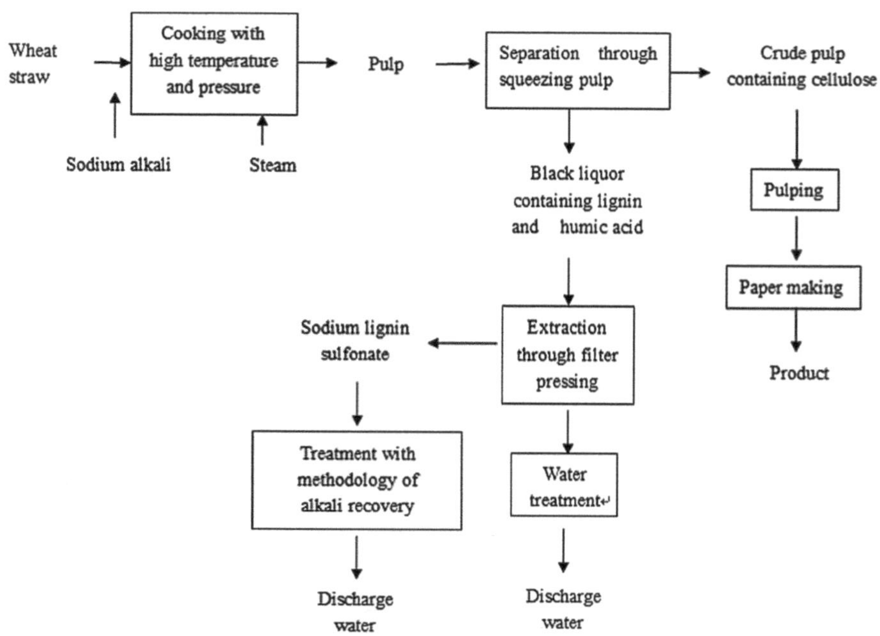

Fig. 6.52 Traditional process of wheat straw chemical pulping

(2) Mechanical pulping

Mechanical pulping is to make the fiber cell in cellulosic materials into pulp by mechanical method coupling with chemical method. This process has many advantages including less chemical consumption, high utilization ratio, less fresh water consumption, no bad smell, less invest, and fast construction. In particular, pollution by chemical pulping is more serious than chemical pulping [129]. According to the instruction, the pollutes in mechanical pulping wastewater are mainly soluble organics and tiny fiber. Compared with chemical pulping, mechanical pulping has better biochemical characteristics, that is to say we can remove COD by biochemical methods in the process of wastewater treatment.

(3) Chemical–mechanical pulping

Chemical–mechanical pulp is obtained by chemical pretreatment and mechanical grinding. Chemical pretreatment is benefit to improve pulp intensity and reduce energy consumption. Chemicals are first used to pretreat the raw materials so as to remove partly hemicellulose, dissolve out small part lignin, and soften intercellular layers. And then, after mechanical grinding of softened chipping, fibers can be made into pulp [130].

(4) Waste paper pulping

Waste paper pulping is the process of secondary fiber reused by waste paper collection and deinking treatment [131]. Less wastewater and pollutes are released in this process because materials have undergone the whole process of pulping, and no new materials are used.

(5) Pulping by steam explosion

In 1926, technology and equipment were invented by W.H. Mason. Saturated steam with 7–8 MPa was used as the medium in the technology. This technology is much required for equipment and operational technology and was applied to fiber board production. It could not be extended because of the high pressure in explosion process. Over the past several decades, amounts of research tests have been carried out on this technology and obtained the pressure reduction up to 1–2 MPa. In late 1980s, steam explosion technology was applied to feed process by Japan and Inner Mongolia Academy of Agricultural and Animal Husbandry Science of China. Kokta, professor of Université du Québec à Trois-Rivières, applied the steam explosion technology to pulping, and the timber is the main material of pulping. And based on this, Stake Technology Company in Canada developed continuous explosion pulping technology. Beijing Forestry University began to study explosion pulping in 1992. Small experiment was carried out in 1993. Middle test was carried out in Jiujiang, Jiangxi, in 1996. This technology was applied to papermaking in Hebei Ningjin Papermaking Company in 1997, and 6000 t pulp was produced from wheat straw. Wuhan Gerun Environmental Equipment Company in Hubei developed the equipment of explosion pulping and finished production experiment in 1999. In 2001, Gerun Explosion Pulping Company was established and production line of ten thousand annually was formed. Lu Wenzhan in South China University of technology also studied the industrial application of explosion pulping. All those researches have verified that steam explosion pulping has many advantages including no direct electrical consumption, high yield, effective, high intension, low pollution, less energy and investment and low cost. It can be applied to multiple production scales with different materials [28].

Steam explosion pulp and chemical pretreatment explosion pulp are two technologies used now.

① Steam explosion pulp (SEP)

The dried materials are added into the explosion tank and heated by steam directly. The pressure in the tank is increased to a certain level, and this pressure is kept for a period of time. Then, the pressure is released immediately to explode the materials. Finally, the SEP can be collected in collecting vessel after being separated by cyclone separator [132].

② Chemical pretreatment explosion pulp (CEP)

Chemical liquid and materials are added into the plastic vessel. Keep this mixed system at room temperature for 24 h. The pre-impregnated materials are added into the explosion tank and heated by steam directly. The pressure in the tank is increased to a certain level, and this pressure is kept for a period of time. Then, the pressure is released immediately to explode the materials, and the CEP can be obtained. The added chemicals are NaOH, Na_2SO_3, $NaHCO_3$, Na_2CO_3, H_2O_2, and so on. NaOH is not only a kind of good swell agent but also the good softener. It is good for fibrillating in inner fiber, improving softness and combining force of the fiber, therefore improving intension of the papers. In addition, the loss caused by acid hydrolysis can be avoided because of the existence of NaOH. Na_2SO_3 has two advantages. On the one hand, it sulfonates the lignin and improves the swell effect. On the other hand, Na_2SO_3 is a kind of antioxidant. It can protect the carbohydrate and lignin from oxidation in high temperature so as to guarantee good intension of the papers [133, 134].

Steam explosion pulping is the new technology based on the treatment of cellulosic materials by steam explosion. Its principle can be described as follows. The smashed raw materials are added into the sealed vessels. The compositions are changed under the given steam, temperature, and pressure. Along with the release of the high pressure, steam in the cell expands suddenly, making the fiber separated and dispersed. In addition, part lignin is separated and the materials are divided into small fiber. Explosion seems to happen in this process. In terms of different raw materials, qualified pulp can be obtained by controlling technical parameters. Chemical pulp is changed into physical pulping by explosion pulping. In technical aspect, the end treatment was developed to middle treatment to reduce pollution. This technology improves the recycling and comprehensive utilization of the resource. Besides, steam explosion pulping can make the other compositions into xylooligosaccharides, protein feed, and organic fertilizer when it is applied to straw papermaking. This can make the most utilization of biomass, providing a method for straw utilization in rural and outlet for small-scale papermaking industry. This technology has undergone middle test and can be applied to industrial production.

Chen Hongzhang developed a method of unpolluted preparation of high-quality pulp by steam explosion degumming with *Broussonetia papyrifera* bark [135]. In this process, the *B. papyrifera* bark was exploded, followed by rinsing and bleaching. 80 % of the pectin and hemicellulose and part lignin were degraded in the unpolluted explosion process. The black organs on the surface can be removed after rinsing, and the bark fibers are broken into loose structure by explosion treatment. This results in the penetration of chemicals in the bleaching process and improvement of white. This method reduces the industrial cost of the papermaking with *B. papyrifera* bark, avoids the environmental pollution, and improves the quality of the paper. This innovation provides new method for high-value utilization of the *B. papyrifera* and will produce great economic and social benefits.

Team of Chen Honghzang breaks through the single utilization of the lignocellulose. They focus on steam explosion technology and fraction of the straw, make the most use of multi-conversion technology, and realize the combined production of grass pulping, bioethanol [136], bamboo pulping, and bioenergy [137]. In addition, they try to develop multiple production of pulping.

Over the past 20 years, the production of industrial pulping, chemical pulping, and mechanical pulping has transferred into chemical–mechanical pulping. This method has the advantages of high yield and quality and less pollution. However, this method demands huge investment and much energy. In terms of the scale of 100 thousand tons one year, 2 thousand million is demanded for industry establishment. However, steam explosion pulping has the advantages of less investment, low cost and energy and environment. The first investment of this technology is just equal to the one out of six of the chemical–mechanical pulping [138]. At present, steam explosion pulping attracts interest of people for its high yield, efficiency, high intensity, low pollution, and less energy consumption. Steam explosion technology is allied not only to pulping, but also to the deinking of waste papers.

6.6.3.2 Deinking by the Method of Steam Explosion

With the development of social economy, waste papers are produced in large amount. China is the second largest consumption state of the papers and paperboards, in 2010. The production of paper and paperboard and waste pulping is 9.27 and 5.305 million tons, respectively [139]. Raw materials of papers are timber, grass, reed, and bamboos, and waste papers are called second fiber which are used to paper production. Reutilization of waste papers has the advantages of less investment, low energy consumption, less raw materials, less chemical consumption, and forest resource protection. Therefore, reuse of papers has increasingly caught the eyes of paper industrials. It has been a long history to produce papers with waste papers. In initial stages, waste papers were collected, washed, and mashed into pulping. It was applied to papermaking of packing paper or the middle medium of multi-boards and industrial papers. Later, with the progress of treatment technology, the quality of reproduced papers was improved a lot. Old newspapers were totally used to produce new papers after deinking by flotation, and the quality of reproduced papers was similar to that of raw fiber paper.

(1) Reutilization of waste papers as raw papermaking materials

It consumes amounts of timber and damages the ecology to produce papers with raw timber. Therefore, city papermaking with waste papers and forest pulp paper has become the tendency of modern papermaking industries. City papermaking also plays the role of elimination of city wastes, reflecting city produce and city elimination concept. Some developed areas are equipped with waste paper recovery basement. In China, recovery of waste paper is scarce to backward, and a large amount of waste papers are burned or reused by small industries to produce poor-quality toilet paper and packing paper. Therefore, deinking waste papers to produce high-quality papers of print and writing is an important road to solve fiber resource shortage problem. At the same time, deinking pulp papermaking can save chemicals and energy consumption, and reduce environmental pollution and production cost. It has great economic and social benefits.

Waste papers are good materials for papermaking industries, compared with timber. Waste papers can not only reduce environmental pollution but also protect forest resources so as to reduce environment damage. Waste papers are used as materials of papermaking, which can reduce 2–3 tons of timber and amount of water, coats, and electricity for every one ton. Waste paper recovery is limited to old newspapers. It has the advantages of large amount and easy recovery as the important composition of waste papers.

In order to produce high-quality production with waste papers, methods for the removal of pollutes in waste papers are required, and printing ink is a serious problem. From 1990s, the amount of office paper has increased along with the improvement of office automation. Composition and properties of the inks (such as ultraviolet solidification and laser jet ink) are different from traditional ink, which increases the difficulty of deinking.

(2) Mechanism of waste paper deinking

It is the key point to solve the problem of deink. This is a combined process of chemical and physical reactions. Chemicals are used to destroy the adsorption of oil to the fiber, and then, with a moderate temperature and mechanical force, oils can be separated from the fiber. This process can be concluded as follows: Loose the fiber, separate the oils from fiber, and remove the oils from the pulping.

(3) Deinking methods

① Chemical deinking

Chemical deinking is the process of stripping the oil from the fiber with chemical under certain temperature and mechanical force followed by washing process, so as to separate the oils from the pulp. Different deinking agents play their role by synergistic effect [140]. Agents usually used are listed in Table 6.31.

② Enzyme deinking

Enzyme deinking adapts the concept of green papermaking recycle economy, and unpolluted production for this technology develops fast. At present, enzymes including lipase, esterase, pectinase, amylase, hemicellulose, cellulase, and ligninase were used.

Enzyme treatment is to attach to the surface of printing ink and fiber, and lipase and esterase can hydrolyze plant-based oils. Cellulase and hemicellulase can hydrolyze cellulose and hemicellulose on the surface of the fiber partly. That is to say enzymes strip tiny fibril on the surface of the fiber, so as to separate and remove the oils after flotation or washing. Deinking effect is related to fiber composition, oil types, print methods, and enzyme composition [142].

State Key Laboratory of Biotechnology of Shandong University, cooperated with Shandong Zhucheng Papermaking Company, succeeded in producing deinking agents for industrial utilization. Their test verified that enzyme deinking has the advantages of high freeness, good drain ability and physics, high whiteness, low remained oils, low energy consumption, and less pollution compared to chemical deinking.

③ Steam explosion deinking

Recoupe Recovery Technology Company in the USA developed steam explosion technology. 50 % concentration of the waste papers is added into the explosion tank in this technology process, and the materials are condensed to plug materials by reciprocating movement and continuously transporting into reactor. The steam heats the materials up to 230 °C, and pressure is 1176.84–2796.45 kPa for several minutes. Finally, the materials were exploded by releasing the pressure through a small discharge valve. By this treatment process, oils can be divided into tiny particles (<75 μm), and then, after purification, screening, and washing, the deinking pulping can be obtained . This technology is the only continuous waste paper treatment technology. It is reported that this technology can recover the low-quality papers effectively and solve some treatment problems such as the removal of plastic melt matters, wax, and rosin. Steam explosion technology has the advantages of simple, low cost and investment, energy saving, and environment-friendly [143].

Researchers in Research Center of Pulping and Papermaking of Universitédu Québec in Canada deinked the waste papers by steam explosion technology and compared it with traditional deinking methods. Sodium sulfite was added in the process of steam explosion deinking method. Newspaper pulping treated by steam explosion method was affected by washing period because it depended on the dispersion of printing ink and washing yield of the tiny fiber. The loss rate was 2 %. Although pulp whiteness in traditional deinking process is higher than that of steam explosion process, steam explosion process can improve pulp whiteness by adding H_2O_2. Pulp by steam explosion deinking process with the addition of sodium sulfite contained little printing ink, and it had high intensity. Lignosulfonate fiber in the pulp increased the intensity and smoothness of the paper.

According to the report of TAPPT, steam explosion deinking is benefit to improve deinking effect. The following condition is required: Temperature is 150 °C; the ratio of solution and paper is 2.5:1; sodium sulfite for its sulfonation is moderate; temperature and pressure of the steam are 165 °C and 0.64 MPa, respectively; explosion time is 1–2 min [144].

Steam explosion can diffuse the ink into soluble particle which is easy to be removed no chemicals are employed when the cellulose is treated by steam explosion. In addition, it can solve some treatment problems including removal of plastic melt matters, wax and rosin, and dispersion of laser print ink. Deinking efficiency can be improved by coupling relative equipment of explosion, screening, and washing [145].

④ Problem and outlook of deinking

In recent years, people propose recycle concept from the prospects of protection of natural resource and living environment, soil maintenance, energy saving, company responsibility, and social cost. Recovery and reuse of the reproduced papers are not only the responsibility of the company, but also the sign of energy saving.

Although the pollutes in waste paper pulping are less than those in chemical pulping, there are still high concentrations of COD_{Cr} and SS in the wastewater. This process still can damage the environment. 50 % of the filling materials, 20 % of the tiny fiber, and 95 % of the printing ink are contained in the wastewaters. In addition, addition of deinking agents increases the difficulty of deinking wastewater [146].

With the development of recovery technology engineering, deinking technology demands improvement further. It is the tendency to reduce water consumption and chemicals in the deinking technology. Particularly, equipment and technology of steam explosion deinking should be improved.

6.6.4 Environmental Materials Manufactured with Steam-Exploded Straw

6.6.4.1 Adsorption Materials Manufactured with Steam-Exploded Straw

(1) Current condition of heavy metal sewage

With the rapid development of industrialization, human beings are facing serious issues of environmental pollution and resource shrinking. Waters are polluted seriously by industrial sewage every year. Harmful matters in sewage enrich in the biological chain and do great harm to ecologic safe and living and health of human beings. Particularly, heavy metal sewage released by metallurgy, electrolysis, electroplate, medicine, and dye industries pollutes the environment badly and damages health of human beings most seriously. Therefore, how to treat heavy metal sewage has been gathering attention all over the world.

At present, three methods (namely chemical precipitation, activated carbon adsorption, and ion exchange adsorption) are used to remove heavy metals in the sewage [147]. In chemical precipitation process, traditional limestone or soda is used to make the heavy metal precipitation in the form of hydroxide. This method must decrease the metal concentration to a certain degree, which is complex. Therefore, chemical precipitation is not economic and efficient. Activated carbon has large specific surface area and void. Therefore, it has the advantages of strong ability of adsorption and high performance of heavy metal removal. However, activated carbon is of high cost, making the total cost of sewage treatment higher and restricting the application of activated carbon absorption method. It is an important method to use ion adsorption in the interface of solid and liquid to control heavy metal pollution. The project of separating heavy metals selectively by ion exchange adsorption has aroused great interest of many people. Over the past several years, many scholars have focused on research on heavy metal adsorbents with low cost. In particular, adsorption material based on low cost, easy accessibility, and environmental natural polymer, cellulose, has gained much attention.

(2) Preparation of adsorption materials with agricultural wastes (straws)

Cellulose is a β-1,4-linked linear polymer of glucose units and the most abundant renewable resource in nature. There are amounts of hydrophilic hydroxyl groups in cellulose molecules. Cellulose molecule is a fibrous and enriched capillary high molecular polymer with the characteristics of much void and large specific surface area. This characteristic endows the cellulose with merit of strong adsorption.

However, adsorption capability of natural fibers is not very strong. It must be modified by chemical methods to endow more strong hydrophilic groups so that fibers can be the functional adsorption materials. Modified cellulosic adsorbents have the same adsorption ability as activated carbon. They are abroad used in water treatment industries because they can chelate with metals and adsorb the metals in water. Also, large specific area makes the hydrophilic environment form easily. Adsorption and desorption rate of modified cellulosic adsorbents is very fast, and their regeneration is easier than adsorption resin. In addition, they also have the characteristics of high stability, special selective ability, and low cost. Therefore, to make the most use of renewable resource to develop new types of modified cellulosic adsorbents and spread its application is an important point of adsorbent research. Process of modified cellulosic adsorbents is shown in Fig. 6.53 [148].

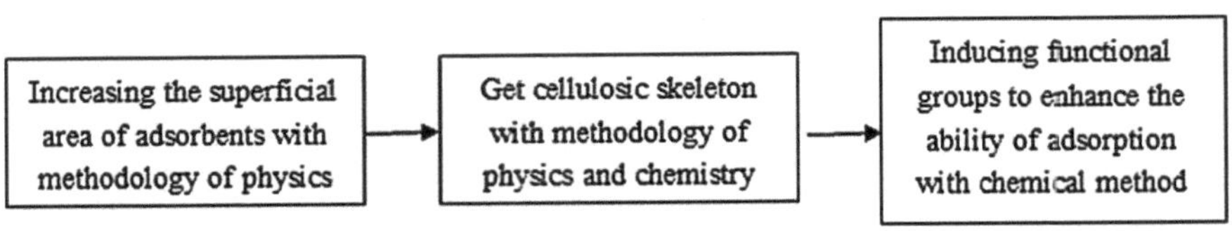

Fig. 6.53 Process of modified cellulosic adsorbents

Table 6.32 Ions absorbed by agricultural waste [147]

Materials	Adsorbed ions
Cellulose	Cr^{3+}, Ni^{2+}, Cu^{2+}
Wheat straw	Fe^{3+}, Cd^{2+}, Ni^{2+}, Pb^{2+}, Co^{2+}
Cotton stalk	Fe^{3+}, Cd^{2+}, Ni^{2+}, Pb^{2+}, Co^{2+}
Corn cob	Cd^{2+}, Ni^{2+}, Pb^{2+}, Cu^{2+}, Zn^{2+}
Bagasse	Zn^{2+}, Ni^{2+}, Pb^{2+}, Cu^{2+}, Cr^{3+}
Wheat bran	Cd^{2+}, Ni^{2+}, Pb^{2+}, Cu^{2+}, Cr^{3+}
Sawdust	Cu^{2+}, Pb^{2+}, $Cd2^{+}$

(3) Evaluation of adsorption effect

Straws are by-product of crops. More than 2 thousand million tons straw is produced every year around the world. Treating heavy metal sewage by straws not only can solve the problem of resource recovery but also get a low-cost method for sewage treatment. Straw is composed by cellulose, hemicellulose and lignin, which has the merits of large specific area, good hydrophilicity and enriched pore. This endows the cellulose natural advantages of heavy metals adsorption and attracts attention of scholars for further research (Table 6.32).

The author presents the thinking of treating sewage with solid wastes, and replacing the expensive activated carbon with steam-exploded straws can reduce the cost of sewage treatment and improve its actual application. Gas cooking and explosion are two processes of steam explosion of straws, and gas cooking provides selectively mechanical separation for explosion. In the process of explosion, inflated gas explodes the materials in the form of shock wave and makes the materials out of shape after being softened. Space in fiber is enlarged rapidly, and more void appears due to this strong shock wave. This results in larger specific areas and can improve its ability of heavy metal adsorption. In terms of this characteristic, applying the steam-exploded straws to sewage treatment is feasible theoretically.

Steam explosion can purify natural plant straw cellulose and damage the cell obviously (Fig. 6.54; [149]). This increases the specific area of fiber and improves the accessibility and reaction ability for chemical agents. Plant straw cellulose chelated with ethanediamine is prepared by alkalization, etherification of alkyl, and affinity substitution reaction of amino. It has fine adsorption ability for heavy metal ions. Test results show that the adsorption for Cu^{2+} and Cd^{2+} can reach 51.8 and 50.7 mg/g, respectively, for 2 h (they are the maximum adsorption). The adsorption is conformed to Freundlich isotherm adsorption basically.

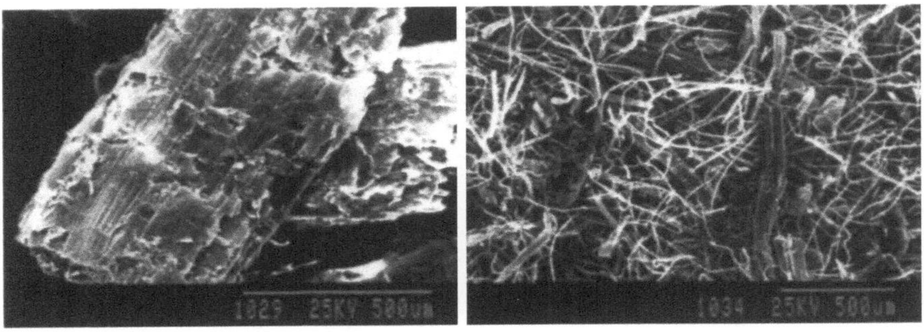

Fig. 6.54 SECs of steam-exploded cornstalk and unpretreated cornstalk

6.6.4.2 Green Construction Materials Manufactured with Steam-Exploded Straw

At present, in Chinese decoration industry, block board is widely used in family and project decoration. Block board is also called big core board because solid wood is used as the core board. It is the main product of decorative tile. However, restricted by technology and quality of tackiness agents, block board in current market can release much formaldehyde. This has damaged public environment and human health seriously.

In order to prepare green board, we must firstly prepare straw fibers. The composition of agricultural straws is complex. Compared with timber, fiber in straws is shorter and contains more extracts and ash and many unfavorable materials for scuffing on fiber surface. In addition, straw fibers are perishable, inflammable, and easy mildew. All those features determined that special technology and equipment are demanded.

Steam explosion technology [150] adapts the technology similar to popcorn technology. Straws are added into the vessel with high temperature and pressure, then opening the vessel immediately to release the pressure and making the straws become fibers (Fig. 6.55). Steam explosion technology combines temperature rise and fiber separation. Compared with methods of separation, electric grinder, and rubbing, steam explosion technology can reduce a step and cost and improve production efficiency.

Straw construction materials are green and light, and replacing timber with it can save forest resource. In addition, this also can avoid the serious pollution caused by

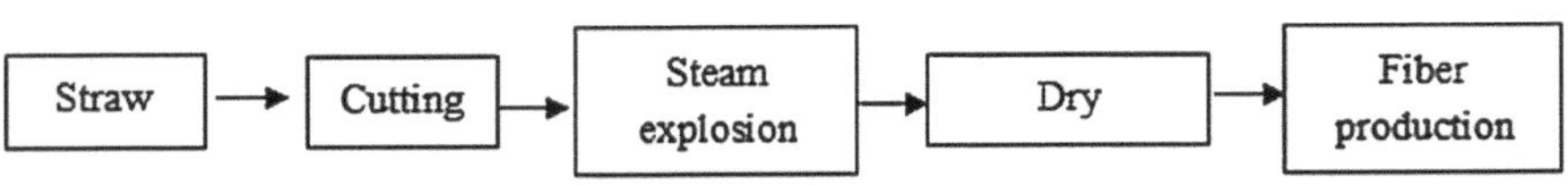

Fig. 6.55 Technology of straw fiber processing based on steam explosion

straw burning. On the other hand, it can also make great contribution to the ecological environment to replace the packing plastics and disposable tableware.

(1) Preparation methods of denatured straw materials [151]

① The straws are exposed to get the steam-exploded straws; ② Phanerochaete chrysosporium (2–15 %) are inoculated into the steam-exploded straws to degrade lignin by solid-state fermentation; ③ denatured straw materials are obtained after thermosetting and dry.

Board or packing materials produced with the denatured straw materials are light. They can be used to replace timber and plastics and applied into construction material industries, packing industries, and agricultural project.

(2) Preparation of degradable material [152]

Straws are mixed directly with ionic liquids or with ionic liquids after treatment of smashing, alkalization, and steam explosion, and the mixed systems are then heated to dissolve the straws and thick system can be obtained. Finally, we can get

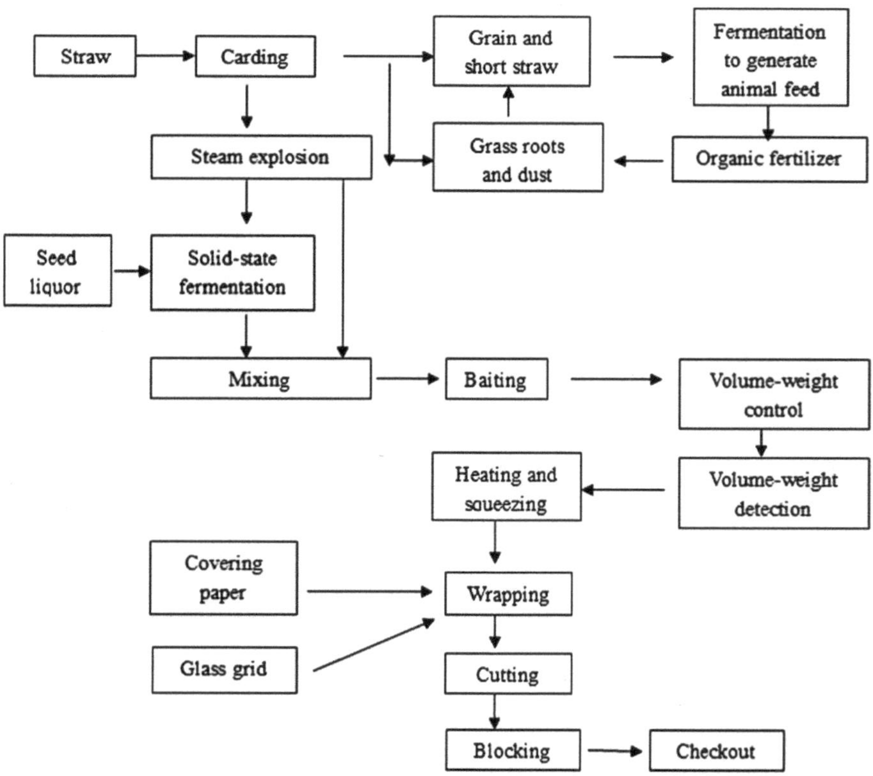

Fig. 6.56 Process chart of preparation of clean packing material with cornstalk

degradable film materials and silk yarn after being diluted by organic solvent and scraping or spinning. Ionic liquids used in this process can be recovered by distilling.

(3) Production of unpolluted packing materials with steam-exploded denatured cornstalk

Taking the cornstalk as an example, the technology of unpolluted production of packing materials is shown in Fig. 6.56 [15].

Green Ecological Company in Heze (based on Institute of Process Engineering, Chinese Academy of Sciences.) has developed denatured crop straw biomass utilization technology to produce environmental natural packing materials. The wastes are used to produce feed, papers, organic fertilizer, and density board. Compared with corresponding materials, density board solves the problem of formaldehyde production, and it has the characteristics of waterproof, non-toxic, smell-less, non-pollution, non-radiative, light, hard, and beautiful. It has proved to be the ideal environmental decorative material outdoors. Utilization of this material can not only protect ourselves but also make contribution to environment protection.

References

1. Li ZX. A review on multipurpose use of apple pomace. J Yellow Cattle Sci. 2002;28(4):58–62.
2. Deng H, Zhang BS, Li XP. Study on preparation of dietary and pectin from apple residue. Food Sci Technol. 2002;5:62–3.
3. Feng WR, Feng WJ. Enzymatic processing of meat co-products into variable products. Food Sci. 2001;22(7):86–7.
4. Zhao XF. Processing and utilization of feather powder. Guangdong Feed. 2002;11(4):13–5.
5. Yang RJ, Zhang WB, Xiao H. A feather protein powder and its preparation method. China Patent, 200910170082.3. 2009.
6. Lin W, Mu CD, Wang KY, Zhang MG, Pan ZC. Conversion of solid leather waste to reusable resources (II): properties of collagen biomaterials and its application in the medicine and cosmetic industry. China Leather. 2001;30(15):8–11.
7. Lv YH, Tang KY, Cao J. Preparation of collagen from tannery wastes and its application in foodstuff industry. Leather Chemicals. 2003;20(3):8–11.
8. Zhang EX, Yu LJ. Utilization situation and development prospects of marine bioactive substance. J Oceanogr Taiwan Strait. 2000;19(3):388–95.
9. Shigematsu M, Akao T, Yamamoto M. New preparation method of chitin by using a steam-explosion. In: Gifu Technique proceeding of the Fourth International Conference on ecomaterials; 1999. pp. 719–722.
10. Chen HZ, Jia XT, Wang XC. A cell wall breaking method of seaweed by steam explosion. China Patent, 02153296.6. 2004.
11. Yang XX, Chen HZ, Li ZH. Steam-explosion of ammoniated corn straw and subsequent solid state fermentation. Chin J Process Eng. 2001;1(1):86–9.
12. Yao ZS. Medicinal plants. Beijing: China Press of Traditional Chinese Medicines; 2002. p. 40–52.
13. Gong QF. Chinese medicine processing. Beijing: China Press of Traditional Chinese Medicines; 2007. pp. 18–26.

14. Liu MY, Wang BC. Advances in new technologies applying to Chinese materia medica extraction. Chin Tradit Herbal Drugs. 2010;41(2):169–75.
15. Chen HZ, Liu LY. Technology of steam explosion principles and applications. Beijing: Chemical Industry Press; 2007. p. 143–55.
16. Kang TG. Chinese traditional medicines identification. Beijing: China Press of Traditional Chinese Medicines; 2003. pp. 124–137.
17. Liu J, Yuan YT, Chen HZ. Ephedrine extraction by breaking herba ephedrae cell wall using super-fine grinding. In: 2nd Chinese national chemical and biochemical engineering annual meeting, Beijing; 2005.
18. Chen HZ, Fu XG. A separation and purification method of chlorogenic acid from leaves of Eucommla Ulmoides. China Patent, 201110233829.2. 2011.
19. Chen HZ, Fu XG. A steam explosion pretreatment method of ginkgo leaves. China Patent, 201110233863.X. 2011.
20. Chen HZ. Medicinal plants process engineering and ecological industry integration. Beijing: Science Press; 2010. p. 48–68.
21. http://www.ipe.cas.cn/hzjl/ydhz/201010/t20101029_2999236.html.
22. Li XS, Ji XT, Chen HZ. A cell wall breaking method of ganoderma spore. China Patent, 02135627.0. 2002.
23. Chen HZ, Li HQ, Zhang SJ. A processing method of single Chinese herb and Chinese compound medicine. China Patent, 200810226455.X. 2008.
24. Chen HZ. Ecological biochemical engineering. Beijing: Chemical Industry Press; 2008. p. 126–50.
25. Chen H. Processing engineering in plant-based products. New York: Nova Science Publishers; 2009. p. 45–76.
26. Zheng H, Zhao R. Production place and chemical composition research of different kinds of *Radix pueraria*. Chin J Manag Chin Med. 2006;14(4):51–3.
27. Wang YF, Hou JK, Pei GY. Cultivation technology for high yield and quality *Radix pueraria*. Bull Agric Sci Technol. 2005;8:30–1.
28. Chen HZ, Xu J, Yao JZ. Studies on multi-level conversion of liquid fuel with straw. Chin J Bioprocess Eng. 2005;3(1):9–13.
29. Chen HZ, Xu J. Modern solid fermentation principles and applications. Beijing: Chemical Industry Press; 2004. p. 86–125.
30. Fu XG, Wang W, Chen HZ. A procedure and equipment thereof for comprehensive utilization of *Radix pueraria*. United States: 8333999. 2007.
31. Japan Energy Society. Biomass handbook. Beijing: Chemical Industry Press; 2007. p. 72–96.
32. Guo P, Mochidzuki K, Zhang D. Effects of different pretreatment strategies on corn stalk acidogenic fermentation using a microbial consortium. Bioresour Technol. 2011;102 (16):7526–31.
33. Grous WR, Converse AO, Grethlein HE. Effect of steam explosion pretreatment on pore size and enzymatic hydrolysis of poplar. Enzyme Microb Technol. 1986;8(5):274–80.
34. Jacquet N, Quievy N, Vanderghem C. Influence of steam explosion on the thermal stability of cellulose fibres. Polym Degrad Stab. 2011;96(9):1582–8.
35. Luo P, Liu Z, Yang CM. Study of simultaneous saccharification and fermentation for steam exploded wheat straw to ethanol. Chem Eng (China). 2007;35(12):42–5.
36. Jiang JX, Zhu LW, Wang K. Simultaneous saccharification and fermentation of steam pretreated lespedeza stalks for the production of ethanol. Biomass Chem Eng. 2006;40 (12):165–8.
37. Fu XG, Chen HZ, Wang WD. Production of ethanol and isoflavones from steam exploded *Radix Puerariae* by solid state fermentation. Chin J Biotechnol. 2008;24(6):957–61.
38. Boluda-Aguilar M, García-Vidal L, González-Castañeda FP. Mandarin peel wastes pretreatment with steam explosion for bioethanol production. Bioresour Technol. 2010;10:3506–13.

39. Boluda-Aguilar M, López-Gómez A. Production of bioethanol by fermentation of lemon (*Citrus limon L.*) peel wastes pretreated with steam explosion. Ind Crop Prod. 2013;41:188–97.
40. Cara C, Ruiz E, Ballesteros M. Production of fuel ethanol from steam-explosion pretreated olive tree pruning. Fuel. 2008;87(6):692–700.
41. Chen WH, Pen BL, Yu CT. Pretreatment efficiency and structural characterization of rice straw by an integrated process of dilute-acid and steam explosion for bioethanol production. Bioresour Technol. 2011;102(3):2916–24.
42. Viola E, Cardinale M, Santarcangelo R. Ethanol from eel grass via steam explosion and enzymatic hydrolysis. Biomass Bioenergy. 2008;32(7):613–8.
43. http://www.ipe.cas.cn/hzjl/ydhz/200809/t20080923_498563.html.
44. Larsen J, Østergaard Petersen M, Thirup L. The IBUS process–lignocellulosic bioethanol close to a commercial reality. Chem Eng Technol. 2008;31(5):765–72.
45. Li DM, Chen HZ. Fermentation of acetone and butanol coupled with enzymatic hydrolysis of steam exploded corn stalk in a membrane reactor. Chin J Process Eng. 2007;7(5):1212–6.
46. Chen HZ, Song YM, Zhang JX. A preparation method of sandy land modified material through solid fermentation of steam exploded corn stalk. China Patent, 200810102982. 2008.
47. Wang L, Chen HZ. Increased fermentability of enzymatically hydrolyzed steam-exploded corn stover for butanol production by removal of fermentation inhibitors. Process Biochem. 2011;46(2):604–7.
48. Wang L. Key process of butanol production from steam-exploded corn stover. China: Institute of Process Engineering, Chinese Academy of Sciences; 2010.
49. Datar R, Huang J, Maness PC. Hydrogen production from the fermentation of corn stover biomass pretreated with a steam-explosion process. Int J Hydrogen Energ. 2007;32(8):932–9.
50. Li DM, Chen HZ. Biological hydrogen production from steam-exploded straw by simultaneous saccharification and fermentation. Int J Hydrogen Energ. 2007;32(12):1742–8.
51. Ren N, Xu J, Su D. Biological hydrogen production from hydrogen-producing fermentative liquid steam-exploded pretreatment of corn straw. J Biotechnol. 2008;136:594.
52. Bauer A, Bösch P, Friedl A. Analysis of methane potentials of steam-exploded wheat straw and estimation of energy yields of combined ethanol and methane production. J Biotechnol. 2009;142(1):50–5.
53. Wang XT, Zhang BL, Song AD. Application of steam-exploded technology to anaerobic digestion of corn stover. Trans CSAE. 2008;24(8):189–92.
54. Song YN, Chen HZ. Study on biogas production by thermophilic solid-state fermentation from steam exploded corn stalk. Chin J Environ Eng. 2008;2(11):1564–70.
55. Estevez M, Linjordet R, Morken J. Effects of steam explosion and co-digestion in the methane production from Salix by mesophilic batch assays. Bioresour Technol. 2012;104:749–56.
56. Snekkenes V, Almqvist L, Trolin D. System and a method for the steam pre-treatment of chips in association with the production of chemical cellulose pulp. United States: 8052843. 2011.
57. Elliott A, Mahmood T. Pretreatment technologies for advancing anaerobic digestion of pulp and paper biotreatment residues. Water Res. 2007;41(19):4273–86.
58. Panter K, Kleiven H. Ten years experience of full scale thermal hydrolysis projects. 2005.
59. Norli M. The cambi thermal hydrolysis process (THP)-dramatically improving sludge digestion and dewatering-11 years experience of full scale project. In: Proceedings of the Gdansk conference 24–26 Oct 2006. Gdansk, Poland; 2006.
60. Chen HZ. Process engineering in plant-based products. Beijing: Chemical industry press; 2010.
61. Chen HZ. Biomass science and engineering. Beijing: Chemical industry press; 2008.
62. Huang J. Chemical technology and materials of biomass. Beijing: Chemical industry press; 2009.
63. Ministry of Science and Technology. Biological base material industry "twelfth five-year" science and technology development special planning. 2012.

64. Liu J, Chen HZ, Li ZH. On the development of research of hemp fiber degumming. Plant Fiber Prod. 2002;24:39–42.
65. Chen HZ, Zhang JX. Vapor explosion of hemp hydraulic opening method and device, China Patent, 200810100972.2. 2009.
66. Chen HZ, Zhang JX. Steam explosion removal of solid impurities such as hemp skin organization method and device. China Patent, 200810100971.8. 2008.
67. Dupeyre D, Vignon M. Fibres from semi-retted hemp bundles by steam explosion treatment. Biomass Bioenerg. 1998;14:251–60.
68. Zhang Y, Yu CW. The degumming process of flax fiber. 2011;32:71–74.
69. Rowell CV. Process for decorticating vegetable fiber and the manufacture of products therefrom. GB Patent. 1932;388:561.
70. Kessler R, Becker U, Kohler R. Steam explosion of flax-a superior technique for upgrading fibre value. Biomass Bioenergy. 1998;14:237–49.
71. Deepa B, Abraham E, Cherian BM. Structure, morphology and thermal characteristics of banana nano fibers obtained by steam explosion. Bioresour Technol. 2011;102:1988–97.
72. Chen YR, Ouyang PK. Steam explosion of the rest of agriculture plants and bandness panels processing. 1994;6:40–42.
73. The ministry of agriculture science and technology education department. 2010. National crop straw resources survey and appraisal report.
74. Chen HZ, Wang N. A kind of crops straw steam blasting method in the process of the hydrolysis of sulfate of dissolving pulp. China Patent, 201110211009.3. 2011.
75. Wang H, Chen HZ. A novel method of utilizing the biomass resource: rapid liquefaction of wheat straw and preparation of biodegradable polyurethane foam (PUF). J Chin Inst Chem Eng. 2007; 38:95–102.
76. Chen HZ, Wang H. A plant straw biomass liquefaction preparation method of polyols. China Patent, 200610114197.7. 2008.
77. Chen HZ, Xie SP. Selective liquefaction of lignocellulose phenol method, China Patent, 200810102984.9. 2008.
78. Xu W, Ke G, Wu J. Modification of wool fiber using steam explosion. Eur Polym. 2006;J42 (9):2168–73.
79. Chen CW, Zhang L, He XM. Convention nutritional components analysis on fruits of *Rhus chinensis Mill.* Anim Husbandry Feed Sci. 2010;31(4):2–5.
80. Chen HZ, Qiu WH. Key technologies for bioethanol production from lignocellulose. Biotechnol Adv. 2010;28(5):556–62.
81. Chen HZ, Liu LY. Unpolluted fractionation of wheat straw by steam explosion and ethanol extraction. Bioresour Technol. 2007;98(3):666–76.
82. Chen HZ. Process engineering of biomass based production. Beijing: Chemical Industrial Press; 2009. p. 46–8.
83. Li AM, Li YB, Gen SY. Evaluation of oxalic acid production technology. Coal Chem Ind. 2006;34(5):58–60.
84. Chen HZ, Li C, Liang SL. Production of oxalic acid by alkali melting and oxidation steam explosion straws in recycling system. China Patent. 2002;00132283:4.
85. Wang D. Current situation of furfural industries and production and application of the derivatives. Chem Intermed. 2004;20:16–8.
86. Li PL, Xiao WP, Chang HY. Development of furfural production technologies. For Ind. 2006;33(2):13–6.
87. Chen HZ, Yu B. One kind of method for preparing furfural, polyether polyol, phenolic resin, and nano silica. China Patent, 201110034318.8.2011.
88. Chang C, Ma XJ, Cen PL. Advances in production and application of levulinic acid: new type green platform chemical. Prog Chem Eng. 2005;24(4):350–6.
89. Cen PL, Mu JH, Zhao CH. Research and development on levulinic acid-a new type green "platform chemical" forms renewable resources. Bioprocess. 2003;1(1):17–22.
90. Liu K, Fang GZ, Ma YL. Study on preparation of levulinic acid by acid hydrolysis of rice straw. Biomass Chem Eng. 2007;41(4):13–6.

91. Jin S, Chen H. Superfine grinding of steam-exploded rice straw and its enzymatic hydrolysis. Biochem Eng J. 2006;30(3):225–30.
92. Xu ZH, Xiong YJ. Research progress of production and application of xylooligosaccharide. Food Ferment Ind. 2002;28(1):56–9.
93. Wang H, Shi B. Preparation of xylooligosaccharides from corncob by enzyme method. Food Sci. 2002;23(5):81–3.
94. Ding XH. Study on the xylitol fermentation from hemicellulosic hydorlysate of corncob. Hang Zhou: Zhejiang University; 2006.
95. Xu Ping, Luo Mei. Xylose production, comsumption and health benefits. New York: Nova Science Publishers; 2011. pp. 120–146.
96. Huang CD, Bai XF, Du YG. The characteristics, production and application of xanthan gum. Microbiol China. 2005;32(2):91–8.
97. Zhang ZG, Chen HZ. Fermentation performance and structure characteristics of xanthan produced by *xanthomonas campestris* with a glucose/xylose mixture. Appl Biochem Biotechnol. 2010;160(6):1653–63.
98. Zhang ZG, Chen HZ. Xanthan production on polyurethane foam and its enhancement by air pressure pulsation. Appl Biochem Biotechnol. 2010;162(8):2244–58.
99. Huang J, Hu JH, Zhu QG. Pharmacological effects of ferulic acid and its derivatives. Prog J Chin Med Mater. 2005;24(4):350–6.
100. Zhang GS. Study on the extraction of ferulic acid from rice bran. J Anhui Tradit Chin Med Coll. 1997;16(6):56–7.
101. Li P, Sun FQ, Zhao MH. Synthesis and application of vanillin. J Hebei Normal Univ. 1999; 2:250–255.
102. Zhao LQ. Study on conversion of isoeugenol to vanillin by microbial method. Wu Xi: Southern Yangtze University; 2006.
103. Deng CJ, Zhong Q, Yang JG. Study of bagasse alkali lignin syringaldehyde and vanillin Separation and purification of syringaldehyde and vanillin. Cellul Sci Technol. 1994;2 (1):61–7.
104. Yang XH. Synthesis and biological activities of novel nitrogen-containing heterocyclic compounds from lignin. Beijing: Chinese Acad Forestry; 2011.
105. Lin L, He BH, Sun RC. High value chemicals from lignocellulosic biomass. Prog Chem Eng. 2007; 19(7):1206–1216.
106. Zhang YC, Tian M, Zhang LQ. Preparation, modification, application progress of silica. Mod Chem Ind. 1998;18(4):11–3.
107. Chen HZ, Yu B. One kind of method for preparing nano-silica with straw, China Patent, 200710062669.3. 2007.
108. Murphy JD, McKeogh E. Technical, economic and environmental analysis of energy production from municipal solid waste. Renew Energy. 2004;29(7):1043–57.
109. Liao L, Feng H, Wang SL. Treatment and disposal of solid waste. Wuhan: Huazhong University of Science and Technology press; 2010. p. 46–60.
110. Su J, Xi BD, Li XJ. Uncertainty and multi-objective optimization model of municipal solid waste management. Environ Pollut Prot. 2007;20(1):129–33.
111. Xi BD, SuJ Jiang YM. Research on optimization of municipal solid waste management model and cost factors. Environ Pollut Prot. 2007;29(8):561–4.
112. Sheng DS, Zheng YG, Yao J. Research on pollutant characteristics of typical solid waste incineration fly ash. Environ Sci. 2011;9:2610–6.
113. Pan XC, Ma ZY, Wang B. Application of plasma technology in treating waste incineration fly ash. Environ Sci. 2008;29(4):1114–8.
114. Zhen XX. Current situation of solid waste and problems in China. Shanxi Archit. 2008;34 (10):44–7.
115. Sun YF, Lin YY, Wang WJ. Resource utilization of solid wastes. Chem Technol Dev. 2012;41(1):44–7.
116. Zhang SJ, Zhao KR, Cui Y. Soil fertilizer. China: Chemical Industry Press; 2009. pp. 1–13.

117. Yang F, Li X, Cui Y. Current utilization of organic fertilizer and development suggestion in China. Chin Soil Fertilizer. 2010;4:77–82.
118. Zhang FS, Wang JQ, Zhang WF. Current situation of utilization of food fertilizer and method for improvement. Acta Pedol Sin. 2008;45(5):915–24.
119. Xu JH, Wang S, Wang N. Inevitability application and the advantages of commercial organic fertilizer products. Mod Agric Sci Technol. 2010;7:324.
120. Shi R, Ding WJ. Advanced business in diversified organic fertilizer. China Agric Means Prod. 2011;25:8.
121. Xu HW, Ma CB. Current situation and suggestion on commercial organic fertilizers in China. China Agric Technol Extension. 2007;23(3):43–5.
122. Chen HZ, Li ZH. A method of ecological fertilizer production by solid-state fermentation with steam-exploded straw: China Patent, 201123915.8. 2001.
123. Cao ZL. Consideration and current situation of Chinese paper industry. China Pulp Paper. 2009;28(10):63–6.
124. Lin QY. Evaluation and prospect of pollution prevention of non-wood pulp in China. China Pulp Paper. 2006;25(5):47–56.
125. He BH. Principles and engineering of papermaking. 3rd ed. Beijing: China Light Industry Press; 2010. p. 22–48.
126. Chen HZ. Biotechnology of lignocellulose. 2nd ed. Bejing: Chemical Industry Press; 2011. p. 188–92.
127. Liu F, Wu JH, Wei TT. Research on anaerobic biodegradability of chemical pulping waste water. China Pulp Paper Ind. 2009;4:50–3.
128. He XY, Lv KYK, He M. Unpolluted technology of chemical pulping and papermaking with wheat straw. Environ Prot Chem. 2009;29(3):256–9.
129. Liu Z. Generality of pulping and papermaking. Beijing: China Light Industry Press; 2012. pp. 42–56.
130. Li HB, Fang GG, Deng YJ. Research on pretreatment methods of chemical–mechanical pulping with weat straw. Chem Ind For Prod. 2009;29(2):81–4.
131. Chen JX. Advance of research on pulping technology. China Paper Mak. 2003;22(2):43–48.
132. Kokta B, Ahmed A. Steam explosion pulping. In: Environmentally friendly technologies for the pulp and paper industry. 1998. pp. 191–214.
133. Li HK, Li PY. Test on bleaching performance of gas exploded poplar pulping. China Paper Mak. 2004;25(5):36.
134. Dou JL, Liu YC, Liu LS. Research and applications of steam explosion pulping. Sci Technol Cellul. 2007;15(2):69–73.
135. Chen HZ, Peng XW, Zhang ZF. A method for rice paper preparation with steam exploded paper mulberry bark: China Patent, 200910078225.8. 2009.
136. Chen HZ, Fu XG, Zhang ZF. A method for coupling production of pulp and ethanol with grass: China Patent, 200710121392.7. 2007.
137. Chen HZ, Qiu WH. A method for preparation of ecological material and energy with steam exploded bamboo: China Patent, 201110034248.6. 2011.
138. Song XL, Jiang JX. Advances in steam explosion pulping. Hunan Papermaking. 2008;4:17–9.
139. National Development and Reform Commission, Ministry of Industry and Information Technology, the State Forestry Administration. Paper Industry "Twelfth Five Year Plan". East China paper industry. 2012;43(2):1–15.
140. Weng MH, Wang HY. Compare of chemical deinking and enzymatic deinking. Pulp Paper. 2011;30(2):21–2.
141. Yu HY. Waste paper recycling and deinking technology. Southwest Pulp Paper. 2004;33(5):44–7.
142. Zhang SF, Zhang MY, Zhao JL. Advances in enzymatic deinking technology of waste paper. China Pulp Paper Ind. 2006;27(6):42–5.
143. Duan YC, Dong ZQ. Test on industrial enzymatic deinking pulp to produce newsprint. China Paper Mak. 2001;20(5):41–4.

144. Jiang ZD. Waste paper treatment by steam explosion. China Paper Newslett. 2007;6:48.
145. Yang H, Zhang SF. Advances in deinking technology of waste paper. Print Today. 2012;4:65–7.
146. Shi CW. Research on deinking waste water by coagulating sedimentation method. China Paper Mak. 2012;2:40–2.
147. Jiang Y, Huang CJ, Pang H. Advances in cellulose based ion adsorbent. Chem Bull. 2008;12:891–9.
148. Chen LH. Preparation of adsorbents with modified cellulose and adsorption of heavy metal ions. China New Technol Prod. 2009;12:6.
149. Hao HY, Shao ZQ, He MC. Research on physical and chemical modification of lignocellulose and mechanism of adsorption. J Agro-Environ. 2007;26(3):1138–41.
150. Yu ZS. Processing technology of agricultural straw fiber and equipment. Mod Agric Sci Technol. 2009;14:231–2.
151. Chen HZ, Li ZH. Denatured straw material and application. China Patent, 01126544.7. 2001.
152. Chen HZ, Liu LY. A method for degradable material preparation with straw. China Patent, 200510011218.8. 2005.

FSC
www.fsc.org
MIX
Papier | Fördert
gute Waldnutzung
FSC® C083411

Kolibri 360 GmbH
Ferdinand-Jühlke-Straße 7
99095 Erfurt, Deutschland
produktsicherheit@kolibri360.de